D1280097

RIVERSIDE STUDIES IN BIOLOGY

Editors: William C. Steere
   The New York Botanical Garden

   H. Bentley Glass
   *State University of New York
   at Stoney Brook*

THE ALGAE: A REVIEW

G. W. Prescott

MICHIGAN STATE UNIVERSITY

THE ALGAE: A REVIEW

P. H. WELSHIMER MEMORIAL LIBRARY
MILLIGAN COLLEGE, TENN. 37682

HOUGHTON MIFFLIN COMPANY · BOSTON

NEW YORK   ATLANTA   GENEVA, ILL.   DALLAS   PALO ALTO

QK
566
.P7

68-6664

COPYRIGHT © 1968 BY G. W. PRESCOTT. All rights reserved.
No part of this work may be reproduced or transmitted in any
form or by any means, electronic or mechanical, including photo-
copying and recording, or by any information storage or retrieval
system, without permission in writing from the publisher.

PRINTED IN THE U.S.A.

To my patient and ever helpful wife
Terressa

62589

Editor's Introduction

THIS BOOK IS most appropriately titled; although several large and technical reference works for specialists have appeared during the past half century, our need for a general introduction to or a "review" of the Algae has become more and more urgent, a need that, at last, this work satisfies. The enormous diversity in form and function of algae is displayed by innumerable groups that have evolved in an unbelievable number of evolutionary lines since the very beginning of life on earth. Obviously, the author has had to impose upon himself an almost inhuman amount of restraint and selectivity, to such an extent that we marvel at his ability to encompass so great a number of important and significant groups of algae in so small a space. For the skill he has shown in making his decisions of what to include and what to exclude, based on more than 40 years of experience with and research on algae, the author is much to be praised. The reader will soon find that the primary virtues of this book are its high professional standard, its avoidance of unnecessarily technical language, its emphasis on the importance of algae to man and to his environment — and its brevity. The reader should also be grateful for the fact that, to avoid disagreement and confusion, the author has generally adhered to a system of classification and terminology consistent with that found in currently-used reference works. Finally — and a very important point indeed — the author must be commended for his great success in presenting material in such a manner that vacancies in our knowledge of algae become obvious. To give even greater emphasis to this approach, he has pointed out by direct statement where research is needed. In summary, this is a book of ideas as well as of facts, and should provide a wellspring for conceptual, basic, and original thinking about algae.

At the same time that more and more scientific and technical information about algae was accumulating, it became clear that algae also have a rapidly increasing impact on man's environment in many practical aspects. It is generally accepted that the originally most primitive plants — algae — invented photosynthesis, a process which transfers the kinetic energy of sunlight, in the presence of chlorophyll, to potential energy stored in the large molecules of carbohydrates and other metabolic products. Because the photosynthetic process gives off oxygen as a byproduct, algae and other primitive green plants may be given the credit for having completely transformed the originally reducing and ammoniacal atmosphere of Earth into the oxidizing one we take so for granted today. Until early algae evolved photosynthesis, then, no gaseous oxygen occurred in the atmosphere, a circumstance whose impact on animal life as we know it today becomes immediately clear.

Its emphasis on the ecology of algae gives this book an added dimension. The influence of algae on our environment from the very beginning, already stressed, still continues on a vast scale. Coralline red algae contribute to the growth of the great reefs and atolls in warm tropic seas. Many kinds of algae produce water contamination and water pollution, too well illustrated in our Great Lakes, where effluents of human and industrial wastes have provided an over-abundance of nitrogen. Chapters on these overwhelmingly important topics, as well as the commercial and industrial uses of algae and their products, furnish significant and thought-provoking material for the reader.

The rapidly increasing interest in algae we see today, together with the enormous volume of literature that has accumulated, make this book both necessary and timely. We may be certain that the author's avowed aim for this review, "encouraging further study and research," will be successful beyond his own hopes.

William C. Steere, Editor

Bronx, New York

Preface

PRE-LITERATE MAN no doubt was interested in and curious about algae, for then, as now, they were either a nuisance on the one hand or useful and edible on the other. References to algae can be found in ancient Chinese and, later, Greek literature. Theophrastus (300 B.C.), in his De Historia Plantarum, is perhaps the first to declare that algae, fungi, and lichens are definitely plants, and that they are so diverse that "to give a general definition of a plant, and that in a few words, is not possible."

Today, the algae have taken on added economic importance (as food, for commercial products, water contamination, toxin-production, sewage oxidation, etc.). Further, with the development of refined culture techniques and the electron microscope, physiologists and cytologists are employing algae more than ever as subjects of study for fundamental scientific information. The geneticist, limnologist, paleontologist, and plant evolutionist find investigations of algae to be both necessary and highly rewarding. One needs but to consider the current flood of literature dealing with the many aspects of algae (taxonomic, physiological, morphological, ontological) to gain an appreciation of the place that algae hold in human and scientific affairs.

This book has been prepared, then, both for the specialist and especially for the beginning student, because of this burgeoning interest in algae. Hopefully, those who are learning to identify algae for one reason or another will find pertinent information in the pages that follow. Emphasis has also been given to the relationship between algae and water quality and conservation. Finally, the information on life histories and ecology, and their relationship to algal form and structure, should be of interest to the student of alga morphology.

Because of the great variety of plants and the number of phyla involved, it has been necessary to select only a few examples for consideration. The plants discussed are, therefore, mere samples, but an attempt has been made to choose forms which are either commonly seen, or typical of the group to which they belong. Further, space limitations require that only a scant outline of biological problems relating to the algae be presented. It is not possible to treat alga biology in a way that will prove acceptable to all readers. Omissions and abbreviated paragraphs are regretted, and are intented only insofar as a choice of material to be included had to be made.

In the face of the rapidly changing concepts of algal taxonomy (especially in reference to composition of phyla) the system of classification used herein is conservative. It attempts to follow the plan found in most handbooks on algae which the reader will wish to use in addition to this volume. Accordingly it has been considered desirable not to depart from the present, more conventional systematics. There are, however, a few innovations within the Order Chaetophorales which the author has suggested. This book, therefore, is a review aimed at encouraging further study and research. Some of the many areas where research is especially needed have been indicated in the text.

I am grateful to my colleagues who have advised me in the preparation of the book, and especially Dr. C. M. Palmer who patiently and helpfully reviewed and criticized the manuscript. Thanks are also due Dr. W. C. Vinyard who inked many of the drawings. Illustrations were prepared from living material whenever possible or from herbarium specimens. In a few instances they were redrawn from published figures, as indicated. I wish to thank those who either furnished photographic illustration or who gave permission to reproduce them from published sources. Proper acknowledgments for these are given in the proper places.

G. W. Prescott

East Lansing, Michigan

Contents

Editor's Introduction   vii

Preface   ix

1. General Characteristics of the Algae   3

2. Phylum Chlorophyta   37

3. Phylum Cyanophyta   135

4. Phylum Chrysophyta   155

5. Flagellated Phyla   189

6. Phylum Phaeophyta   207

7. Phylum Rhodophyta   233

8. Ecology   279

9. Physiology   331

10. Economics   349

11. Phylogeny and Fossil Algae   367

12. Culturing of Algae   375

Bibliography   383

Glossary   401

Index   416

THE ALGAE: A REVIEW

Chapter 1

Birthplace of the algae. (G. W. Prescott)

General Characteristics
of the Algae

The philosopher has said "Nothing is uninteresting — there are only disinterested persons" — which is a reminder that we become interested when we are informed. This is true for the realm of the "algae," a world of Life which can become downright intriguing when one is informed, and if one wishes to become interested. The chief purpose of this book is to place the algae on review and thereby to point up some of their many biological features (physiology, morphology), their life histories, which in many instances are amazingly complex, their economic importance, and something of their aesthetic qualities. To do this presents at least one major problem: how to deal fairly with nine different phyla of organisms, each with its peculiar morphological and physiological characteristics, each member governed in its distribution by its own ecological requirements.

What Are the Algae

The nine phyla which comprise the "algae" are all those chlorophyll-bearing organisms (and their colorless relatives) which are thalloid, i.e., having no true roots, stems, and leaves, or leaf-like organs. So varied are the plants comprising what are commonly called "algae" that a precise definition is difficult. None of the algae have what may be regarded as true tissues, although some thalli are quite complex. Their sex organs are always one-celled, and none have a sporophyte generation parasitic on the gametophyte, a characteristic which is true for the thalloid liverworts in the Bryophyta. Some of the red algae, however, have what might be interpreted as a parasitic sporophyte. The algae vary in size from unicells 0.5 microns in diameter to the huge seaweeds, some of which may be upwards

3

of a hundred feet or more in length (cf. the giant kelp *Macrocystis pyrifera*). In fact, one unsubstantiated record claims a specimen to have been 700 feet — the longest plant in the world. Between these two extremes are thousands of species of unicellular, colonial, filamentous, or frond-like and bushy plants displaying endless degrees of complexity and of geometric design — the gelatinous and filamentous growths of ponds and streams, the seaweeds of the shore. Many possess great beauty and long have been the object of wonderment, both macroscopically and microscopically, especially since the invention of the compound microscope. In fact the study of algae and, subsequently, the science of phycology developed along with the science of microscopy. Early British, Continental, and American microscopists employed algae and protozoa as subjects for observation, partly because of the appeal of the microscopical universe, and partly for researches in lens resolution, determination of focal lengths, and upon condensers for illumination. The old records of microscope clubs and their published proceedings are replete with notes and notations regarding algae.

Just what organisms are to be included under "algae" varies with points of view, both current and historical. At first only strictly plant-like forms were regarded as algae (a name derived from the Latin for scrubbage or sea-wrack) — the plant life washed onto the beach or which grew along sea coasts. There emerged a gross classification of these plants into blue-green (Cyanophyceae), green (Chlorophyceae), brown (Phaeophyceae), and red (Rhodophyceae). Diatoms were grouped separately as the Bacillariophyceae.

Still later a recognition of the similarity to the algae of certain swimming, protozoa-like but pigmented organisms required the inclusion of the Volvocales, for example, into the green algae (Chlorophyta). Further, the possession of many characters held in common between other protozoan-like flagellated organisms (Chrysophyceae) and strictly plant-like forms, such as the yellow-green algae (Xanthophyceae), demanded that they be given a place in the realm of *phykos*, the Greek word for algae and one which Latins borrowed and spelled *Fucus*. (The latter is currently the generic name for one of the common and widely distributed brown rock-weeds of ocean shores.) Today in most systems of animal classification the flagellated organisms are assigned to the Phytoflagellata, although this means illogically grouping decidedly different forms within a single category (e.g. Dinoflagellata associated with *Euglena*). One plan recommends placing into the phylum Protista all one-celled and colonial, pigmented and motile organisms together with the strict Protozoa. To do this would fail to give a place for the filamentous and algal-like relatives of these same protozoa-like organisms (e.g. *Phaeothamnion, Dinothrix*). The similarity of the protozoan Phytoflagellata to algae was pointed out first by Klebs in 1893.

The student in biology often is heard to complain about duplicate, over-lapping, or inconsistent classification systems for plants and animals; the question repeatedly arises: "Why don't they work out a standard classification and stick with it?" One soon learns that ideas concerning classification systems continually vary as more and more facts are disclosed which require modification of previous concepts. Further, we come to realize that as long as there are three men on earth there will be at least two different interpretations of facts, possibly three, and we may find that none of them is correct. So it is necessary to adopt a system of classification which appears to be the most consistent, the most nearly natural, and the one which forms the most helpful backdrop against which to arrange our ideas. Then we can organize our thinking and communication.

The most widely and currently used algal classification system is presented below. It cannot be considered the "modern" system because even now this classification is undergoing revision — partly as a result of electron microscopy which has revealed many characteristics that are of taxonomic importance in grouping or in separating organisms or in both. The plan employed here, in which the author has introduced his own interpretations and concepts, varies only in certain minor respects from those proposed in certain standard reference works and texts.

Their Importance

There are many reasons for studying algae, but only a few can be mentioned here and it is impossible to list these in any order of importance. First, the role of algae in various sciences requires familiarity with their names (systematics) and their physiology. Much of what we know and are continuing to learn about the mechanisms and the products of photosynthesis come from algal physiology studies. Furthermore, a great deal of what we know about the behavior and the composition of protoplasm has been learned by experimental work with laboratory cultures of both fresh-water and marine algae. Likewise, nutritional requirements of plants, the selection of elements, the role of vitamins, the response to trace elements, the fixation of nitrogen, and numerous other kinds of information about the physiology of protoplasm have come from algal investigations. This is partly true because so many algae lend themselves well to laboratory culture.

Another area in which a knowledge of algae plays an important role is that of limnology and oceanography. The effects of algae on water chemistry and vice-versa, productivity of organic matter and the relation to the food chain, to bottom sediments, to light penetration (quality and quantity), are all involved.

Further, medical science and research related to medicine involve algal studies and experimentation. Mention in this connection might be given to cancer research, skin sensitization and allergies, assay of biologicals, etc.

Many aspects of fishery biology deal with algae: fish food, parasites, killing of fish directly or indirectly (Red Tide, e.g.). Other strictly economic aspects of the algae, especially of the seaweeds, are too numerous to mention here (see p. 349), but if one asks what algae are good for, the answer could be that many are useful as food and food-stuffs. Many marine algae especially, long have been used to supplement diets of maritime peoples throughout the world. It is possible that the fresh-water, and currently famous, alga *Chlorella* may yet become suitable for human food; even at present, however, algae are much used in the Western World for domestic animal and fowl food-stuffs.

There is a surprisingly long list of ways in which substances derived from marine algae are useful in commerce and industry. On the other hand, algae can also kill domestic animals, cause shell-fish poisoning (toxins), spoil water supplies, ruin recreational sites, etc. (see Table 10.2).

Classifications

The characteristics of the multitudinous forms of algae basic to a classification system are:

1. Pigments: kinds (chemical composition), relative amounts.
2. Reserve food products or assimilatory products of photosynthesis; their chemistry.
3. Flagellation: type and number of flagella; insertion; morphology.
4. Cell wall: chemistry; physical features, some of which are revealed only by electron miscroscopy.
5. Presence (Eukaryotic algae) or absence (Akaryotic algae) of a true nucleus.
6. Life history and reproduction: reproductive organs and methods. (The latter are less constant and often are not useful as a basis for classification.)

In many, if not most, instances it is a particular *combination* of these characteristics that either delimits an algal phylum or determines the classification of a particular species. Thus, as studies of algae progress, the necessity for further knowledge of life histories becomes more and more evident. Repeatedly discoveries are being made to show that a sedentary alga bearing one generic name is the non-motile phase of a motile form identified as another genus. Frequently life history studies disclose that a species is but a life cycle stage of one bearing a different name.

This is true for both marine and fresh-water algae — a situation which continually vitalizes algal taxonomy.

One of the chief objectives of systematics in biology is to arrange organisms in such a way as to show their phylogeny and genetical relationships. A recent proposal (Chapman, 1962), is helpful. Here the "algae" are grouped into what are thought to be associations of classes that are likely descendants from a common ancestry. These are:

I. Euphycophyta, to include Charophyceae, Chlorophyceae, Phaeophyceae, Rhodophyceae.
II. Myxophycophyta, Myxophyceae (Cyanophyceae).
III. Chrysophycophyta, to include Chrysophyceae, Xanthophyceae, Bacillariophyceae.
IV. Pyrrhophycophyta, to include Cryptophyceae, Dinophyceae.

This system does not recognize the Euglenophyceae (euglenoids) or the Chloromonadophyceae (chloromonads). Such a classification is based largely on pigment chemistry or upon pigment combinations, for it seems reasonable and likely that pigment similarities are fundamental and imply kinship.

Phyla and Orders

The advance in algal classification may be evaluated when a comparison is made with the system employed in 1800 and before. Such a system divided all algae into four groups (genera): *Conferva, Ulva, Chara, Fucus.* Below is a synopsis of contemporary algal classification. The characteristics of the respective phyla will be considered as each is discussed further on.

I. Phylum Chlorophyta (Green Algae). Chlorophyll predominant; food reserve starch

A. CLASS CHLOROPHYCEAE.

1. Order Volvocales. Motile in the vegetative state and with motile reproductive cells (spores and gametes); isogamous (sex cells similar); anisogamous (gametes slightly differentiated); oogamous or heterogamous (egg and sperm).
2. Order Tetrasporales. Gelatinous colonies of essentially unicellular forms; reproductive cells motile but vegetative cells may assume motility; isogamous reproduction.
3. Order Ulotrichales. Unbranched filaments with or with-

out basal-distal differentiation; chloroplast a parietal plate; wall in one section; reproduction isogamous or anisogamous.

4. Order Microsporales. Unbranched filaments with cell wall peculiarly constructed in two sections; chloroplast a parietal network; isogamous or anisogamous sexual reproduction.

5. Order Cylindrocapsales. Unbranched filaments of palmelloid cells with a massive chloroplast; cells enclosed in lamellated mucilage; oogamous reproduction.

6. Order Sphaeropleales. Plants filamentous, unbranched, and without basal-distal differentiation; chloroplasts band-like; reproduction oogamous.

7. Order Ulvales. Foliose or sheet-like thalli, or hollow tubes, with basal-distal differentiation; essentially composed of laterally adjoined filaments; sexual reproduction isogamous or anisogamous.

8. Order Schizogonales (Prasiolales). Uniseriate or multiseriate filaments (sometimes with false branches), becoming foliose and frond-like expanses; cells with axial, stellate chloroplasts; mostly lacking in sexual and asexual reproductive elements.

9. Order Chaetophorales. Uniseriate, branched filaments with basal-distal differentiation; branches tapering apically and often terminating in setae-like extensions; chloroplast a parietal, ulotrichoid plate; sexual reproduction isogamous or anisogamous.

10. Order Coleochaetales.[1] Branched filaments, erect or prostrate on a substrate and often laterally adjoined to form a disc; cells frequently with walls bearing hairs; sexual reproduction predominantly oogamous (rarely isogamous).

11. Order Trentepohliales. Plants filamentous and branched, erect or both erect and prostrate; without tapering of the axis or branches and without hairs; sexual reproduction isogamous.

12. Order Cladophorales. Branched or unbranched uniseriate filaments with basal-distal differentiation; cell walls thick and lamellate; cells coenocytic; chloroplast a parietal net; asexual reproduction by zoospores; sexual reproduction isogamous or anisogamous.

[1] Name proposed without diagnostic definition.

13. Order Siphonocladales. Semi-siphonous, coenocytic filaments of segments or vesicles, with basal-distal differentiation; segregative cell division in many forms; chloroplast a reticulum (sometimes dense); sexual reproduction isogamous or anisogamous. (This order, according to some systems of classification, includes the Cladophorales.)

14. Order Siphonales. Unsegmented, coenocytic filaments as architectural units, these usually closely entwined and arranged to form macroscopic fronds, bracts, feathery tufts, branched macaroni-like strands; isogamous, rarely oogamous. (Most of the marine green algae belong here; a few [**Dichotomosiphon,** e.g.] are fresh-water.)

15. Order Oedogoniales. Branched or unbranched filaments with basal-distal differentiation; cells mostly larger at the anterior end; cell division peculiar, involving an interpolation of a new wall section; chloroplast a parietal net-work; asexual reproduction by zoospores, sexual oogamous, with differentiated cells forming sex organs.

16. Order Zygnematales (Conjugales). (Subphylum Conjugatae.) Unicellular or filamentous without basal-distal differentiation; chloroplast relatively large, axial or parietal; asexual reproduction occasionally by parthenospores;[2] sexual reproduction by the metamorphosis of the vegetative cell protoplast to form iso- or anisogametes, uniting by conjugation.

17. Order Chlorococcales. Unicellular or colonial aggregates; cells lacking the ability to carry on vegetative cell division; cells coenocytic; vegetative reproduction by autospores or autocolonies; asexual reproduction by zoospores (rarely); sexual reproduction by isogametes, anisogametes, or (rarely) oogamous.

B. CLASS CHAROPHYCEAE (STONEWORTS).

1. Order Charales. Macroscopic, filamentous with basal-distal differentiation, the thallus showing definite nodes and internodes which bear whorls of branches of limited growth and special branches differentiated to form sex organs; no zoospores; reproduction oogamous.

---

[2] A spore similar in size and shape to zygospores of a species but formed without conjugation, i.e. sexually.

II. **Phylum Euglenophyta (Euglenoid Algae).** Chlorophyll predominant in oval, diffuse, or star-shaped chloroplasts (some members are colorless); motile by one, two, or three flagella; unicellular or incidentally colonial; food reserve paramylum.
1. Order Euglenales. Unicellular. Zoospores and gametes lacking.
2. Order Colaciales. Colonial, cells attached on stalks, anterior end downward in a mucilaginous capsule; vegetative cells becoming motile by metamorphosis of a vegetative cell to form a uniflagellate zoospore.

III. **Phylum Chrysophyta (Yellow-green Algae).** Carotenoids or xanthophyll pigments predominant in variously shaped chloroplasts; food reserve oil and leucosin; flagella usually two and unequal in length and in morphology; sexual reproduction isogamous or (rarely) by modified oogamy.

A. **Class Chrysophyceae.** Mostly flagellated, unicellular or colonial (some forms palmelloid), rarely filamentous; chloroplasts yellowish; flagella one, or two and unequal.
1. Order Chrysomonadales. Uniflagellate; assuming a temporary amoeboid stage.
2. Order Rhizochrysidales. Amoeboid, but with a temporary flagellate stage.
3. Order Chrysocapsales. Non-motile cells united (usually) in gelatinous colonies (comparable to the Tetrasporales in the Chlorophyta).
4. Order Chrysosphaerales. Unicellular or colonial; non-motile; cell division internal as in the Chlorococcales of the Chlorophyta.
5. Order Chrysotrichales. Branched filaments with basal-distal differentiation (comparable to the Chaetophorales of the Chlorophyta).

B. **Class Bacillariophyceae (Diatoms).** Unicellular, colonial, or filamentous; cell walls siliceous and constructed of two overlapping parts; carotenoids and diatomin pigments dominant. Reproduction by cell division, statospores, and sexually by isogametes and by a modified oogamy. (Diatom classifications at present, as in the past, are subject to varying concepts of specialists. The conventional and usually acceptable plan recognizes two orders.)

1. Order Centrales. Cells mostly circular in top (valve) view (or isodiametric) and with ornamentation (pits, striae, etc.) radial; cell walls without a raphe.
2. Order Pennales. Cells elongate, rectangular, crescent, key-shaped, cigar-shaped, or boat-shaped in valve view; wall ornamentation bilaterally symmetrical; one or both valves with a raphe or a pseudoraphe (see p. 181).

C. **Class Heterokontae (Xanthophyceae).** Unicellular, colonial filamentous or siphonaceous; carotene often predominant; flagella two, different in length; reproduction isogamous, anisogamous; oogamous.

1. Order Rhizochloridales. Unicellular, with a rhizopodial protoplasmic extension, with or without an envelope (lorica).
2. Order Heterocapsales. Non-motile, colonial, usually attached, gelatinous thalli; cells often able to resume a motile condition directly (comparable to the Tetrasporales of the Chlorophyta).
3. Order Heterococcales. One-celled or colonial, unable to carry on ordinary cell division, reproduction by autospores and through internal cell division (comparable to the Chlorococcales of the Chlorophyta).
4. Order Heterotrichales. Branched or unbranched filaments, with or without basal-distal differentiation (except when attached in early sporeling stages), comparable to the Chaetophorales of the Chlorophyta.
5. Order Heterosiphonales. Vesicular or siphonaceous coenocytes (comparable to the Siphonales of the Chlorophyta).

IV. **Phylum Pyrrhophyta**[3] **(Dinoflagellates).** Dorsiventrally differentiated (usually), motile, unicells with two laterally attached and morphologically different flagella (in most forms); one major group with the cell wall in geometrically arranged plates; cells usually with a longitudinal (ventral) furrow and a transverse furrow; carotenes, xanthophylls, and peridinin predominating pigments; food reserve starch or oil, reproduction by cell division, cysts, or rarely by conjugation of individuals **(Ceratium).**

---

[3] Usually written incorrectly Pyrrophyta in current literature.

A. **Class Desmokontae (Desmophyceae).** Cells without a transverse furrow (girdle), and with apical flagella.

B. **Class Dinokontae (Dinophyceae).** Cells with transverse and a longitudinal furrow; flagella laterally attached.

1. Order Gymnodiniales. Dinoflagellata without a cell wall but with a periplast that may be spirally striated.

2. Order Peridiniales. Dinoflagellata with a wall constructed of definite plates, specifically variable in number and arrangement.

3. Order Dinocapsales. Palmelloid dinoflagellates, enclosed in a mucilage and non-motile, but forming dinoflagellate type of zoospores.

4. Order Dinococcales. Dinoflagellata without plates in the wall, stationary, occurring as attached or free-floating cysts, forming dinoflagellate type of zoospores but not carrying on ordinary cell division.

5. Order Dinotrichales. Simple or sparsely branched filaments, usually creeping and prostrate; dinoflagellate type or zoospores formed in reproduction.

V. **Phylum Phaeophyta (Brown Algae, Brown Seaweeds).** Branched, tufted filaments, or complexes of filaments to form prostrate or erect thalli, fronds, or foliose expansions (usually with anchoring organs and a basal-distal differentiation); fucoxanthin pigments predominant; food storage as soluble carbohydrates; motile reproductive cells with subapical or lateral flagella. Reproduction by zoospores, iso-, aniso-, and heterogametes. (The subphyla, Classes, and Orders which comprise the Phaeophyta vary according to proposals by different students. Below, a conservative and widely accepted plan is followed.)

I. **Subphylum Phaeosporeae**

A. **Class Isogeneratae.** Alternation of similar generations in the life cycle.

1. Order Ectocarpales. Branched, uniseriate filaments with basal-distal differentiation, varying from microscopic to macroscopic, commonly forming bushy tufts; reproduction isogamous and anisogamous.

2. Order Sphacelariales. Branched filaments becoming multiseriate (with apical cell growth); reproduction isogamous.

3. Order Cutleriales. Branched, flat, ribbon-like or fan-shaped thallus, with tufts or hairs at the apices of the branches, growth by cells at the base of the hairs (trichothallic); alternation of similar (isomorphic) generations, or (rarely and paradoxically) by dissimilar (heteromorphic) generations.

4. Order Dictyotales. Frond-like, branched ribbons, often with a pad-like holdfast; alternation of isomorphic generations; growth by an apical cell or marginal meristem.

5. Order Tilopteridales. Branched, uniseriate filaments with basal-distal differentiation; reproduction by non-motile spores (monospores); sexual reproduction unknown.

B. Class Heterogeneratae. Alternation of dissimilar generations.

1. Order Chordariales. Complexes of crustose or erect filaments enclosed by a cartilaginous mucilage in which three regions ("tissues") can be identified; sporophyte macroscopic, gametophyte microscopic.

2. Order Sporochnales. Sporophyte a branched thallus with tufts of hairs at the apices; sporangia grouped in a swollen receptacle; growth intercalary; gametophyte microscopic.

3. Order Desmarestiales. Plants a frond-like thallus, flat or round strands with pinnately arranged branches; an axial filament enclosed by a wide cortex; growth trichothallic; alternation of generations heteromorphic.

4. Order Dictyosiphonales. Sporophyte tubular (one-celled with thick walls), saccate, or a foliaceous thallus two cells thick; some forms parenchymatous; alternation of heteromorphic generations.

5. Order Laminariales. Sporophyte large fronds with holdfast, stipe, and expanded leaf-like portions, with elaborate medulla, cortex, and "epidermis"; alternation of generations heteromorphic.

II. **Subphylum Cyclosporeae.** Plants frond-like, branched, with holdfast and leaf-like expansions; reproduction only by spores which metamorphose to form gametes; no gametophyte generation; reproduction oogamous; organs contain in conceptacles.

VI. **Phylum Rhodophyta (Red Algae).** Phycoerythrin the dominant pigment; food storage floridean starch; no motile cells.

I. **Subphylum Bangioideae.** Simple thalli of branched (rarely unbranched) filaments or membranous fronds; no pit connections between cells; relatively simple, heterogamous sexual reproduction organs, life cycle also simple, the gametophyte dominant, the diploid confined to the zygote.

1. Order Porphyridiales. Unicellular forms of uncertain taxonomic position.
2. Order Goniotrichales. Uniseriate or multiseriate filaments. Reproduction by cell-division and by monospores.
3. Order Bangiales. Attached, unbranched, multiseriate filaments or fronds. Reproduction by monospores and by carpogonia.
4. Order Compsopogonales. Branched, arbuscular filaments, the axis enclosed by a cortex of small, brick-like cells. Reproduction by monospores. No carpogonia known.

II. **Subphylum Florideae.** Plants attached; filaments, expanded sheets, or complexes of filaments which are mostly arbuscular and highly gelatinous; reproductive organs and life cycles complex and much involved.

1. Order Nemalionales. Mostly multiaxial (sometimes uniaxial) fronds (**Nemalion** a gelatinous branched cylinder); female organ (carpogonium) on a simple branch; auxiliary cell (see p. 240) developing from one of the cells composing the carpogonial branch; reduction division (meiosis) ordinarily occurring after fertilization in the carpogonium; tetrasporophyte (a generation which produces spores in groups of four) present in some genera.
2. Order Gelidiales. Flattened, branched, uniaxial filamentous fronds; carpogonial branch simple, and the carpogonia clumped; auxiliary cell (see p. 240) not formed; life history with male, female, and tetrasporophytes.
3. Order Cryptonemiales (Coralline Algae). Incrusting or erect, and mostly calcium-encrusted thalli, uni- or multiaxial; carpogonial branches specialized and sometimes clumped, with auxiliary cells on special branches; mostly with male, female, and tetrasporophyte plants in the life history.
4. Order Gigartinales. Highly branched, erect thalli; filamentous, membranous, or prostrate; carpogonial branches

short and unspecialized; auxiliary cell formed from a vegetative cell in an unspecialized filament; mostly with male, female, and tetrasporophyte plants in the life history.

5. Order Rhodymeniales. Multiaxial fronds, with short carpogonial branches; auxiliary cells from a branch that grows from the supporting cell (the cell which gives rise to the carpogonial branch); male, female, and tetrasporic plants in the life history.

6. Order Ceramiales. Carpogonial branch formed from a supporting cell that is cut off laterally as a pericentral cell;[4] auxiliary cell formed from the supporting cell following fertilization; male, female, and tetrasporic plants in the life history.

VII. **Phylum Cyanophyta (Blue-Green Algae).** Unicellular, colonial, and filamentous algae in which phycocyanin usually predominates; cells without a true nucleus; lacking motile cells; lacking sexual reproduction.

I. **Subphylum Coccogoneae.** Cells solitary or colonial, enclosed in copious mucilage.

1. Order Chroococcales. Cells mostly spherical; solitary or colonial in mucilage; reproduction by fission only.

2. Order Chamaesiphonales. Cells mostly elongate; club-shaped cells solitary, or gregarious, attached; reproduction by endospores.

3. Order Pleurocapsales. Cells arranged to form prostrate clumps or strands, or somewhat pseudofilamentous; reproduction by endospores. (Herein included with Chamaesiphonales.)

II. **Subphylum Hormogoneae.** Plants multicellular filaments.

1. Order Pscillatoriales.[6] Filaments unbranched, without differentiation; sheath present or absent.

2. Order Nostocales. Filaments unbranched, with differentiation of certain cells to form heterocysts (Plate XI, Fig. 147) and akinetes.[5]

[4] Pericentral cells are cut off from and surround the main axial filament (see Plate XXI, Fig. 263-b).

[5] A spore formed from a modified, thick-walled vegetative cell (see Plate XI, Fig. 114-b).

[6] See Drouet, 1968, for a rearrangement of the Oscillatoriaceae.

3. Order Scytonematales. Filaments with differentiated cells and with false branching (see Plate XI, Fig. 150); often forming tufts.
4. Order Stigonematales. Filaments with differentiated cells (heterocysts); with true branching; often forming mucilaginous clumps, or feathery tufts (see Plate XI, Fig. 152).
5. Order Rivulariales. Filaments tapering from base to apex; heterocysts and akinetes basal; false branching in some.

VIII. Phylum Cryptophyta (Blue and Red Flagellates). Compressed, unsymmetrical or slipper-shaped flagellated cells with one or two flagella, usually of unequal length and either apical or subapical; xanthophylls or chlorophyll predominant in plate-like chloroplasts; food reserve starch-like carbohydrates.

1. Order Cyptomonadales. Cells motile.
2. Order Cryptococcales. Cells non-motile, cyst-like, forming cryptophycean zoospores in reproduction.

IX. Phylum Chloromonadophyta (Chloromonads). Unicellular, biflagellate cells; chlorophyll predominating in radially arranged chloroplasts (some members colorless); food reserve oil; cells with trichocysts.

1. Order Chloromonadales (the only order).

Occurrence of Algae[7]

In general, algae are aquatic and, like other water inhabitors, often are more widely distributed than are terrestrial species. But algae are highly selective of particular habitats and are known to require specific chemical and physical conditions. Of course all organisms in one sense are aquatic, and this possibly reflects the aquatic origin of terrestrial beings. Some creatures live on or in water; others exist with at least some of their surface (roots, e.g.) exposed to a film of water. Still others (terrestrial animals) absorb needed quantities and carry water around with them, returning periodically for replenishment.

But some algae exist well when surrounded only by a film of water and hence occur on and even under the soil (subterranean algae), sometimes even to a depth of a meter or more. On sandy beaches, where quartz permits the passage of light, a profuse growth of algae and other organisms occurs, forming a densely green stratum (psammon) just beneath the

[7] See Chapter 8, Ecology.

surface. Algae that live on moist rocks (lithophilic), wood, or soil are said to be *aerial*, or more properly subaerial.

Many algae occur only in salt water (euryhaline), a few exist equally well in brackish water, and a smaller number of species occur in both fresh and salt water (*Prasiola, Enteromorpha, Cladophora*).

Hot springs and geyser waters are populated by mostly blue-green algae. Some of these are specifically *thermal*, whereas others, though commonly occurring at normal temperatures, are adjustable to temperatures as high as 85°C. Diatoms have been reported from water moderately hot (40°C), but green algae are conspicuously absent in hot springs.

In contrast, genera such as *Chlamydomonas, Scotiella, Raphidonema*, and many others occur in ice and snow; when abundant they produce the red snow of high altitudes. Although these are mostly green algae, many of them, especially when encysted, contain a red pigment (haematochrome) that develops in cells exposed to intense illumination. Such a flora is known as *cryoplankton* or *cryobiota*.

It is not surprising that many algae, both marine and fresh-water, have assumed the habit of living on other plants (*epiphytic*), whether these be other algae or higher plants, such as terrestrial vegetation in moist tropics. Some algae are specifically related to a particular host, whereas others are only incidentally epiphytic but do seem to select plant tissues rather than other substrates for their attachment. Some species grow within or among the cells of host plants as *endophytes* (*Anabaena* in cycads), and in such instances are in part *parasitic* (*Cephaleuros* in tea leaves), producing pathological conditions. Still others are wholly parasitic.

Similarly, algae may live on (*epizoic*) or within (*endozoic*) animals. Examples include Zooxanthellae in corals; *Chlorella* (*Zoochlorella*) in sponges and *Hydra*; *Characium* on the antennae of mosquito larvae; *Basicladia* on turtles; blue-green algae in the intestinal tract of mammals; *Chlorella* beneath the scales of fish.

Whereas many algae are attached (*sessile*) or *benthic*, a host of species drift and are buoyed in water as *plankton*. When an organism floats in open water it is known as *euplankton* (true plankton); when it is unattached but living among algal mixtures near shore and in weed beds it is said to be in the *tychoplankton*. Plankton of rivers is called *potamoplankton*; of ponds, *heleoplankton*. Organisms which drift but are attached to or are suspended by the surface film are known as *neuston* (cf. **Nautococcus** in Plate I, Fig. 1). When attached or sedentary many algae form a coating or a slimy film over the surface of submerged objects constituting what is known in German as *Aufwuchs*. Sometimes the term *periphyton* is used to describe algae growing on or around higher plants (emergent reeds, etc.) especially at the water level.

Although often not specifically confined to flowing water, certain species of fresh-water algae are well-adjusted to and are seemingly selective of currents (*Cladophora* spp, *Stigeoclonium* spp). Also many marine algae are adjusted to the severe movements of tidal waters and to wave action (*Fucus*, *Postelsia*). Attached stream algae can be referred to as rheophilic, a category which would include lithophilic algae — those forms, such as *Nostoc parmeloides* and many other Cyanophyta (*Phormidium*, *Stigonema*, *Gloeocapsa*), which characteristically attach themselves to rocks. Marine algae include many species which are rock-inhabiting (often encrusting). Sand and mud of course are not suitable substrates for attachment, although some forms (*Fucus*, *Enteromorpha*) are able to grow on sand and gravel unattached.

A few algae such as *Hyella* in the Cyanophyta and *Gomontia* in the Chlorophyta are shell-boring (calciphilic); others are wood-boring (lignophilic).

Of considerable biological interest is the commensal association of algae and fungi to form lichens. Different species of fungi growing with different species of algae produce different "species" of lichens. Blue-green algae primarily are involved, but unicellular (*Trebouxia*) and filamentous (*Trentepohlia*) green algae also may occur. At least in some associations the fungi parasitize the algal cells.

Cytology

CELL WALL

The majority of algae have a two-layered wall: the inner is firm and contains microfibrils; the outer is gelatinous and amorphous. The wall is composed of various carbohydrates such as cellulose, pectin, mucilage, and in some instances may contain proteins also. Not infrequently the wall is impregnated with calcium, iron, silicon, or chitin. The carbohydrates are either mucilaginous and water-soluble, or non-soluble. Among the former are included cellulose, mannose (to a lesser degree), and chitin (to an even lesser degree). The latter are referred to as pectin substances (e.g., amyloids or callose). Rather significantly the wall of blue-green algae contains diaminopimelic acid, a substance lacking in other algae but present in bacteria — another bit of evidence suggesting phylogenetic relationship between Cyanophyta and the Schizophyta.

Composition of the cell wall varies from phylum to phylum as well as within phyla; details will be taken up in the discussion of respective groups. In general, however, we can state that cellulose takes two forms: cellulose-I, typical of higher plants; and cellulose-II, mercerized by treatment with alkalis. Cellulose-I is found in *Cladophora*; cellulose-II in *Ulva*, *Ulothrix*, and probably others.

Some forms, however, have no true wall (*Pyramimonas, Gymnodinium, Euglena*) but only the bounding (plasma) membrane of the cytoplasm, known as a *pellicle*. This may be variously striated or ornamented. In several unicellular algae (*Pteromonas, Trachelomonas, Dinobryon*) the organism (with its wall or pellicle) is enclosed by a shell, or *lorica*, composed of various substances, mostly cellulose and carbohydrate complexes, and sometimes impregnated with iron.

In some algae the wall contains definite simple or complex pores which function in mucilage discharge; in others (colonial or multicellular forms) pores provide for intercellular protoplasmic connections (plasmodesmata) (some Cyanophyta and Rhodophyta, e.g.). There are instances where the wall is constructed of two equal or unequal sections which adjoin variously and which separate when the cell undergoes division (Diatoms, Desmids, Tribonema).

Thanks to development of electron microscope techniques we now know much more about the micro-physical structure of the wall. Specifically we know that the wall is not a layer of homogeneous material. The details vary from group to group and in some instances the characters disclosed help to strengthen ideas concerning relationship; for others, previously held ideas of classification have been corrected. Commonly, the algal cell wall has a non-crystalline layer and an outer layer of fibrils (dispersed crystalline material), all of a carbohydrate chemistry. The fibrillar layer, composed of cellulose-I, has a pattern of fibrils lying at right angles to one another, with sometimes a third series of fibrils extended at another angle (see Chlorophyta cell wall, p. 39). The growth and extension of cell walls is related to and determined by the arrangement and rearrangement of fibrils.

Cytoplasm

Within the wall is a reticular layer of cytoplasm, bounded by a plasma membrane, which may form strands transversing the cell cavity. There are vacuoles (with a tonoplast) but these are lacking, or very minute, in most Cyanophyta. Vacuoles are large and favorable for study in some of the Siphonales such as *Valonia, Codium*, and in *Vaucheria*. Especially motile algae, and particularly those in fresh water, have contractile vacuoles; sometimes there is a primary reservoir surrounded by a number of smaller ones. Mitochondria are detectable in several groups, though not in the Cyanophyta. They are bounded by membranes and are important in cell physiology as the originators of enzymes which oxidize carbohydrates and synthesize proteins. These same enzymes are involved in the transfer of electrons in photosynthesis, a process known as the tricarboxylic-acid cycle. In those algal groups in which the xanthophylls and carotenes are predominant the mitochondrial surface is increased by means of extensions. Commonly the mitochondria show as slender bodies (threads or granules), and may occur in the lumen as well as in the cytoplasm.

Some cytological studies employing the electron microscope have shown a Golgi apparatus to be present. In *Pedinomonas* the Golgi apparatus consists of a body surrounded by numerous small vesicles. Such bodies are especially evident in desmid cells at the margins of chloroplasts, and are described as appearing like an aggregation of flattened vesicles. In motile forms the bodies may lie about the nucleus. Some cytologists claim that there is no Golgi apparatus comparable to that of animal cells.

Chondriosomes, which are metachromatic granules thought to be volutin, occur in the Chlorophyta, diatoms, and some euglenoids. The volutin of diatoms, however, is thought to be identical with leucosin or stored food material of the Chrysophyta.

Nucleus

Except in the Cyanophyta, there is a definite nucleus, with a nuclear membrane and nucleoli, as is found in higher plants. Chromosomes of quite varied shape are formed during mitosis, a process that involves spindle fibers except in the Dinophyceae (*Pyrrhophyta*) and some red algae. In some nuclear divisions the chromatin material (granules) may gather at an equatorial plate during metaphase and then pass to the poles during telophase to form new nuclei. Chromosomes are small and often numerous, varying in count from five to 48 or more. Both their small size and certain interfering cellular substances make the task of counting them a difficult one. Polyploidy occurs frequently under artificial conditions, resulting in some of the many recognized "strains" of species. Mitosis is of regular occurrence but there may be amitosis as for example in the Charales. In some of the euglenoids division of the chromatin material occurs within the nuclear membrane. The Dinophyceae are curiously lacking in the spindle fibers and centrosomes which occur in other algae, and are peculiar in having the chromatin in bead-like strands. Algal nuclear division may or may not be accompanied by wall-formation. Coenocytic cells or "units" may develop (*Cladophora*, Siphonales), or septations may form independent of nuclear division.

Algae which reproduce sexually have a meiotic division, usually with the formation of spores (meiospores or tetraspores) at the end of a diploid phase of the life cycle. Rarely, however, gametes (sex cells) are produced through meiosis (*Codium*, diatoms). In many algae which are sexually dioecious (separate male and female plants) reduction division results in two kinds of spores, male gametophyte- and female gametophyte-producing spores (see life histories below), indicating the presence of sex chromosomes.

EYE-SPOT

An intriguing organelle in motile algae and in reproductive elements of many non-motile algae is the eye-spot or pigment spot. This animal-like organelle is apparently light-sensitive and directs the movement of swimming cells. In some instances, however, certain motile cells are phototactic even though not provided with an eye-spot.

Structurally, the eye-spot varies from group to group. In the Volvocales, for example, one construction is that of a layer of pigment chambers. In the euglenoids there are carotinoid granules in a colorless matrix. The pigment (red or blackish) is a haematochrome, at least in part, and may be anterior, median, or even posterior in the cell, on the edge of the chloroplast, or near the base of the flagella. It may be a simple, cup-shaped plate, as in the Volvocales, or in a protoplasmic net-work of droplets.

During cell multiplication the eye-spot divides but it may arise *de novo* in an individual. In the sea lettuce (*Ulva*) the eye-spot comes from the fragmentation of a colored granule that appears suddenly just before the protoplast begins to undergo cleavage to form zoospores. In some cells, especially those located anteriorly, the eye-spot is accompanied by a lens-shaped plate which receives and directs light to it (see Euglenophyta, p. 189). The eye-spot in the Dinoflagellata is a complex *ocellus*, and the pigment exhibits amoeboid movement, as in *Trachelomonas* (Plate XIV,

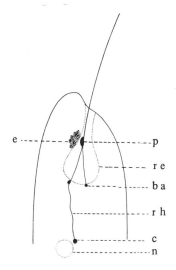

TEXT FIGURE 1.1

Neuromotor apparatus (one of several types) in *Euglena*. BA, basal granules (blepharoplasts); C, centriole (either posterior or anterior to nucleus); E, eye-spot; N, nucleus; P, photoreceptor; RE, reservoir; RH, rhizoplast.

Fig. 198). The colorless flagellates (*Polytoma*, e.g.) have pigment spots similar to those of the pigmented colonial flagellates; that is, a cluster of polygonal bodies comprises the eye-spot, each containing a core of thinner material as seen by permanganate fixation.

Centrosomes, lacking in the Dinoflagellates, appear in the Chlorophyta, Rhodophyta, and Phaeophyta, either just within or exterior to the nucleus. During nuclear division the centrosome enters into the formation of spindle fibers. In motile forms of the Chlorophyta the centrosome is joined by a fine protoplasmic thread (*rhizoplast*) to a fiber (*paradesmose*) which adjoins the two granules (*blepharoplasts*) that lie at the base of the flagella. This constitutes an incipient nervous system and is referred to as a *neuromotor apparatus*. When the motile cell becomes quiescent, the rhizoplast and the basal granules disappear. Silver staining has shown fine (see Text Figure 1.1) fibrils in the ectoplasm that are connected with the flagellar structure. It is assumed that the centriole in non-motile algae is a relic of a motile ancestor. Of particular interest is the fact that this organ is present in some red algae, a group in which there is no motility.

FLAGELLA

Organs of locomotion vary from one to three (rarely four or more) and may be apical, subapical, or lateral in point of origin. Flagella are said to be *isodynamic* if they have a single movement (propulsion) and *hetero-dynamic* if one (or two) is used for lateral vibration or for turning movements, attachment, etc. Ordinarily there is a granule at the base of each flagellum, but these have not been found in *Ulva* and *Cladophora* (see Text Figures 1.1, 1.3). Oedogoniales (Chlorophyta) and *Derbesia* (Chlorophyta) have multiflagellate swimming cells where there is a ring-shaped centrosome and the flagella arise from a double row of granules. The number and morphology of flagella vary from phylum to phylum, as well as within a group. The electron microscope has revealed structural characteristics showing that flagella morphology once thought to be peculiar to respective algal groups is possessed by genera in several phyla. There is a bewildering number of variations and modifications in the finer details of flagellar structure which invite investigation. Cross section examination of flagella show that almost invariably there are two axial, central fibrils surrounded by nine others,[8] all enclosed by a sheath which is an extension of the plasma membrane. In a few forms the axial fibrils are coiled; in all forms each of the nine peripheral fibrils is composed of two smaller fibrils. Whereas these nine fibrils extend to the basal body, the two central fibrils terminate just short of the granule. In the region between the basal granule

[8] The total number of fibrils varies, some flagella having nine (or ten).

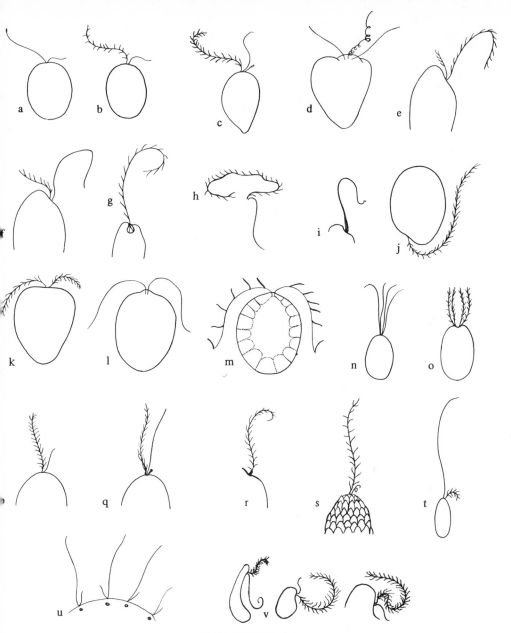

TEXT FIGURE 1.2

Types of flagella found among algal cells. a, *Anisomonas*; b, *Thallassomonas*; c, *Synura*; d, *Chrysochromulina*; e, *Cryptomonas*; f, *Chilomonas*; g, *Euglena*; h, *Gyrodinium* (flagella only); i, *Chromulina*; j, *Pedinomonas*; k, *Bipedinomonas*; l, *Chlamydomonas*; m, *Haematococcus*; n, *Draparnaldia* (zoospore); o, *Platymonas*; p, *Ochromonas*; q, *Synura*; r, *Micromonas*; s, *Mallomonas*; t, *Vaucheria* (**gamete**); u, *Vaucheria* (zoospore); v, *Phaeophyta* **flagellation**.

and the flagellar shaft there is a star-shaped pattern of fibrils (in *Chlamydomonas*) which interconnect one of the two fibrilar components of the nine peripheral fibers. Whether these ultramicroscopic structures play a role in the neuromotor apparatus is not known.

There are four[9] general types of flagella (with variations) (see Text Figure 1.2). One is the *simple* flagellum, a slender, smooth whip which,

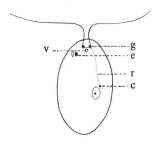

TEXT FIGURE 1.3

Neuromotor apparatus in a volvocoid cell. C, centriole; E, eye-spot; G, basal granules (blepharoplast), interconnected by a fibril, the paradesmose; R, rhizoplast; V, contractile vacuoles (2) at right angles to the granules. The centriole may be intranuclear or extranuclear.

at least in those forms so far investigated, does not taper to a point, but is the same diameter throughout. The second is the *acronematic*, a smooth whip which abruptly terminates in a fibril (flimmer). A third type, with variations, is the *pleuronematic* in which there are lateral fibrils or flimmers or *mastigonemes*. When the flimmers arise on opposite sides of the flagellum it is said to be *pantonematic* (probably radial in arrangement); when the fibrils are unilateral the flagellum is *stichonematic*. Occasionally there is an apiculus as well as lateral fibrils; in such cases the flagellum is said to be *pantocronematic*. Still another type of flagellum-like structure is the *haptonema*, which appears especially in marine flagellates such as *Chrysochromulina*. This is often coiled, may be long or short, and even "buried," or difficult of observation. It has a different number of fibrils than the other flagella.

Pigments

Perhaps the most obvious and arresting characteristic of the algae is their colors — variable and attractive in hue and bewildering in chemistry. Each phylum has its own particular combination of pigments and, in general, a

---

[9] Deflandre, 1934.

characteristic color. Although a wealth of information has been gleaned from investigations of algal pigments and of their role in photosynthesis, much more research is needed. Remembering the age of the algae it is not surprising that they have developed, in addition to those also possessed by higher plants, a number of pigments that are peculiar to them (see Table 1.1). Interestingly enough the pigmentation of higher plants is very similar to that of the Chlorophyta, the phylum from which land plants are thought to have evolved. It must be pointed out that several phyla include colorless members — for example certain species and genera in the Euglenophyta, the Pyrrhophyta, and a few Chlorophyta. Nevertheless, some colorless flagellates have been shown to possess plastids (*Polytoma*, e.g.). These plastids contain the same tubular microstructures as possessed by *Chlamydomonas*.

Occurring in the nine recognized phyla of algae are five chlorophylls, 20 xanthophylls (the majority of which are known in only a few groups), five carotenes, and seven phycobilins (red or blue). The phycobilins are described as being tetrapyrrolic compounds joined to globulin-proteins. Anthocyans (red or purplish) may occur also. In general, the pigments can be listed as follows:

Chlorophyll-*a*, -*b*, -*c*, -*d*, -*e*
Carotenoid Hydrocarbons
    Carotene-*a*, -*B*, *E*-, -*y*, flavicin, lycopene
    Chromolipoid: Haematochrome
        B-Carotene in **Trentepohlia**
        Ketonic Carotenoid: euglenarhodone in
        Haematococcus
        Unknown metonic pigments in **Protosiphon**
        (red forms)
Oxycarotenes
    Xanthophylls: Lucein, Zeaxanthin, Violaxanthin, Flavoxanthin, Neo-
    xanthin, Siphonein, Siphonoxanthin, Fucoxanthin, Neofucoxanthin,
    Diatoxanthin, Dinoxanthin, Neodinoxanthin, Peridinin, Myxoxanthin,
    Myxoxanthophyll, Aphanicin, Aphanizophyll, Aslaxanthin, Oscilloxan-
    thin, Taraxanthin, Neofucoxanthin-*A*, Neofucoxanthin-*B*, Antheraxan-
    thin, Cryptoxanthin
Proteinaceous or Phycochromoproteids
    Phycobilins: *r*-Phycoerythrin, *c*-Phycoerythrin, *r*-Phycocyanin, *c*-Phy-
    cocyanin, Phycoerythrin-*x*, *B*-Phycoerythrin, Allophycocyanin

The dominant (abundant) pigments are Chlorophyll-*a*, coloring the Chlorophyta green; carotene and diatomin in the Chrysophyceae; the

TABLE 1.1

CHLOROPHYTA	EUGLENOPHYTA	PHAEOPHYTA
Chlorophylls	Chlorophylls	Chlorophylls
Chlorophyll-a	Chlorophyll-a	Chlorophyll-a
Chlorophyll-b	Chlorophyll-b	Carotenes
Carotenes	Carotenes	B-Carotene
a-Carotene	a-Carotene	Xanthophylls
Euglenarhodone (some)	Euglenarhodone (some)	Violaxanthin
B-Carotene	B-Carotene	Flavoxanthin
Xanthophylls	E-Carotene	Neoxanthin
Lycopene (y-Carotene)	Flavicin	Neofucoxanthin-A
Lutein	Xanthophylls	Neofucoxanthin-B
Siphonein	Zeaxanthin	
Zeaxanthin	Violaxanthin	
Siphonoxanthin	Flavoxanthin	
Violaxanthin	Neoxanthin	
Astaxanthin	Others ?	
Neoxanthin		
Cryptoxanthin		

CHRYSOPHYTA

A. Bacillariophyceae	B. Chrysophyceae	C. Xanthophyceae
Chlorophylls	Chlorophylls	Chlorophylls
Chlorophyll-a	Chlorophyll-a	Chlorophyll-a
Chlorophyll-c	Chlorophyll-c	Chlorophyll-c
Carotenes	Chlorophyll-d	Carotenes
B-Carotene	Chlorophyll-e	a-Carotene
E-Carotene	Carotenes	B-Carotene
Xanthophylls	a-Carotene	E-Carotene
Fucoxanthin	B-Carotene	Xanthophylls
Neofucoxanthin-A	E-Carotene	Flavacin
Neofucoxanthin-B	Xanthophylls	Flavoxanthin
Diatoxanthin	Flavacin	
Diadinoxanthin	Lutein	
	Zeaxanthin	
	Violaxanthin	
	Flavoxanthin	
	Neoxanthin	
	Fucoxanthin	
	Neofucoxanthin-A	
	Neofucoxanthin-B	
	Diatoxanthin	
	Diadinoxanthin	
	Dinoxanthin	
	Neodinoxanthin	
	Peridinin	
	Myxoxanthin	
	Myxoxanthophyll	

PYRRHOPHYTA

Chlorophylls
  Chlorophyll-*a*
Carotenes
  B-Carotene
  E-Carotene
Xanthophylls
  Flavicin
  Flavoxanthin
  Diadinoxanthin
  Dinoxanthin
  Neodinoxanthin
  Peridinin

RHODOPHYTA

Chlorophylls
  Chlorophyll-*a*
Carotenes
  B-Carotene
  E-Carotene
Xanthophylls
  Flavicin
  Violaxanthin
  Flavoxanthin
  Neoxanthin
  Fucoxanthin
  Neofucoxanthin-*A*
  Neofucoxanthin-*B*
  Diatoxanthin
  Diadinoxanthin
  Dinoxanthin
  Neodinoxanthin
  Peridinin
  Myxoxanthin
  Myxoxanthophyll
Phycobilins
  r-Phycoerythrin
  r-Phycocyanin
  B-Phycoerythrin

CYANOPHYTA

Chlorophylls
  Chlorophyll-*a*
Carotenes
  a-Carotene
  B-Carotene
  E-Carotene
Xanthophylls
  Flavicin
  Violaxanthin
  Flavoxanthin
  Lutein
  Zeaxanthin
  Neoxanthin
  Fucoxanthin
  Neofucoxanthin-*A*
  Neofucoxanthin-*B*
  Diatoxanthin
  Diadinoxanthin
  Dinoxanthin
  Neodinoxanthin
  Peridinin
  Oscilloxanthin
  Aphanizophyll
  Antheraxanthin
  Myxoxanthin
  Myxoxanthophyll
Phycobilins
  c-Phycoerythrin
  c-Phycocyanin
  Allophycocyanin

CRYPTOPHYTA

Chlorophylls
  Chlorophyll-*a*
  Chlorophyll-c
Carotenes
  a-Carotene
  E-Carotene
Xanthophylls
  Zeaxanthin
  Diadinoxanthin
  Cryptoxanthin
  Dinoxanthin
Phycobilins
  c-Phycocyanin
  Phycoerythrin
  Phycoerythrin-x (?)

CHLOROMONADOPHYTA

Chlorophylls
  Chlorophyll-*a*
Carotenes
  B-Carotene
Xanthophylls
  Lutein monoepoxide
  Antheraxanthin
  Hydroxylated lutein epoxide
  Other Xanthophylls (?)

characteristic yellowish-green or brown of the Chrysophyta; fucoxanthin, which colors the Phaeophyta; phycoerythrin, which colors the Rhodophyta; and phycocyanin, which colors the Cyanophyta.

Of the five known chlorophylls, only -a is found in all algae, whereas -b occurs in the Chlorophyta and the Euglenophyta, a circumstance which has led to the speculation that these two are phylogenetically related. Chlorophylls may account for as much as 6% of the dry weight, but amounts are usually much less (0.5–1.5%). Naturally chlorophylls are the important photosynthetic pigments. Light absorption in the chlorophylls of Chlorophyta is greater at 405–430 mμ and at 640–680 mμ; it would naturally follow that the greatest photosynthetic rates occur in relation to these two absorption peaks.

The red (650–680 mμ) and the blue rays (400–450 mμ) are absorbed by chlorophylls, whereas blue and green light rays (430-500 mμ band) are absorbed by carotenes and xanthophylls. The carotenoids are not only protective, acting as screens to light, but are also useful in the transfer of energy of light waves to chlorophyll. Further there is evidence that carotenoids actually perform as co-enzymes in the photosynthetic process. In this transfer carotenoids accept otherwise destructive oxygen molecules. We do not know how universally true it is but at least in some cultured algae carotenoids, as well as phycoerythrin, also act with chlorophyll in the photosynthetic process by absorbing some light. In fact it has been shown experimentally in some algae that the water soluble pigments absorb the light and that photosynthesis is related more to these than to chlorophyll-a.

Fucoxanthin also serves as a supplementary light-absorbing pigment in both Phaeophyta and Bacillariophyceae (Chrysophyta).

Chlorophylls, carotenes, and xanthophylls are fat-soluble, whereas phycobilins are water-soluble, occurring only in the red and blue-green algae (although phycoerythrin has been found in the Cryptophyta). Of these R-phycoerythrin and C-phycocyanin are the most abundant, with the former absorbing blue, green, and sometimes yellow rays, and the latter absorbing green, red, and yellow. The B-phycoerythrin found in one species of *Porphyra* (Rhodophyta) absorbs rays at 545μ, while the blue pigment allophycocyanin, which occurs in the Rhodophyta (but not the Cyanophyta), absorbs at 650–654 mμ.

The same algal species growing in different habitats shows variations in the relative abundance of pigments. Doubtless, pigment composition is important in determining the vertical distribution. Although Rhodophyta, for example, can live at a 200-foot depth or more, Chlorophyta are restricted to upper or shallow water zones. Brown algae in turn grow well (if not better) in water of medium depth. The general adaptability of Phaeophyta to moderately reduced light seems to explain horizontal distribution as well, for they grow luxuriantly in fog-shrouded regions and in those parts of the world which are cloud-covered much of the time (north Pacific coasts, the Subantarctic, and the Arctic, which can successfully nurture the growth of brown and yellow-pigmented algae).

Rhodophycean species growing in deep water are richer in phycoery-thrin than are individuals growing in shallow water or in the intertidal zones (*Chondrus crispus*, e.g.). Because red light rays are absorbed rapidly in the upper levels of water, only green and ultraviolet rays penetrate deeply. Hence Rhodophyta can live in abysmal depths because of the ability of phycobilins to make use of such rays in photosynthesis. Cyano-phyta in general show pigment adaptation in relation to light intensity, which accounts in part for their ability to grow well both in subdued and in direct light (soil and rock surfaces).

CHLOROPLASTS

Except in the Cyanophyta pigments are contained in a plastid, the chloroplast. This organelle varies in morphology throughout the algae and reference will be made to it under respective phyla discussions. The chloroplast may be a parietal plate, disc, or network, or it may be an axial band, stellate body, an oval body, a lobed disc, or a parietal ring. In the Cyanophyta there is no chloroplast, but the pigments often appear concentrated in a peripheral zone of the protoplast. This area is generally referred to as the chromoplasm.

In some nomenclatures the pigment-bearing body is called a *chloro-plast* when chlorophyll is the predominating and masking filament (Chlor-ophyta, Euglenophyta), and *chromatophore* when pigments other than chlorophyll are dominant. More recently it has become customary to use the term chloroplast in referring to those bodies which have a demonstrably lamellated structure. Chromoplast refers to colored plastids in bacteria, worms, and other animals in which there are no lamellae.

The basic structure of the chloroplast is very similar throughout the "plant" kingdom: a body which has a double outer membrane enclosing bands of lamellae (lipoproteins), interspersed by a more or less homog-enous, aqueous matrix. In *Astrephomene*, for example, the chloroplast has a membrane enclosing discs or plates in parallel stacks of usually three. The interspersed matrix contains about 80% of all the water in the chloroplast. In the Cyanophyta the lamellae (not organized into a chloroplast) are scattered in the chromoplasm.

An organelle usually found in the chloroplast, or lying on its surface, is the *pyrenoid*, a proteinaceous granule which functions as a starch-ac-cumulating or -concentrating center. In at least some algae the protein-aceous material becomes interspersed and continuous with the chloroplast lamellae. When the protoplast divides to form zoospores the pyrenoids may disappear, and then reappear in the swimming spores. Sometimes the organ divides when the cell divides vegetatively.

RESERVE FOOD AND NUTRITION

Although most algae are autotrophic, other nutritional methods and combinations of methods are employed. Photosynthesis constructs organic compounds from carbon dioxide and water through the use of light as an energy source. A few algae, such as *Chlamydobotrys*, use organic compounds (*photo-organotrophic*); others are in part photosynthetic but need carbohydrates, such as sugars or acetate, for some energy. Still others, such as members of the Volvocales, carry on photosynthesis with light as an energy source, but are *heterotrophic* (i.e., they use organic compounds in the medium) at night (the nutrition is referred to as *mixotrophic*). A number of algae can use particulate matter in their heterotrophic nutrition (some Dinoflagellates, *Chrysochromulina*, e.g.), and are thus said to be *phagotrophic*. Nutrition through photosynthesis is *holophytic*.

Inorganic substances are used by some organisms in culture (*chemosynthetic* or *chemolithotrophic* nutrition) but how widespread this is in nature is not known. In all these types of nutrition it appears that various vitamins are needed, especially vitamin B_{12}.

Some of the final products of photosynthesis and of metabolism using other types of syntheses are seen in the reserve food materials that collect in the algal cell (see Table 9.1, p. 335). Included are proteins, oils, and various carbohydrates; their presence depends upon the metabolism within respective phyla. For example, amylose, or common starch $(C_6H_{10}O_5)$, occurs in the Chlorophyta. In the Euglenophyta a solid starch-like carbohydrate, paramylum, is found. Pyrrhophyta accumulate reserves of both starch and oil. The Chrysophyta use oil and a carbohydrate leucosin plus chrysolaminarin. Phaeophyta store their food as soluble carbohydrates (including at least one alcohol, mannitol) and as laminarin, a polymer of glucose (*B-D*-glucopyranose). The Rhodophyta accumulate a peculiar solid carbohydrate, floridean starch (a glucose residue), and some cholesterols, whereas the Cyanophyta have either a glycogen type of food reserve or a cyanophyte starch (amylopectin) together with some proteins.

Growth

Increase in the size of the cell, whether followed immediately or not by cell division, is under the control of hormones or hormone-like regulators within the cell. Growth involves the elaboration and deposition of new material in regions where the wall is stretching, or the interpolation of new sections, girdles, or sleeves.

Polarity is observable in the anterior end of a cell, or of a plant, where elongation and new wall formation often occur more rapidly. Auxins determine polarity, at least in plants, and in some instances light is the factor which triggers the necessary auxin. Physical contacts with substrates or the presence of other cells may likewise stimulate auxin action. Such inherent polarity can be seen in the development of spores and germlings of plants, and in the development of branches in the anterior end of both multicellular plants and unicellular Siphonales thalli. *Bryopsis* germlings (Plate VIII, Fig. 104) similarly show a directional growth in response to light, and *Ulothrix* and *Trentepohlia* are known to be positively phototrophic.

In the development from *Fucus* zygotes (see Text Figure 6.1, p. 230) polarity is determined at the first division, when an apical (outer) cell and a lower (basal) cell are formed. A rhizoid promptly grows out of the lower cell in a direction opposite to the source of light.

The zoospores of *Oedogonium* are polarized but the anterior end of the spore becomes the base of the plant. Elongation occurs in a direction opposite to the apex of the spore, and the base of the spore (posterior pole) becomes the apical cell of the germling. Culture experiments with *Enteromorpha* and *Ulva* have demonstrated an axial gradient in the thallus. Such a gradient involves a greater degree of osmotic pressure at the anterior end. Jacobs (1951) reports on polarity of an auxin behavior in *Bryopsis*. When a thallus (see Plate VIII, Fig. 104) of this plant is cut and inverted, and indolyl acetic acid is applied to the free, basal end, the branch apices develop rhizoids. Experiments with *Acetabularia* (Plate VIII, Fig. 100) also demonstrate polarity. Here, the one nucleus in the siphonous plant is in the basal portion of the thallus in the rhizoidal region. Notwithstanding the remoteness of the terminal lobes, the apical region maintains its polarity and a strong regenerative capacity.

Reproduction

Reproduction in the algae occurs in three general ways, with variations in certain species. Vegetative reproduction is common to all algae and includes multiplication by cell division or by fragmentation — any method, in short, that uses only vegetative cells and does not employ any specialized structure, whether cell, or organ. Asexual reproduction is accomplished by using differentiated or specialized cells or organs capable of directly multiplying the plant without uniting with any other cells. Many different kinds of spores are involved in asexual reproduction, particularly the swimming zoospore. Zoospores are equipped with one, two, four, or many flagella (variously attached), and commonly contain a bit of chloroplast and a pigment-spot. The zoospores are produced frequently and often in large numbers and so multiply the plant greatly. Their motility enables them to distribute the species; the eye-spots enable them to do so advantageously. Zoospores (produced one to many within a cell) are haploid in almost all instances and give rise to haploid or sexual generations. They may be produced in unspecialized cells or in differentiated zoosporangia. Zoospores may be formed from the same plant which also produces sex cells (gametes) or from a separate, diploid generation. Whereas zoospores have no wall, the *aplanospore*, many of which are produced within a cell, is enclosed by a wall and is non-motile. When an aplanospore forms an especially thick wall, suitable for dormancy, it is called a *hypnospore*. A special kind of aplanospore, the *endospore*, is formed when the entire content of a cell, or only a portion of the protoplast, is cut into small, reproductive, non-motile elements either simultaneously or successively (Chamaesiphonales in the Cyanophyta, e.g.). Usually these are naked.

When an entire vegetative cell, especially in filamentous forms, lays down a much-thickened wall and concentrates reserve food it forms an *akinete*. This spore can either germinate in place to form a branch, or may persist after death of the plant and produce a new generation. Akinetes may be borne singly or in series; sometimes an entire filament becomes converted to these spores.

Some algae cannot undergo ordinary cell division but multiply vegetatively by dividing the cell content into small replicas of the parent which are called *autospores* (e.g., *Oocystis*, *Tetraedron* in the Chlorophyta; see Plate III, Fig. 42).

Monospores are produced singly, usually in a special cell called the *monosporangium*. The latter occurs in the so-called primitive Rhodophyta especially, although a vegetative cell may here serve also as the monosporangium.

Tetraspores, usually produced by reduction division, are formed in groups of four — hence the name. These are mostly produced in special cells, *tetrasporangia* (commonly found in the Rhodophyta).

Androspores are a special type of zoospore produced in differentiated cells of Oedogoinales filaments known as *androsporangia*. Androspores germinate to form dwarf male plants only.

Spores produced within the female organ (carpogonium of the Rhodophyta) or near it after fertilization, are called *carpospores*. These are non-motile, either haploid or diploid, and give rise either to a haploid (sexual) or to a diploid (tetrasporophyte) generation.

Spores produced directly from a diploid cell by reduction division (meiosis) may be called *meiospores*, and can be either motile or non-motile.

At times the contents of a cell form a thick-walled cyst within the mother cell wall. The cyst wall either can be in two parts, as in the diatoms, or can have a plug in a silicious wall (as in the Chrysophyceae). Such cysts are referred to as *statospores*.

Rarely, as in some Cyanophyta, a short section of a filament will become invested by a thickened membrane and the unit, separated from the main filament, will serve in reproduction as a *hormospore*.

A *zygospore* is a thick-walled, encysted zygote formed by union of sex cells (gametes). In germination it produces either haploid spores (by meiosis) or a diploid generation which in turn produces spores by meiosis.

Sexual reproduction comes at the end of a "growing season," or may be induced by unfavorable or critical changes in the environment. In sexual reproduction specialized elements are produced, either in unspecialized, vegetative cells or in the male sex organ (*antheridium*) or female sex organ (*oogonium*) (*carpogonium* in the Rhodophyta). These sex cells are incapable ordinarily of producing a new plant by themselves, but must unite (syngamy) with another cell to form a zygote. Such cells are called *gametes*. When the uniting gametes come from the same individual the plant is said to be *homothallic*; when they come from different plants the species is said to be *heterothallic*. When the two uniting gametes are similar in size, shape, and behavior, and do not show any recognizable maleness or femaleness, they are called *isogametes*. If there is enough difference so that a degree of maleness and femaleness is evident, they are called *anisogametes*. Both may be the same shape and motile, but one may be slightly larger and sluggish in movement, the other smaller and more active (characteristic of a male gamete). When sexuality is clearly evident and the gametes are different in size, shape, and/or behavior — when, in short, there is a clearly defined egg and sperm — they are called *heterogametes* (oogamous reproduction).

Life History and Alternation of Generations

The alternation of generations (*gametophyte* with *sporophyte*) which characterizes the life cycle of the plant type of organism had its beginnings among the algae. Throughout the algal groups there are varying degrees of life history complexity but the basic plan is the same: a sexual plant (gametophyte) produces gametes which unite to form a diploid asexual generation. The latter forms spores by meiosis, and these in turn grow into new gametophytes. The two generations may be similar in form (*isomorphic*) or different in size and shape (*heteromorphic*). Hence,

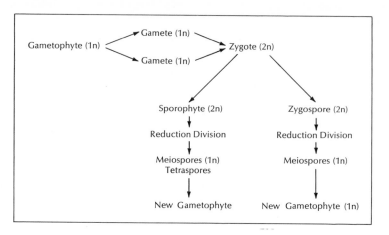

CHART 1.1   Outline of Plant Life History

algae may be said to belong to Isogeneratae or Heterogeneratae, depending on their life history. A knowledge of the type of life history used by a plant is important for a number of reasons, especially in reference to classification and physiology.

The zygote produced by gametic union behaves differently from group to group and even within groups; the variations will be considered further along. In general, the diploid zygote follows one of three behavior plans. (1) It may form a thick-walled resting cell or cyst, as previously mentioned, called a zygospore. Upon germination meiosis occurs to form four (or more) haploid zoospores, aplanospores, or at least four haploid nuclei which are capable of initiating new plants. (2) The zygote may germinate by meiosis promptly without forming a zygospore to produce haploid, reproductive elements, as in many Rhodophyta. (3) In most instances, however, the non-resting zygote germinates to form a diploid plant (or filamentous growth in many Rhodophyta) which, when mature, eventually produces spores (tetraspores or meiospores) by reduction division.

The gamete-producing generation is nearly always haploid; correspondingly the spore-producing plant is diploid. The gametophyte generation thus begins with meiosis and ends with fertilization, whereas the sporophyte begins with syngamy and ends with meiosis. In the "lower" algae the sporophyte consists of only the diploid zygospore. The plan of a life cycle is shown in Chart 1.1. The many variations will be discussed in appropriate places.

In many instances zoospores and gametes are similar in respect to their morphology and motility. Thus sex cells probably developed in the evolution of reproductive methods as specialized or metamorphosed zoospores. In other words, gametes (especially isogametes) are zoospores lacking some chemical, some vitality, to carry on their reproductive destiny alone; instead they need to pool or to complement their chemical, hormonal, or electrical equipment by uniting with an appropriate cell. Although no firm rule can be applied there is, in general, an evolution of sexual reproduction — isogamy to oogamy — that parallels developing degrees of complexity in morphology. The most advanced forms of algae are oogamous and sometimes possess complex life histories.

Duration

Algae can be classified according to the duration in time of the two generations. A useful scheme proposed by Feldmann (1937) refers mostly to the marine algae, but is applicable to the fresh-water forms as well:

I. **Annual Plants**

   A. Ephemerophyceae. Found the year round; plant producing several generations a year; reproductive elements develop without a resting period: **Cladophora** p.p., **Enteromorpha, Monostroma, Polysiphonia.**

   B. Eclipsiophyceae: Found in obvious state (larger of two generations) during part of the year only; plants passing remainder of year as a microscopic vegetative organism: **Sporochnus, Asperococcus.**

   C. Hynophyceae. Algae found in the obvious (large) state during part of the year only; passing remainder of time in a dormant resting stage, either as a spore, akinete, zygospore, quiescent germling, etc.: **Ulothrix, Vaucheria, Spirogyra, Chara, Porphyra.**

II. **Perennial Plants**

   A. Phanerophyceae. Entire plant perennial; erect: **Codium, Fucus** p.p., **Chara** p.p.

   B. Chamaephyceae. Entire plant perennial; a crust and prostrate: **Hildenbrandtia, Lithophyllum.**

   C. Hemiphanerophyceae. Only part of erect plant perennial: **Sargassum, Cladophora** p.p., **Laminaria** p.p.

   D. Hemicryptophyceae. Only basal part of thallus persisting: **Cladostephus, Gymnogongrus, Acetabularia.**

Chapter 2

Bryosis plumosa, a *siphonaceous green alga.*
(Reproduced from Nature Printed British Sea-
weeds, London, 1860)

Phylum Chlorophyta

Chlorophyta includes the green algae, though literally translated the name means merely "green plants." One classification system uses the term Chlorophycophyta, or "green algal plants." Starch is the storage product, identifiable by staining with IKI, which gives a blue-black reaction. This phylum is composed of an unknown number of species, perhaps as many as 20,000, with more being discovered and named continually. There are, for example, 11,000 species of desmids alone (a group of the Conjugales; see p. 118). The diversity of size, form, and complexity is perhaps greater than in any of the other phyla, although in structure they are not as advanced as are the brown and red algae.

The range of architecture extends from minute unicells no more than a micron or two in diameter to four-feet-long *Chara* and the large, leafy, or strand-like green algae of the ocean. Perhaps fewer species occur in salt water than in fresh water, where they seem to have had their major evolution, if not origin. They live in both standing and flowing waters, attached or planktonic. A few are subaerial whereas others are epiphytic or parasitic on higher plants (see pp. 17, 324). Included in their morphological variation are motile and non-motile unicells, swimming and non-swimming colonies, branched and unbranched simple filaments, cushion-like thalli, sheets, siphonaceous and coenocytic filaments, complexes and aggregates of tubular threads to form penicillate tufts, stalked discs, and branched strands of macroscopic size.

The green algae are probably the latest group of algae to have evolved. Even so, fossil records, especially of the calcium-encrusted forms, date from the Silurian and the Pre-Cambrian. Some of the presently recognized orders have representatives in the Ordovician, the Dasycladales for example being known from the Permian. The Charales (Stoneworts) are also known from the Silurian, although in a somewhat simpler morphology than today's. And because of their relatively advanced stages even in this period, one can only speculate as to their true age.

Cytology

PIGMENTS

Almost by definition, the most conspicuous feature of the Chlorophyta
is their green pigments — chlorophylls — contained in variously shaped
bodies — the chloroplasts. In addition to chlorophyll-*a* there is chloro-
phyll-*b*, B-carotene, Y-carotene, a-carotene (at least in the sperm of
Charales), and many xanthophylls: lutein, zeaxanthin, violoxanthin, neoxanthin, siphonein, siphonoxanthin, lycopene, and astaxanthin (see Table
1.1, p. 26). Chlorophyll-*a* is considered to be the precursor of chloro-
phyll-*b*, a segment found only in one other phylum, the Euglenophyta.
This circumstance is used as evidence by some to justify the inclusion of
the Euglenophyta as a subphylum (the Euglenophytina) of the Chlorophyta. The amount of chlorophyll varies decidedly from plant to plant and
from time to time. For example, in *Chlorella* chlorophyll was found to
constitute 6.6% of the dry weight when cultured in the shade, but 3.3%
of dry weight when grown in the light.

Carotinoid pigments are yellow and orange with an aliphatic or alicytic
chemical structure. They occur in at least two recognizable classes: as
oxygen-free hydrocarbons (the carotenes), and as oxygenated derivatives of
these (the xanthophylls). B-Carotene is responsible for the brick-red or
orange-red color of the aerial, filamentous alga *Trentepohlia* which grows
on rocks and tree trunks. This alga is especially prevalent in the humid
tropics, where it often enters into combination with fungi to form the
lichen *Coenogonium*. Another carotene, a ketone carotenoid, is responsible
for the red color in the motile *Haematococcus* when encysted. Astaxanthin
also causes red coloring in some green algae as well as in some *Euglena*.
Anthocyans, rare among algae, mask the green of some forms such as
Mougeotia capucina, which occurs as clouds of light purple filaments in
soft water or acid habitats.

The B-type of carotene is more abundant in the green algae than in
other groups. In this respect, as in many others, they are similar in pigmentation to higher plants, although B-carotene is still more abundant
in higher plants than in green algae. Y-carotene is rarely found in the
green algae but curiously it is more abundant in chlorophycean male
gametes than in female.

CHLOROPLASTS

The chloroplast which contains the pigments is sometimes axial, plate-
like, or massive; usually, however, it is parietal, lying just within the cell
wall. More varied here than in other phyla, it may be cup-shaped, a mesh-

work, ribbons, oval discs, or a complete or incomplete ring. In the desmids and some Volvocales, the chloroplast is ribbed with flanges.

The chloroplast is composed of pairs of lamellae (from one to six) with a matrix between. The lamellae unite to form a disc. The grana characteristic of higher plant chloroplasts are lacking (but are present in *Micrasterias* and eventually may be demonstrated in other genera). The pyrenoid or starch-collecting body is also lamellated, but here the lamellae are thicker than those of the chloroplast and are continuous with them. No doubt there is a great variability in pyrenoid structure, as yet unrevealed.

The Cell Wall

Contrary to what might be expected for such relatively simple plants, the cell wall is not a homogeneous layer of amorphous material. In the Chlorophyta the cell wall commonly occurs in two (or three) layers, an inner firm membrane composed of lamellae, and outer mucilaginous and pectose layers. In *Urospora* and *Codiolum* there is, apart from this inner layer, a "cuticle" which, as shown by the electron microscope, is amorphous except in *Cladophora*, where it has parallel microfibrils. The inner membrane is composed mostly of pectin, cellulose, or celluose in combination with other carbohydrates of a polysaccharide nature. In the Cladophorales, for example, cellulose comprises as much as 41% of the wall material. These plants lack the outer mucilaginous layers and hence are subject to much epiphytism from other algae, the filaments sometimes being completely encased by blue-green algae and diatoms. In some cell walls lipids and proteins also occur; in others, hemicellulose. The Siphonales walls contain much pectin and callose rather than cellulose.

The wall carbohydrates may be soluble, insoluble, or both. Soluble carbohydrates include cellulose-I and, at times, cellulose-II, a regenerated or crystalline reconstruction resulting from the precipitation of cellulose in solution. At least in walls of *Halicystis*, a marine, siphonaceous genus, and in *Hydrodictyon* (the Water-Net), cellulose-II has been found by X-ray defraction. The presence of cellulose-I, cellulose-II, or both varies throughout the Chlorophyta; by contrast, no cellulose at all has been detected thus far in the Oedogoniales, for example. As many as six sugars have been found in the walls of green algae, whereas xylose and mannose have been found in the plume-like marine alga *Bryopsis*. Tiffany (1924) reported chitin in the Cladophorales but this has been doubted by some.

The inner cellulose layer may be impregnated with calcium. (The outer layer of the Siphonocladales [Dasycladales] is similarly impregnated.) In the Charales (most species of *Chara*) there is a superficial or external deposition of lime. It has been suggested that the calcium is deposited through bacterial action rather than as a result of photosynthesis, wherein simple lime is formed from the removal of carbon dioxide from carbonates. If this were the condition, however, we should find calcium occurring on other related species of algae associated with the same bacteria.

Other variations in wall composition include chitin in some Cladophorales walls as well as in *Oedogonium*. Iron has been found in the walls of desmids and *Oedogonium*, as have deposits of iron, in at least some habitats, on the walls of *Cladophora* (possibly related to bacterial action). The deposition of the iron is one of numerous physiological questions still awaiting study.

In one order, Volvocales, a few genera have no wall at all; instead, the outer membrane of the cytoplasm serves as a protective pellicle (*Pyramimonas*, e.g.)

The electron microscope has revealed many physical features of the algal cell wall not detectable by the light microscope. Herein lies an ever broadening field of research. Walls of some green algae have been shown to be basically similar to those of higher plants. The inner wall occurs in two phases or strata: one is continuous and amorphous, and the other is a dispersed phase with two or three layers of carbohydrates which, as microfibrils, assume different patterns in respective genera or families.

The consistency of arrangement of microfibrils, their chemistry and physics, excite the imagination of the cytologist who seeks an explanation of the process and controlling mechanism by which the living protopast regulates the highly refined details found within the outer, non-living wall material.

The fibrils mostly are in a network at right angles to one another; there may also be a third set of fibrils crossing through the other two. Biochemical studies have shown that these fibrils are composed of glucose or xylose, together with an overall layer of mannose. Variations in pattern occur according to Orders. Dawes (1966) found, for example, five different patterns of fibril arrangement in the Chlorophyta. Investigators continually examine the microstructure of walls to learn whether some groups or genera of algae may be incorrectly included in some Orders as now constituted. In group I no fibril structure shows; in group II microfibril pattern is reticulate; in group III microfibrils are axial in the wall; in group IV microfibrils are parallel, and form lamellae; in group V there are spiral cross-fibrils, with the transverse in a loose spiral and the parallel in a tight spiral.

One example may be cited to illustrate the relationship between cytoplasm and wall structures. In *Spirogyra*, when filaments become juxtaposed for conjugation, a "spot" occurs in the region of the wall where the subsequent conjugation protrusion is to be formed. Vesicles are then formed in the cytoplasm and these, plus globular bodies with a thick membrane, push through the cytoplasm membrane and through the "spot." They thus function in some unknown way to break down the cross-walls of the conjugation tube and permit passage of the gamete.

FLAGELLA

In general, the motile cells of the Chlorophyta have two (rarely four) equal-length (isokont) flagella attached in the apical region. An exception, as mentioned previously, is in the Oedogoniales, where motile cells bear a crown of flagella (stephanokont) arising from a double row of granules (see p. 93). Usually the flagella are smooth and whip-like (simple), but in a few instances there are two pleuronematic of equal length; cf. *Haematococcus* and *Bipedinomonas* (pantonematic). *Polytoma* has four pleuronematic and *Anisomonas* has two simple flagella, one long and one short. The flagella have the standard 9-2 fibrillar organization (see p. 22). In *Pedinomonas*, according to the electron microscope, four "roots" originate in the antiflagellar region, extend through the cell, and then converge to join the base of the flagellum.

CYTOPLASM

The protoplast is bounded by a plasma membrane and in most species there are strands of cytoplasm traversing the cell cavity. In some Volvocales there are intercellular connections of cytoplasm. Those genera or orders not possessing any cytoplasmic vacuoles (cf. the Volvocales) have instead one to several contractile vacuoles, mostly in the apical, flagellar region. The contractile vacuoles, diastolic and systolic, are thought to have an excretory function. In several desmid genera there are vacuoles containing granules of waste material (gypsum).

The cell vacuoles are relatively large in some of the Siphonales and in the huge cells of the Charales. The cell sap maintains a physiologically appropriate osmotic pressure which must be higher for the algae living in sea than those living in fresh water.

Metachromatic granules have been found in some chlorophycean cells as well as chondriosomes. The latter possibly are a different form of a plastid. Also mitochondria, previously mentioned, and Golgi bodies occur in the green algae. Tetrahedral crystalloid bodies and spherical bodies of crystalline material are found in *Cladophora pellucida* and in *Bryopsis* and *Derbesia*.

Food Storage

Whereas starch is the principal storage product derived from glucose, other substances of a nutritional nature are found in the green algae. The A-spectrum of algal starch is similar to that found in cereals, and the B-spectrum in *Chara* and *Volvox* starch is at least similar to that found in tubers of higher plants. Several algae, such as *Polytoma* and *Dunaliella*, contain amyloproteins. In such instances it accounts for as much as 87% of the food reserve. In a few forms fats and oils also occur.

Various carbohydrates include glucose (e.g., callose), found in the siphonaceous *Caulerpa*; fructose, in *Cladophora*; polymeres of fructose, in some of the Dasycladales; and inulin, in *Acetabularia*. At least ten species of green algae contain sucrose.

Reproduction

The Chlorophyta exhibit as much variation in reproduction as they do in architecture. Many reproduce by cell division only, whereas others make use of spores (see p. 32). In such instances sexual reproduction may include isogamous, anisogamous, or heterogamous methods, with or without special sex organs. Most of the green algae have an alternation of generations involving a unicellular or multicellular gametophyte and a single-celled diploid stage (the zygospore). But, as will be described in appropriate places, a few genera have an alternation of similar generations. (See Table 2.1 for diagrams of different kinds of life histories in the green algae.)

Representative Orders

Order Volvocales (Subphylum Chlorophyceae)

The name Volvocales is derived from the fact that plants are "rollers" or "flyers" in the vegetative state, with two (rarely four or eight) flagella arising from blepharoplasts anteriorly in cells. Some students recommend the elevation of this order to a class, Volvophyceae, under the Chlorophyta. Microscopically a colony of *Volvox* presents a beautiful sight, with the many thousands of cells arranged in a perfectly spherical colony, rolling and turning as the flagella beat in a coordinated fashion. In a few genera the flagella are pleuronematic; in most, however, they are simple. There are at least six families and about 45 genera (one-celled or colonial), some of which contain numerous species (e.g., *Chlamydomonas*, with about

TABLE 2.1   Types of Life Histories in the Green Algae

1. **Chlamydomonas**

   one-celled gametophyte (1n) ⟨→ gamete (1n) →⟩ zygote (2n) ⟶ zygospore (2n)

   gamete (1n)

                                                    zoospores (1n) ← reduction division

             metamorphosis to form adult individual gametophyte (1n)

2. **Ulothrix, Oedogonium, Chaetophora,** and most filamentous Chlorophyta

   many-celled gametophyte (1n) ⟨→ gamete (1n) →⟩ zygote (2n) ⟶ zygospore (2n)

   gamete (1n)

   many-celled gametophyte (1n) ⟵ zoospores (1n) ⟵ reduction division

3. **Monostroma, Cladophora**

   multicellular gametophyte (1n) →gamete (1n)↘ zygote (2n)→ multicellular sporophyte (2n)
                                  ↘gamete (1n)↗

               multicellular gametophyte (1n)⟵ zoospores (1n)⟵ reduction division

4. **Codium** and the Siphonales

   macroscopic plant (2n) ⟶ reduction division ⟨→ gamete (1n) →⟩ zygote (2n)
                                               gamete (1n)

                                                       macroscopic plant (2n)

5. **Chlorochytrium**

   unicellular gametophyte (2n)⟶ reduction division ⟨→ gamete (1n) ↘ zygote (4-flagella)
                                                      gamete (1n) ↗

                 metamorphosis to form unicellular gametophyte (2n)

6. **Conjugales** (including Desmids)

   unicellular or multicellular gametophyte (1n) ⟨→ gamete (1n) (metamorphosed content of cell)
                                                  gamete (1n) (metamorphosed content of cell)

   4 nuclei (1n) ⟵ meiosis ⟵ zygospore (2n) ⟵ zygote (2n) ⟵ conjugation (syngamy)

   one, two (rarely four) new gametophytes (according to whether one, two or all of
   the 4 nuclei are functional (1n)

43

400 species, and more being described continuously). Many of the "higher" green algae have volvocoid types of reproductive cells (gametes and zoospores); many of these cells have a volvoid type of chloroplast. This order is thus thought to be the chlorophycean prototype, and it well may be that what appear to be several phylogenetic lines of development in the Chlorophyta had their origin in the Volvocales (see Chart 2.1). Within the order itself there is an easily constructed evolutionary series from unicellular genera (*Carteria, Chlamydomonas*) to simple colonies of few cells and no cellular specialization (*Pandorina, Pascherina*) to larger colonies of many thousands of cells, cellular specialization, and anisogamous or oogamous reproduction, as in *Eudorina, Pleodorina*, and *Volvox*.

Practically all of the Volvocales are fresh-water in habitat, and many show a preference for water enriched with nitrogen and organic substances. Barnyard pools and drinking troughs are frequently opaquely green because of *Eudorina, Chlamydomonas*, or *Pandorina* blooms. A few species (e.g. in *Brachiomonas*) occur in brackish environments,

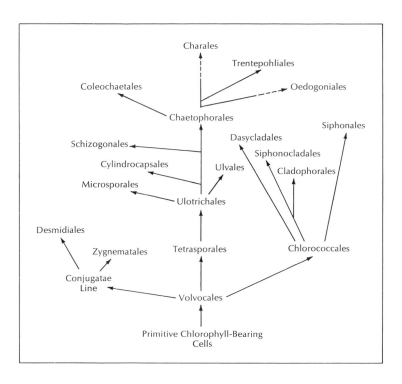

CHART 2.1   A Suggested Phylogenetic Arrangement of the Chlorophyta

whereas the genus *Dunaliella* is found in marine, inland brine, or fresh waters.

Many members of the Volvocales, especially *Chlamydomonas*, have been used for investigations of cellular physiology and of reproductive phenomena in algae. Culture studies have shown that there are homothallic and heterothallic strains of a single species; that is, strains in which gametes from individuals in the same culture will fuse, and strains in which gametes must fuse with those of another clone. Light, temperature, and micro-elements introduced into the culture medium have all demonstrated highly refined adjustments and variabilities, sometimes resulting in gamete fusion, sometimes inhibiting mating of gametes. A reduction in nitrogen, for example, seems to induce sexual reproduction in cultures of *Chlamydomonas*. Because this genus exhibits so many variations in cytological features and in reproductive habits under artificial conditions, it is thought probable that many of the numerous varieties and species of *Chlamydomonas* have been described incorrectly, that these so-called species are only incidental variants and not true taxa.

Study of the behavior of gametes, and the subsequent genetics, has led to studies of nuclei. The chromosome number in *Chlamydomonas* varies from eight to as many as 38, but reports on numbers in certain species seem to depend on interpretations of the investigator. In other genera the number varies from five, in one section of *Volvox*, to 17 in *Gonium pectorale*. Other sections of *Volvox* have from 13 to 15 chromosomes.

The volvocalean life history usually involves the alternation of a one-celled diploid (sporophyte) zygospore stage with the formation of four zoospores (or .aplanaspores) when the zygospore germinates. But the numerous genera (and species) invite cytological and life cycle studies. An unusual genus, *Chlorobrachis* (*C. gracillima*), has been reported to be the diploid (sporophytic) stage of another plant, *Pyrobotrys gracilis*.

FAMILY POLYBLEPHARIDACEAE (PRASINOPHYCEAE P.P.)

This family is composed of unicellular, oval, or lobed organisms which have from one to as many as eight flagella (*Polyblepharides*). It is a unique family in that cells have no wall but only a firm membrane which is the outer boundary of the cytoplasm. The chloroplast is a parietal cup.

Certain members of this family, together with some of the Tetrasporales (see pp. 53, 55), have been assigned to the Prasinophyceae, a new group separate from the Volvocales. The basis for this is the cytology of the reproductive cells. Representatives of this family occur in fresh water or, as in the case of *Dunaliella*, in both brackish and salt water. **Dunaliella** is an oval, biflagellate (simple flagella) organism lacking an eye-spot; its cells are frequently red with haematochrome (see Plate I, Fig. 3). Species of this organism occur in a wide range of salinities; *D. tertiolaeta*, for example, has been grown in media varying from 3.5% to 120% salt.

Pyramimonas Schmarda, 1850 (Plate I, Fig. 2), is well-named because of its pyriform shape (broader at the anterior end as seen in front view). In end view cells are equally four-lobed, with a flagellum arising in each of the concavities between the lobes (quadriflagellate, simple).

   The cup-shaped but lobed chloroplast has a basal pyrenoid, and there is an eye-spot.

   Besides cell division these species may reproduce by cysts and by isogametes. A zygospore results from gametic union and this germinates in the usual way to form four haploid zoospores. As far as known species are all fresh-water.

Pedinomonas Korshikov, 1923 (Plate I, Fig. 4), is an odd genus in which oval cells have a single, pantonematic flagellum that is directed backward. The cytology and reproduction are similar to characteristics of *Pyramimonas*.

Stephanoptera Dangeard (Plate I, Fig. 5), is a pear-shaped cell with six longitudinal lobes. It lacks a wall and has two flagella, and is found in brackish water or brine lakes.

FAMILY CHLAMYDOMONADACEAE

   This is a large family of unicells (about 20 genera). There are two or four (*Tetraselmis*) equal flagella, and a cell wall. In the biflagellate species the flagella may emerge through the same canal or through individual ones. The chloroplast varies in shape, even within the same genus, as in the type genus *Chlamydomonas*, for example, where it may be cup-shaped, net-like, laminate, rarely stellate, and occasionally H-shaped, sometimes ridged. *Polytoma* and a few other genera lack chlorophyll. There usually is an eye-spot and from one to several pyrenoids. The cells are mostly oval or elliptic but some (*Chlorogonium*) are fusiform or spindle-shaped and a few (*Lobomonas, Brachiomonas, Chlorobrachis*) are lobed.

Chlamydomonas Ehrenberg, 1833 (Plate I, Fig. 6) with its hundreds of species, invites wonder that a minute, green cell can express itself in so many genetically distinct taxa. Many individuals can be found in a

PLATE I

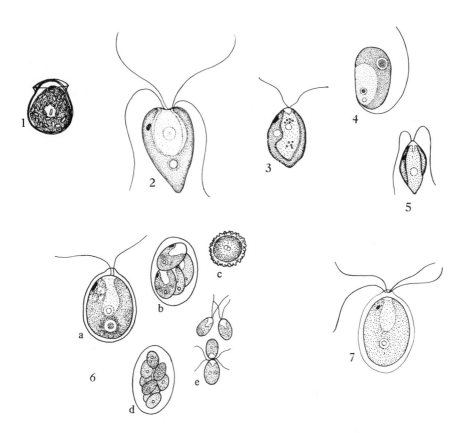

Fig. 1.   **Nautococcus pyriformis,** neustonic cell with floating cap (redrawn from Javornicky)

Fig. 2.   **Pyramimonas tetrarhynchus,** cell showing four flagella, eye-spot and pyrenoid

Fig. 3.   **Dunaliella paupera** (redrawn from Pascher)

Fig. 4.   **Pedinomonas minor** (redrawn from Korchikoff)

Fig. 5.   **Stephanoptera gracilis** (redrawn from Smith)

Fig. 6.   **Chlamydomonas** sp: a, vegetative cell with cup-shaped chloroplast and pyrenoid; b, cell division to form "zoo-spores"; c, gamete-formation; d, gametes uniting; e, zygo-spore

Fig. 7.   **Carteria** sp, cell with four flagella

47

PLATE I

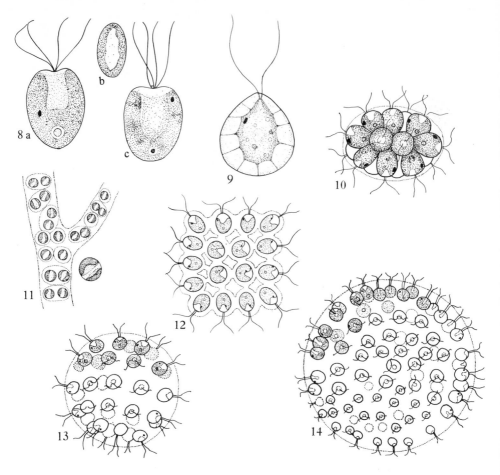

Fig. 8.   **Platymonas elliptica;** a, vegetative cell in "front" view; b, end view to show compressed form; c, "front" view of another species

Fig. 9.   **Haematococcus lacustris,** vegetative cell showing extensions of protoplast to the wall

Fig. 10. **Pandorina morum,** colony

Fig. 11. **Palmodictyon viride,** portion of "filamentous" colony

Fig. 12. **Gonium pectorale,** colony

Fig. 13. **Eudorina elegans,** colony

Fig. 14. **Pleodorina californica,** colony

PLATE I

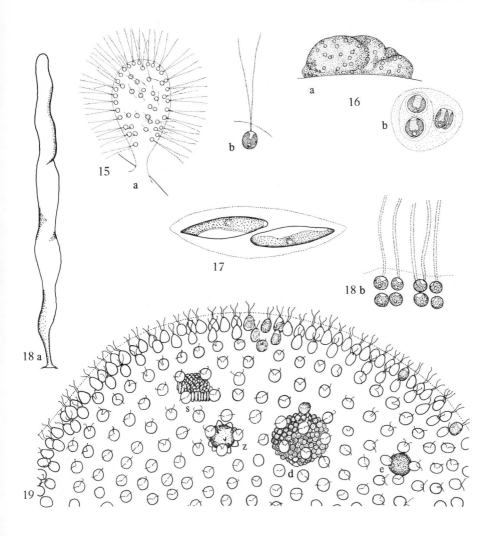

Fig. 15. **Apiocystis Brauniana:** a, colony; b, cells with pseudocilia

Fig. 16. **Palmella mucosa:** a, gelatinous colony; b, cells showing lamellate sheaths

Fig. 17. **Elakatothrix viridis,** two-celled colony

Fig. 18. **Tetraspora cylindrica:** a, habit of colony; b, cells in quartet with pseudocilia

Fig. 19. **Volvox aureus:** portion of spherical colony with D, daughter colony; E, egg; S, sperm plakea; Z, spiny-walled zygospore

habitat; watering troughs, rain barrels, and laboratory aquaria are often opaquely green with their numbers. *C. halophila* has been described from salt water. One species is a well-known producer of red snow in high altitudes.

The wall may be smooth at the anterior end, or there may be one or two apical papillae. The inner wall is thin, smooth, and, as determined by the electron microscope, is very finely striated with parallel cellulose fibrils. The chloroplast (shaped as described above) has one or more pyrenoids with starch sheaths.

As in the Polyblepharidaceae, asexual reproduction occurs when the cell nucleus undergoes division, followed by a longitudinal division of the protoplast. There are two or four more subsequent divisions all within the original cell. New flagella arise from fragments of the original blepharoplast, a wall is formed around each portion of the protoplast, an eye-spot appears, and through gelatinization of the mother cell wall the units escape as "zoospores." They then simply enlarge to become mature, vegetative cells.

There is considerable variation in sexual reproduction. In a majority of species isogametes are formed when a vegetative cell becomes quiescent and loses its flagella. The contents then become divided into from eight to 16 biflagellate portions. Although morphologically alike the gametes are physiologically different and are referred to as either "plus" or "minus" with opposites fusing in pairs to form a zygote. At least for some species it has been determined experimentally that hormones are produced by gametes and are passed into the medium. Androtermones are produced by the male or (−) gametes and gynotermones by the female (+). In addition a hormone, called a *gamone*, functions in attracting gametes to one another. The gamone is thought to be produced by the sheath of the flagella, since it is known that the flagella play an important part in gamete copulation. According to Moewus, gamones have been determined in two forms of a crocetin dimethyl ester, a cis- and a trans-. If a cis-crocetin is in abundance the hormone behaves as a female; by contrast, an abundance of trans-crocetin determines a male hormone. How universally true this is among all species of *Chlamydomonas* and among other algae is not known and some phycologists have cast doubts on the behavior of such hormones. It is clear, however, that there are many variables in the physiology of sexual reproduction, and the whole problem constitutes another area for fruitful research.

Anisogamy appears when gametes occur in two sizes, sometimes the fused pair being carried about by the action of the larger. Some species have a type of reproduction which approaches oogamy.

Carteria Diesing, 1866 (Plate I, Fig. 7), are less seldom seen than *Chlamydomonas*. They may be mistaken, however, for that genus because of shape similarities, but *Carteria* cells are equipped with four flagella. The parietal, cup-shaped chloroplast may or may not have a pyrenoid. A characteristic volvocoid eye-spot is present.

Sexual reproduction is isogamous (with a slight degree of anisogamy). Oddly enough, according to one report, *Carteria ovata* is but the diploid expression of *Chlamydomonas variabilis*. This is a reminder of the necessity of making more cytological investigations, especially of the unicellular Volvocales.

Platymonas G. S. West, 1916 (*Tetraselmis*, 1878) (Plate I, Fig. 8), are both fresh-water and marine quadriflagellate cells. They are oval-elliptic in "front" view with a concave apex from which four flagella arise. In end view the cells are compressed-oval with the flagella appearing in two pairs. There is a single, cup-shaped (parietal) chloroplast with one pyrenoid and a lateral pigment-spot. The cell wall is thin and may not be evident except during cell division. It has been suggested that this genus should be included with *Carteria*.

Species occur in the tychoplankton of lakes and in tidal pools which are enriched with organic matter (high in nitrates).

FAMILY SPHAERELLACEAE (HAEMATOCOCCACEAE)

In this family the biflagellated unicells have a wide, mucilage-filled space between the protoplast and the cell wall. A commonly seen member is *Haematococcus lacustris* (Girod.) Rostaf. (Plate I, Fig. 9), which occurs in rock pools, bird-baths, etc. The cells encyst when the water becomes warm, and when the oxygen-content is low. Like other organisms which are exposed to strong light under such conditions the pigment haematochrome develops and the pool of water becomes blood-red, or reddish granulations appear in the bottom of cement pools. The cysts germinate under suitable conditions, forming either isogametes or zoospores.

FAMILY VOLVOCACEAE

In this family all members are colonial. **Pandorina** Bory, 1824 (Plate I, Fig. 10), is an ovoid colony of pear-shaped cells, essentially a cluster of eight *Chlamydomonas* zoospores enclosed in a common gelatinous sheath. The cell contents are replicas of many *Chlamydomonas* species, with a parietal, cup-shaped chloroplast, contractile vacuoles, pyrenoid, an eyespot, and two flagella. Reproduction occurs by cells dividing internally to form a daughter colony. Sexual reproduction is by iso- or anisogametes.

Gonium Mueller, 1873, is a flat, rectangular plate of four, 16, or 32 cells, each with its individual sheath which has processes that adjoin it to its neighbors (Plate I, Fig. 12). The colony has a characteristic toppling locomotion, and is found either in the tychoplankton or euplankton. Each cell in the colony can form a daughter colony.

Sexual reproduction is by isogametes. The zygote (with meiosis) gives rise to a four-celled colony. From these, later, two of the four produce a female (+) and two a male (−) colony (physiologically). Like many genera in the order which have been studied in culture, *Gonium pectorale* shows great variation in respect to suitability of gametes for syngamy. There are many plus and minus clones detectable within the same species.

Eudorina Ehrenberg, 1832, is a globular or spheroidal colony of from 16 to 64 spherical cells, the cells interconnected by protoplasmic strands (Plate I, Fig. 13). In one species the colonial sheath has "posterior" lobes. Cell morphology is essentially that of *Chlamydomonas*, but the flagella emerge through cone-shaped apical canals. The colonies have an active rolling motion.

Vegetative reproduction is by daughter colony-formation. Sexual reproduction is anisogamous and colonies are either homothallic or heterothallic (see p. 45). Certain cells within the colony enlarge and serve as biflagellate female gametes. Other cells divide to form a disc of biflagellate sperm, with fertilization occurring within the parent colony. The zygote forms four zoospores, three of which disintegrate. The fourth eventually divides to form a small colony.

Pleodorina Shaw, 1894 (Plate I, Fig. 14), is somewhat similar to *Eudorina*, but the colonies have as many as 128 cells of two sizes. The larger cells are arranged in one sector of the gelatinous sphere, smaller at the opposite pole. The small cells are strictly vegetative. Larger cells are both vegetative and reproductive, forming either anisogamous or heterogamous gametes. When daughter colonies are produced they are formed as hollow spheres, with the anterior pole of the cells directed inwardly. An inversion of the colony occurs by means of an invagination on one side. This continues until the layer of cells has pushed its way through an opening opposite the place of invagination. The anterior end of the cells is thus directed outwardly. (See *Volvox* below.)

Most species are heterothallic. Reproduction is similar to that of *Eudorina*, but at times the enlarged female gamete may lose its flagella and function as a non-motile egg (heterogamous). The *plakea* of antherozoids undergoes inversion as do the vegetative colonies. Presumably the zygote behaves as in *Volvox*.

Volvox Linnaeus, 1758 (Plate I, Fig. 19), has the largest and the most impressive colonies of any genus in the family, containing as many as 50,000 individuals. They are often large enough to be seen easily with the unaided eye. The oval or pyriform cells are arranged at the periphery of the gelatinous matrix and in some species there are intercellular connections. In favorable habitats veritable "blooms" may develop during summer months. Interest in this unique genus has induced a considerable amount of study by morphologists, cytologists, and physiologists.

Colonies are either monoecious or dioecious according to species Among the many thousands of cells a few (in one sector) can withdraw to the watery interior and divide to form daughter colonies (one to several forming at one time, depending on the species). The daughter colony invaginates and then inverts through a *phialopore* (as in *Pleodorina*). Other cells withdraw and form a packet (*plakea*) of antherozoids, and still others metamorphose to form non-motile eggs. The plakea swims as a group to a colony in which eggs have been formed. The plakea dissociate and the antherozoids behave independently to fertilize the eggs. The zygote forms an oospore (zygospore) with either a smooth or spiny wall. As usual meiosis occurs when the zygospore germinates, but only one nucleus of the four potentials is used to form a single zoospore. This eventually initiates the formation of a new colony of but a few cells. This colony inverts and forms successive generations of daughter colonies, the number of cells per colony increasing with each generation.

Order Tetrasporales

In this order volvocoid but non-motile cells are embedded in copious mucilage, often forming colonies of macroscopic size. The order is sometimes included under the Volvocales. Colonies may be attached, gelatinous, tubular or bulbous masses, or pyriform microscopic sacs growing on filamentous algae. A few are free-floating. In general they resemble a palmelloid state (see glossary) of volvocalean algae. The chloroplast is a parietal cup, with one pyrenoid. In some genera there is an eye-spot and contractile vacuoles. There are four families.

In some genera cells are able to throw out flagella and swim away. A peculiarity is the presence of long, fine, hair-like false flagella (pseudocilia) in several genera which are sheathed by firm mucilage until the hairs emerge from the colony (Plate I, Fig. 15). The cells revert to a volvocoid type when zoospores or isogametes (32 per cell) are formed. The zygospore is the only diploid stage in the life history in most forms, *Tetraspora gelatinosa* being an exception. Vegetative reproduction is accomplished by cell division.

FAMILY PALMELLACEAE

Palmella Lyngbye, 1819, emend. Chodat, 1902 (Plate I, Fig. 16), has globose or ellipsoid cells arranged in soft, amorphous gelatinous colonies (sometimes red). Cells, enclosed by individual sheaths, have a parietal chloroplast and one pyrenoid. The dormant, unflagellated stage of some volvocoids (e.g., *Chlamydomonas*) is referred to as palmelloid because of the similarity to this genus.

Palmodictyon Kuetzing, 1845 (Plate I, Fig. 11), is of interest because of the tendency for spherical cells to assume a linear arrangement and to form false filaments — suggesting a possible link with the Ulotrichales. Zoospores and akinetes are used in reproduction. Apparently sexual reproduction is unknown.

FAMILY TETRASPORACEAE

Tetraspora Link, 1809 (Plate I, Fig. 18), has spherical cells arranged in groups of four (or two) in long gelatinous strands or as balloon-like masses. It occurs mostly in cold, flowing water or springs. *Tetraspora cylindrica* (Wahlb.) Ag. is sometimes a foot or more in length and forms conspicuous streaming growths on rocks. Some species are planktonic clumps. In young colonies especially, cells bear a pair of pseudocilia arising from the anterior end of the cell. They may be more easily detected when stain is applied or when microscope illumination is reduced. They lack the fibril composition characteristic of true flagella, having only the nine peripheral ones. These decrease in number toward the apex. The pseudocilia are shed when cells form zoospores or gametes. The thin-walled isogametes show a typical "clumping" behavior when released — a characteristic of iso- and anisogametes in the Volvocales. The zygote in one species (*T. gelatinosa*) develops a new colony without meiosis. This colony with diploid cells produces 2n zoospores (supposedly) which in turn grow into diploid colonies. Eventually a colony gives rise to haploid gametes and it is thought that reduction division must occur here. This indicates an alternation of isomorphic generations. Otherwise the zygospore of other species produces aplanospores by meiosis from which colonies of haploid cells are developed.

Apiocystis Naegeli, 1849 (Plate I, Fig. 15), is a microscopic, attached, pear-shaped colony of *Tetraspora*-like cells which also have pseudocilia.

Schizochlamys A. Braun, 1849 (Plate II, Fig. 21), forms floating, amorphous gelatinous masses. The spheroidal, flattened cells have as many as four or eight pseudocilia. In this genus there is a wide space between the protoplast and the wall occupied by mucilage. The four flagella arise from the flattened side of the cell through as many pores. The fact that new cells are formed within a parent cell, the pieces of the old cell wall remaining about the daughter cells, suggests that this genus should be included in the Chlorococcales which reproduce by internal cell division.

FAMILY CHLORANGIACEAE

Stylosphaeridium Geitler et Gimesi, 1925 (Plate II, Fig. 22), is an example of attached, stalked tetrasporine cells which characterize this family. These are invested by a tough membrane, and appear as hat pins emerging from the mucilage of colonial algae such as *Coelosphaerium*.

Chlorangium Stein, 1878 (Plate II, Fig. 23), is characterized by ovoid cells attached anteriorly and downwardly by gelatinous stalks to microfauna. The cells form dendroid colonies by repeated cell division and mucilage secretion. The cells have two laminate chloroplasts and two anterior vacuoles, giving a volvocoid appearance. There is no pyrenoid, however. In reproduction a cell may become motile (two flagella) and escape from the sheath. The anterior end of the zoospore adheres to the substrate and produces a gelatinous stalk. This plant should be compared with *Colacium* in the Euglenophyta.

Prasinocladus Kuckuck, 1894 (Plate II, Fig. 20), forms a stalked, branched colony with cells at the end of mucilage tubes.

FAMILY COCCOMYXACEAE

This family is quite different from the other members of the Tetrasporales and possibly should be excluded. Genera which comprise this family, however, are able to divide and multiply by cell division. The cells are oval or fusiform, solitary or in colonies. A common plankton form is **Elakatothrix** Wille, 1898, which has fusiform cells enclosed in a similarly shaped sheath, the cells lying somewhat parallel. Reproduction is by cell division, rarely by akinetes (Plate I, Fig. 17). **Dispora** Printz, 1914, is a plate of somewhat irregularly arranged oval cells (Plate II, Fig. 24) with a single parietal chloroplast lacking pyrenoids. Reproduction is by cell division and fragmentation. It should be compared with *Crucigenia*.

Order Chlorococcales

This is a diversified and artificial assemblage of ten or more families of one-celled and colonial plants which have in common the inability to undergo ordinary cell division. Instead the contents of a cell divide to form zoospores or to form miniatures of the mature individual (known as autospores) which then enlarge to form adult plants. Some colonies of unconnected cells result from daughter cells being enclosed in a common membrane (*Oocystis*, Plate III, Fig. 45), the membrane being an old, sometimes much swollen mother cell wall. Or the daughter cells may become adjoined in various positions to form colonies or coenobia (*Scenedesmus, Pediastrum*).

There is an almost endless variety of cell and colony shape. Likewise there is a variety of chloroplast form. The volvocoid type of cell is frequently seen in reproductive elements, some with an eye-spot as in *Trigonidium* Pascher. Cells may be round, oval, reniform, pyramidal, cylindrical, or needle-like. The wall may be smooth, warty, spiny, or reticulate. The electron microscope shows *Pediastrum* to have a double meshwork of fibrils in the wall involving spheres and interconnecting threads. Cells are uninucleate when young but become coenocytic. It is thought possible that the Chlorococcales may have arisen from certain volvocoid cells which become multinucleate when their cell division (cytokinesis) does not accompany mitosis. This is further indicated by some cells having volvocoid vacuoles. No doubt the Chlorococcales are polyphyletic and as a group they exhibit two expressions, Azoosporic and Zoosporic (Zoosporineae), the former reproducing by autospores. In some forms, division of the cell is through simultaneous cleavage to form elements, whereas in other genera the division is successive. In sexual reproduction there is isogamy, anisogamy, and (in a few instances) oogamy.

This is a panktonic order, many forms becoming dominant in the flora and producing near "blooms." As such they are important elements in the food chain. Several become especially troublesome (*Hydrodictyon*, Plate III, Fig. 40) in recreational waters. It is significant that no euplanktonic Chlorococcales are known to be marine. Some are soil-inhabiting, where they may live as saprophytes in organic matter, especially in nitrogenous wastes. A few are found in the oozing sap of trees, and others (e.g. *Trebouxia*, Plate II, Fig. 26) are associated with fungi to form lichens. Species of *Chlorella* are endozoic, producing green *Hydra*, sponges, and protozoa (e.g. *Ophrydium*). The curious *Glaucocystis*[1] is regarded as an oval chlorococcalean cell endophytized by blue-green algal protoplasts.

---

[1] Classified in Cyanophyta.

PLATE II

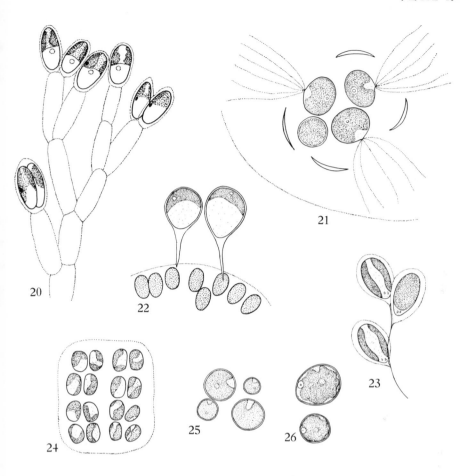

Fig. 20.   **Prasinocladus lubricus,** portion of branched colony

Fig. 21.   **Schizochlamys gelatinosa,** four cells from large colony showing pseudocilia (varying from four to eight)

Fig. 22.   **Stylosphaeridium stipitatum,** epiphytic on **Coelosphaerium**
colony

Fig. 23.   **Chlorangium stentorinum,** a few-celled colony on a microcrustacea

Fig. 24.   **Dispora crucigenioides,** plate-like colony

Fig. 25.   **Chlorococcum** sp, cells from soil

Fig. 26.   **Trebouxia Cladoniae,** cells from a lichen

PLATE II

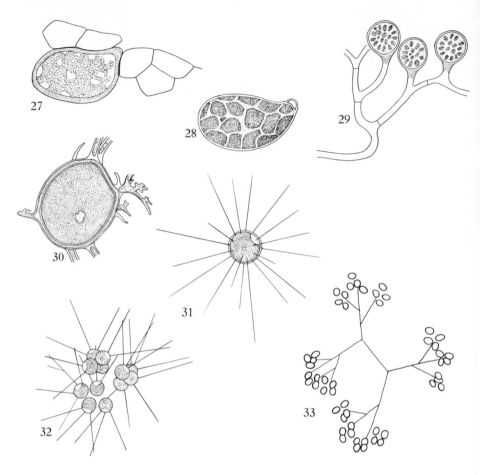

Fig. 27. **Chlorochytrium Lemnae,** cell within thallus of **Lemna**

Fig. 28. **Kentrosphaera** sp, irregularly shaped cell from soil

Fig. 29. **Phyllobium sphagnicola,** portion of thallus, endophytic in **Sphagnum,** showing akinete-formation

Fig. 30. **Rhodochytrium spilanthidis,** irregularly shaped cell within **Ambrosia** (redrawn from Smith)

Fig. 31. **Golenkinia radiata**

Fig. 32. **Micractinium pusillum,** small colony

Fig. 33. **Dictyosphaerium pulchellum,** colony showing interconnecting fibrils

PLATE II

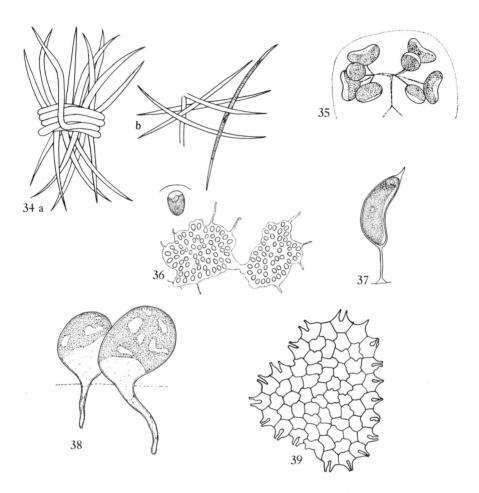

Fig. 34.   **Ankistrodesmus:** a, **A. spiralis,** colony of spirally twisted cells; b, **A. falcatus,** individual cells

Fig. 35.   **Dimorphococcus lunatus,** portion of colony of reniform cells with interconnecting fibrils

Fig. 36.   **Botryococcus Braunii,** portion of compound colony

Fig. 37.   **Characium** sp, cell epiphytic on a filamentous alga

Fig. 38.   **Protosiphon botryoides,** balloon-like cells on soil

Fig. 39.   **Pediastrum Boryanum** fa., an irregularly shaped colony

FAMILY CHLOROCOCCACEAE

Chlorococcum Fries, 1820 (Plate II, Fig. 25), is a genus of spherical cells, solitary or gregarious, nearly always found on and in soil, on wet rocks and wood. There is a parietal chloroplast with one pyrenoid. The cells are often irregular in shape with knob-like thickenings. Reproduction is by biflagellate zoospores and by isogametes, the latter developing from a palmella stage. Cells of this genus are very similar to many other small, green cells belonging to other genera, or to stages in the life history of other algae. Hence culture studies are often needed to make identification (see Starr, 1955).

Trebouxia de Puymaly, 1924 (Plate II, Fig. 26), takes the form of round, green cells which occur with fungi to form lichens. Reproduction is by biflagellate zoospores and by isogametes.

FAMILY ENDOSPHAERACEAE

Relatively large, irregularly-shaped cells characterize this family. Some live in the soil; some are endophytic.

Chlorochytrium Cohn, 1875 (Plate II, Fig. 27), a globular, oval, or moniliform cell, occurs as an endophyte in *Lemna* and (marine) in *Porphyra* and other algae. The wall is relatively thick and lamellate, sometimes with irregular knobs. The chloroplast is a parietal plate at first but becomes massive. The nucleus undergoes meiosis, followed by nuclear proliferation. Around the nuclei biflagellate isogametes are cut out which upon escape fuse to form quadriflagellate zygotes. These swim about for a time and then settle on a host. The resulting germ tube penetrates the host tissue and the contents of the zygote migrate into an internal vescicle which enlarges to form the mature cell. *Chlorochytrium*, therefore, is a diploid which has no haploid generation.

Kentrosphaera Borzi, 1883 (Plate II, Fig. 28) in this family is unique in having sausage-shaped, asymmetrical cells with thickened knobs. The chloroplast is axial and has processes extended toward and spread at the cell wall. Species live in moist soil and, though uncommon, are widely distributed, particularly in Antarctica.

An oddity is **Phyllobium** Klebs (Plate II, Fig. 29), an endophyte of *Sphagnum* with thread-like, tubular cells that are inflated at the tips where akinetes are formed. *Phyllobium* reproduces sexually by motile anisogametes. Another endophyte is the parasitic red unicell **Rhodo-chytrium** Lagerheim (Plate II, Fig. 30), which inhabits ragweed leaves.

FAMILY MICRACTINIACEAE

In this family one-celled or colonial individuals bear long, needle-like spines. **Microactinium** Fres. (Plate II, Fig. 32) and **Golenkinia** Chodat (Plate II, Fig. 31) have oogamous sexual reproduction. In these plants one of the cells metamorphoses to serve as an egg, with a receptive portion protruding from the wall. In other cells biflagellate male gametes are formed. The zygote forms a thick-walled warty or spiny stage.

FAMILY DICTYOSPHAERIACEAE

Dictyosphaerium Naegeli, 1849 (Plate II, Fig. 33), is a common and al-most ubiquitous genus. In this plant round or oval cells in groups of four are arranged at the ends of radiating, dichotomously branched fibrils, the fibrils having come from the break-down of the old cell wall within which the colony was formed. There is a cup-shaped chloroplast and one pyrenoid. The colony is enclosed in a thin mucilage which is sometimes difficult to discern. Species are all planktonic, but may be found in such places as the liquid in pitcher plants. Like *Golenkinia*, sexual reproduction is oogamous. Some believe that at times motile elements are released to act as zoospores.

Dimorphococcus A. Braun, 1855 (Plate II, Fig. 35), is a genus of reni-form cells similar in arrangement to *Distyosphaerium* but not enclosed in a definite mucilaginous sheath. As far as is known reproduction is by autospores only.

Botryococcus Kuetzing, 1849 (Plate II, Fig. 36), is a colonial form in which oval cells are rather compactly and radiately arranged within a tough gummy or rubbery mucilage. Because of oil this mucilage is opaquely yellow or orange. The colonies are often adjoined by strands to form multiple associations. There is a parietal chloroplast and one pyrenoid; both oil and starch are used in food storage. Reproduction is by colony fragmentation and autospores. Because of the oil and the brownish color, *Botryococcus* at one time was classified as a chrysophyte. Later it was given its own family in the Chlorophyta, and recently was transferred to its present position. The plants are highly buoyant plank-ters. They often occur in blooms sufficient to give water an oily taste and a "fishy" odor. In Scotland can be found an oil-rich "Botryococcus Coal" that was formed by the accumulation of these plants in ancient seas.

FAMILY CHARACIACEAE

Characium A. Braun, 1849 (Plate II, Fig. 37), are often overlooked by microscopists because they are unicells attached to filamentous algae or to microfauna such as mosquito larvae and crustaceans. The cells are mostly fusiform, oval, or elliptic, on a long or short stalk. The chloroplast is usually single and parietal, with one pyrenoid. Many species have a sharp point or spine at the apex. They are easily confused with *Characiopsis* of the Chrysophyta because the cells are similarly shaped and have the same habit of growth. *Characium* gives a positive starch-iodide test. Asexual reproduction is by zoospores which escape from the cell apex in some species. Sexual reproduction is by iso- or anisogametes. These are biflagellate and have an eye-spot.

FAMILY PROTOSIPHONACEAE

Protosiphon Klebs, 1896 (Plate II, Fig. 38), illustrates an extreme coenocytic condition and a tendency to produce a siphonaceous thallus. An associate is *Botrydium granulata*, a coenocytic, bulbous plant in the Chrysophyta. The plants (*P. botryoides*) grow as minute bulbils on moist soil. The bulbs have a tubular portion extending below ground as a rhizoid. There is a large, net-like chloroplast, many pyrenoids, and an abundance of starch. Reproduction is frequently by aplanospores and by isogametes. Plants sexually are either homothallic or heterothallic.

FAMILY HYDRODICTYACEAE

This family is comprised of regularly-formed colonial genera. Although each genus is highly different from any other in appearance, they are classified together because in each instance zoospores become adjoined within a mother cell without being discharged so that a miniature parent colony is formed. Further, sexual reproduction of a peculiar type is similar.

Pediastrum Meyen, 1829 (Plate II, Fig. 39), is distinct because cushion-like multinucleate cells are geometrically arranged in flat, circular plates, the cells being in multiples of two and varying in number according to the number of zoospores that entered into the formation of the colony during the previous generation. The peripheral cells may be polyhedral and bi- or tetra-lobed and somewhat different in shape from the internal cells. The colony may be continuous or perforate, with interstices.

There is a parietal, diffuse chloroplast, one or more pyrenoids, and several nuclei. The walls are composed of cellulose derivatives that are very resistant to decay. Hence *Pediastrum* colonies are found in bog and well-borings in a fossil or subfossil condition. These represent both extant and extinct species. The wall has an inner, continuous membrane overlayed by a pattern of fibrils. Externally the wall may be smooth or variously marked with granules, or reticulate. Sometimes there are bristles, especially at the tips of the outer free lobes. In some arctic lakes *Pediastrum* species are known to produce growths reaching bloom proportions.

Besides multiplying by auto-colonies isogametes are used in sexual reproduction. The zygospore resulting from gametic union in turn produces zoospores by meiosis. The zoospores are released, swim for a time, and then become dormant, forming a polyhedral resting spore. The large polyhedron germinates by producing a number of zoospores which cannot escape and so become quiescent, forming a small plate (autocolony) which eventually is discharged in a vesicle.

Hydrodictyon Roth, 1800 (Plate III, Fig. 40), the familiar and unique Water Net, has the same type of reproduction and life history found in *Pediastrum*. In the most common and widely distributed species (*H. reticulatum*) the cylindrical cells are adjoined three together at end walls, repeatedly, so that five- or six-sided meshes are formed, the whole constituting a cylindrical net. The nets vary in size from microscopic to (more rarely) as much as two feet in length. This genus has the distinction of being the first alga to be mentioned in literature, judging from a reference in one ancient Chinese poem, *Bible of Poems*. At least one species has the cells arranged in a flat or saucer-like expanded meshwork.

Cells are coenocytic, and the chloroplast (in fully grown cells) is reticulate with numerous pyrenoids. In *H. reticulatum* the wall does not contain cellulose-II as does *H. patenaeforme*. In fact it is not certain that *H. reticulatum* contains cellulose at all (Kreger, 1960). Within any cell hundreds of biflagellate zoospores are cut out. These swarm but are not permitted to escape and so become quiescent, with poles adjoined to form a network. Eventually, the mother-cell breaks down, having contributed its entire protoplast to zoospore-formation. The old net dissociates, the end walls of the cells break open, and the young nets slip out. The zoospores in the young nets, oval at first, elongate immediately and continually until a mature net is again formed. Thus a net with 1000 cells can produce 1000 nets. This very efficient repro-ductive rate explains why in a very short time *Hydrodictyon* may become very troublesome, forming floating and entangled mats in recreational sites, in gold-fish ponds, irrigation canals, etc.

It is noteworthy that when *Hydrodictyon* cells produce their biflagellate isogametes the mother-cell wall cooperates by forming escape pores.

FAMILY COELASTRACEAE

Coelastrum Naegeli, 1849 (Plate III, Fig. 41), has oval or polyhedral cells arranged in hollow, planktonic, geometrically shaped colonies, the cells being interconnected by extensions of their sheaths. The sheaths, composed of a pectic material, may be only slight protrusions or they may be elongate arms, thus determining the degree of reticulation. There is a characteristic parietal, cup-shaped chloroplast and one pyrenoid. Reproduction is through the formation of autocolonies, all cells of a colony usually entering into autospore-formation simultane-ously. Sometimes a single aplanospore will form in a cell. This gives rise to autospores which in turn arrange themselves to form a daughter colony.

FAMILY OOCYSTACEAE

This is a large and probably polyphyletic family in which there are as many as 40 genera and hundreds of species. The disinguishing character-istic is the formation of autocolonies of unadjoined cells within mother cells. Plants, mostly colonial, are unicellular when the colonies dissociate. Cells exhibit a great range of shape: spherical, oval, lunate, acicular, polyhedral (**Tetraedron,** Plate III, Fig. 42), pyramidal. The wall is smooth, spiny, warty, or ridged; the chloroplasts typically parietal, one to four or many per cell, each with a pyrenoid. Members of this family are planktonic and are important in the food chain of aquatic animals.

Chlorella Beijerinck, 1890 (Plate III, Fig. 43), are cultured for their high protein production, sometimes commercially, and for information on their antibiotic and oxidation capacities. The round or oval cells are commonly found in moist soil and are easily confused with *Chlorococ-cum*, culturing often being necessary to make identification. Some "species" are referred to *Zoochlorella* as endozoophytes in *Hydra* and sponges. Species are both marine and fresh-water.

There is one thin, parietal chloroplast either with or without pyre-noids. Autospores are the only known reproductive elements. Repro-

PLATE III

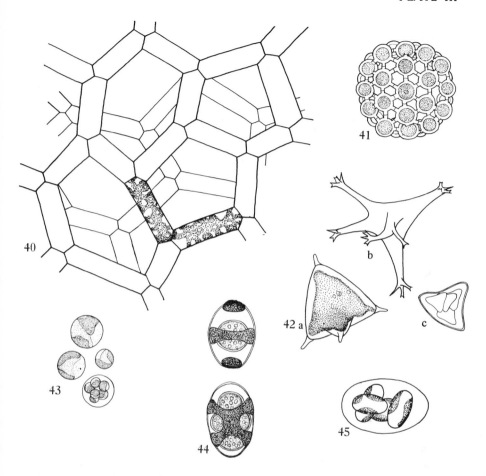

Fig. 40. **Hydrodictyon reticulatum,** portion of cylindrical net

Fig. 41. **Coelastrum microporum,** hollow colony showing intercellular sheath connections

Fig. 42. **Tetraedron:** a, **T. regulare;** b, **T. limnecticum;** c, **T. muticum** with autospores

Fig. 43. **Chlorella vulgaris,** few cells, one in reproduction by autospores

Fig. 44. **Gloeotaenium Loitelsbergerianum,** cells in small colony arrangement, showing dark bands of material between them

Fig. 45. **Oocystis parva,** mother cell with four daughter cells (autospores)

PLATE III

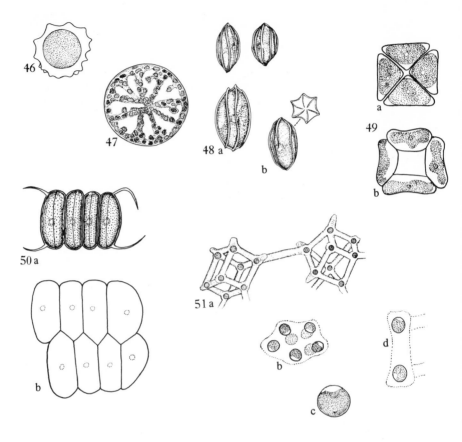

Fig. 46. **Mycanthococcus antarcticus,** cell from snow field (redrawn from Kol)

Fig. 47. **Eremosphaera viridis,** cell showing irregular, lumpy chloroplasts

Fig. 48. **Scotiella** spp; a, aquatic species; b, cell from snow field

Fig. 49. **Crucigenia:** a, **C. tetrapedia;** b, **C. crucifera**

Fig. 50. **Scenedesmus** spp

Fig. 51. **Pectodictyon cubicum:** a, portion of compound colony (redrawn from Taft); b, young colony; c and d, cells showing chloroplasts

PLATE III

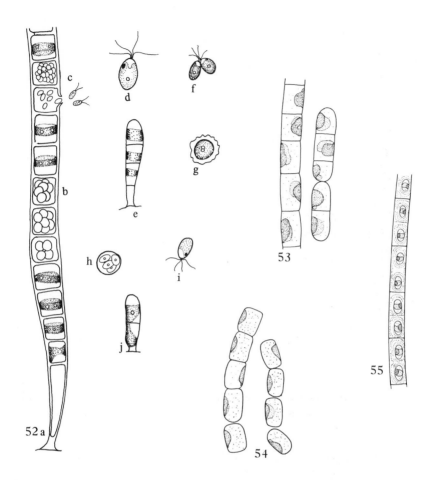

Fig. 52.   **Ulothrix zonata:** a, filament with holdfast; b, zoospore-formation; c, gamete-formation; d, zoospore from filament; e, sporeling produced by zoospore; f, gametes fusing; g, zygospore; h, zygospore germinating with meiosis; i, zoospore from zygospore; j, germling produced by zoospore from zygospore

Fig. 53.   **Hormidium** sp, portion of filament; one fragmenting

Fig. 54.   **Stichococcus bacillaris,** filaments of cells from tree bark

Fig. 55.   **Binuclearia tatrana,** filament; some cells with two protoplasts

PLATE III

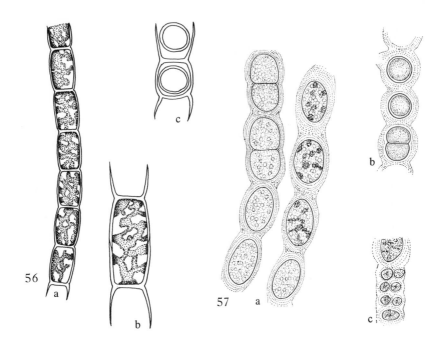

Fig. 56. **Microspora pachyderma:** a, portion of filament; b, one cell showing skein-like chloroplast and wall structure; c, akinete-formation

Fig. 57. **Cylindrocapsa geminella:** a, vegetative filament showing lamellate walls; b, oogonium with zygote; c, antheridia, immature

duction is very rapid and leads to bulky productions in mass cultures. Interest is directed toward *Chlorella* to provide oxygen for possible use in space flights.

Gloeotaenium Hansgirg, 1890 (Plate III, Fig. 44), is an oddity in which two or four spherical cells are enclosed in a sheath with X-shaped bands of dark, gelatinous material.

Oocystis Naegeli, 1855 (Plate III, Fig. 45), or "egg-cyst," is well-named. Oval or elliptic cells are enclosed in the old mother-cell wall. There are sometimes two or three generations or families of cells within cells, all enclosed by a much-extended old mother-cell wall. Some species have lemon-like thickenings of the wall at the poles. Reproduction is by autospores and, more rarely, aplanospores formed singly within a cell.

Mycanthococcus Hansgirg, 1890 (Plate III, Fig. 46), is a spherical uni-cell that occurs in green snow. Cells have a thin, smooth wall in the vegetative condition, but when the cells encyst the wall thickens and becomes spiny. Reproduction is by autospores only.

Eremosphaera De Bary, 1858 (Plate III, Fig. 47), is one of the largest green algal cells, a beautiful globe with numerous oval, plate-like chloroplasts arranged in radiating strands and also parietal within the wall. The chloroplasts are lumpy and irregular because of the attached starch grains. Cells may be 500μ or more in diameter. This genus, especially *E. viridis*, is nearly always found in acid bogs, being closely associated with desmids. Reproduction is by autospores formed two or more within a cell.

Ankistrodesmus Corda, 1838, emend, Ralfs, 1848 (Plate II, Fig. 34), are slender, needle-like or fusiform cells, either solitary or in clumps; tycho-planktonic and euplanktonic. Reproduction is by autospores. Species often produce dense, green, clouded growth in aquaria, and are some-times troublesome in fish culture.

Scotiella Fritsch, 1912 (Plate III, Fig. 48), is a genus of oval cells which have longitudinally ridged walls (of various design according to species). There are one or two parietal chloroplasts. Some species are commonly found in snow, where they are red with haematochrome. In classifica-tion this genus is sometimes associated with the Tetrasporales.

Family Scenedesmaceae

In this family plants reproduce likewise by autospores but the situation is different from the Oocystaceae because daughter cells arrange themselves to form miniature colonies within the parent (**Crucigenia,** Plate III, Fig. 49). A breakdown of the old cell wall liberates the colonies which then increase to a mature size. Motile swarmers are produced at times under culture conditions, as in *Scenedesmus* for example.

Scenedesmus Meyen, 1829 (Plate III, Fig. 50), is the type genus and one that includes many species. Oval or fusiform cells are adjoined side by side in two's or four's or multiples of four. There is a parietal, platelike chloroplast and usually one pyrenoid. Unlike most other chlorococcalean plants *Scenedesmus* appears to be uninucleate. The wall may be smooth or bear spines, ridges, and teeth. This genus is very popular among culturists for studies in genetics and responses of cells to various chemical substances, production of antibiotic material, etc. Reproduction is by autocolonies and (at least in culture) by zoospores.

Pectodictylon Taft, 1945 (Plate III, Fig. 51), is an unusual plant in which eight spherical cells are distantly arranged in cubical fashion, the cells adjoined remotely by gelatinous tubes, and in multiple cubes so that complex colonies are formed. As far as is known reproduction is by autospores.

Order Ulotrichales

This order as conceived here includes unbranched filamentous Chlorophyta which have a parietal chloroplast with one or more pyrenoids, and which use iso- or anisogamous sexual reproduction. An anomalous genus *Uronema* Lag. has been known to branch (rarely). This genus probably should be placed in the Chaetophoraceae. The plants are, therefore, multicellular and not colonial as in the previously considered orders. Some have basal holdfasts, at least when young. The filaments are often gregarious because so many zoospores germinate in close proximity in favorable situations, forming profuse tufted growths. Others are solitary and tychoplanktonic.

The composition of this order varies according to individual opinions. Some students extend the limits to include the Chaetophorales, Ulvales, and the Microsporales. Because of the parietal chloroplast and the volvocoid type of motile cells (zoospores and gametes), the Ulotrichales conceivably arose from the Volvocales through intermediary forms in the Tetrasporales.

FAMILY ULOTRICHACEAE

Ulothrix Kuetzing, 1833, emend. Mattox et Bold, 1962 (Plate III, Fig. 52), is a marine and fresh-water genus, the filaments being attached and basal-distally differentiated, or free-floating, intermingled with other algae. In the sea, species occur in the intertidal zone, sometimes just above the high tide level, and commonly they are epiphytic. In fresh water a common species, *U. zonata*, grows best in cold, flowing water. Certain species or strains of species of *Ulothrix* are recognized as indicators of the mesosoprobic zone in polluted waters.

The basal cell of the filament forms a holdfast and does not divide following the first division in the germling stage. The cells are cylindric or quadrate and have a parietal, band-like or ring-like chloroplast with one or more pyrenoids.

In asexual reproduction two sizes of quadriflagellate zoospores are formed, four or eight per undifferentiated cell. These escape through a lateral spore, swim away and settle down, anterior end first, germinate by cell division, and so form new filaments. In some instances zoospores remain in the parent cell and become aplanospores.

Iso- or anisogametes are similarly cut out of any vegetative cells except the basal. They are twice as numerous and half as large as the zoospores and are biflagellate. Species are homothallic or heterothallic. The zygote continues to swim for a time, then encysts as a zygospore. Zoospores or aplanospores are produced by meiosis when the zygospore germinates (see life histories, pp. 33, 43).

Hormidium Klebs, 1896, emend. Mattox et Bold, 1962 (Plate III, Fig. 53), is mostly fresh-water but some species occur in salt water. With its cylindrical cells it is similar to *Ulothrix* but has a smaller chloroplast that folds around much less of the very thin cell wall. The filaments have no basal-distal differentiation, and have a tendency to fragment into short sections. The plants may be intermingled with other algae or grow gregariously on moist soil or tree trunks along with *Stichococcus*. Zoospores or aplanospores are borne singly in *Hormidium*. Ecological studies show that *Hormidium* species are pioneers on newly exposed or barren soil. In culture, *Hormidium* has shown an ability to deaminate nitrogenous substances.

Stichococcus Naegeli, 1849, emend. Mattox et Bold, 1962 (Plate III, Fig. 54), has cylindrical cells arranged in very short filaments. Even these tend to dissociate so that cells often occur singly in aggregates on damp soil or other moist aerial substrates. Cells have a folded, parietal chloroplast, rarely with a pyrenoid. Cell division and fragmentation are the only known methods of reproduction. Mostly *Stichococcus* is subaerial, or on soil and in fresh water, but at least one species (*S. cylindricus* Butcher) is marine. Culture studies indicate that this is synonymous with the common fresh-water *S. bacillaris* Naeg.

Binuclearia Wittrock, 1886 (Plate III, Fig. 55), occurs as filaments of undifferentiated cylindrical cells in which there is a pair of protoplasts. When the protoplast divides into two there is a delayed cross-wall formation. The spaces between the protoplasts and the wall are filled with layers of mucilage. Each protoplast has a small laminate chloroplast without a pyrenoid. It is thought that zoospores must be formed.

Order Microsporales

This order has one family (Microsporaceae) and one genus (*Microspora*).

Microspora Thuret, 1850, emend. Lagerheim, 1888 (Plate III, Fig. 56), usually is included in the Ulotrichales. It is regarded as a separate order on the basis of the parietal, reticulate, or bead-like chloroplast, quite different from the ulotrichoid, and because of the architecture of the cell wall which is composed of two sections that overlap in the midregion. When filaments fragment, the cells dissociate not at the cross walls but in the middle of the cell so that H-shaped or projecting pieces are formed. Large, single aplanospores are formed in *Microspora*, as well as akinetes wherein a filament becomes converted to a chain of thick-walled resting cells. Also biflagellate or quadriflagellate zoospores are formed in asexual reproduction. Sexual reproduction probably occurs but has not been observed.

Order Cylindrocapsales

Like the Microsporales this is an order with one family, Cylindrocapsaceae, and with two genera, *Cylindrocapsa* and *Cylindrocapsella*. These plants may be included in the Ulotrichales but consistency demands that they be considered separately from that order.

Cylindrocapsa Reinsch, 1867 (Plate III, Fig. 57), has oval or subquadrate cells with thick, lamellate walls and is enclosed in a mucilaginous sheath of the same material. The chloroplast is massive and somewhat stellate and often obscured by starch. There is a single, central pyrenoid.

Plants are attached at first but soon become free and intermingled, rather sparingly, among other algae. Frequently the filaments fragment and form palmelloid stages. Also the filaments may become biseriate.

In asexual reproduction one, two, or four zoospores are formed in a cell. Sexually *Cylindrocapsa* is oogamous. A vegetative cell enlarges and an increase in wall thickness occurs, while a lateral pore is formed simultaneously. This cell becomes an oogonium containing a single egg. The egg becomes red, as do the antheridia formed by a vegetative cell undergoing several divisions into box-like units. Each one of these cells produces two biflagellate antherozoids. The life cycle otherwise is similar to that of *Ulothrix*. Sexual reproduction in one species follows somewhat the complex habits of some *Oedogonia*, another characteristic which seems to justify separating *Cylindrocapsa* from the Ulotrichales.

Order Sphaeropleales

This is an order in which long, coenocytic cells form long, unbranched filaments without basal-distal differentiation. There is one family (Sphaeropleaceae) in fresh water and one unique genus (*Sphaeroplea*).

Sphaeroplea Agardh, 1824 (Plate IV, Fig. 58), consists of long cylindrical units with narrow, ring-like chloroplasts which vary in shape with age. The cell is divided into protoplasmic sections by large vacuoles. At the time of cell division there is a peculiar type of cross-wall formation involving a remarkable increase in length of the filament. A vacuole appears and divides a protoplast into two parts. The vacuole continues to enlarge and elongate so as to separate the two protoplasts further and further. Sooner or later a cross wall forms between the two protoplasts.

Sexual reproduction is usually oogamous but in one species anisogamous. In the most common species (*S. annulina*) some cells, without changing shape, cut out a large number of spherical eggs. Other cells in the same filament divide the contents into hundreds of biflagellate antherozoids. Numerous pores form in the walls of the egg-bearing cells, thus permitting the sperm to enter. Zygospores are red, with thick, decorated walls. After a dormant period, which may endure for years, they germinate as usual to form four zoospores. In the anisogamous species the unequal motile gametes fuse external to the gametangia.

It is obvious that this genus has characteristics like the Cladophorales (coenocytic units), parietal chloroplasts and anisogametes like the Ulotrichales, and, further, has a combination of characteristics which seem to justify its separate category.

Order Chaetophorales

This order is characterized by plants having branched filaments that taper to setae or hair-like apices, although some have rather briefly tapering tips. Associated with this form of growth are branched plants which have much of the same habit, but which taper little, if any. The cells are essentially ulotrichoid with a parietal chloroplast and one or more pyrenoids. Reproduction is mostly isogamous; though in some instances, anisogamous. As conceived here the order excludes those families which, although including branched filaments, do not have branches tapering to setae but have walls bearing hairs, and which are predominantly oogamous. It is suggested that the order should include two families, Chaetophoraceae and Protodermataceae.

Family Chaetophoraceae

This family includes plants which have branched filaments with basal-distal differentiation. Branches terminate in sharp points or in setae which may be several cells in length. Genera are both fresh-water and marine. Many have the thalli enclosed in either firm and tough or in soft and amorphous mucilage. As interpreted here the Chaetophoraceae includes the following genera: *Chaetophora* Schrank, *Stigeoclonium* Kuetz., *Cloniophora* Tiff., *Draparnaldia* Bory, *Draparnaldiopsis* Smith et Klyver, *Microthamnion* Naeg. (?), *Tellamia* Batters, *Pilinia* Kuetz., *Fritschiella* Iyen., *Fridaea* Schm., *Caespitella* Vischer, *Ireksokonia* Meyer, *Iwanoffia* Pascher, *Trichodiscus* Welsford, *Pseudochaete* W. et. W., *Chaetotheke* Dür., *Chaetomnion* Skuja, *Tumulofilum* Berger.

There are two general plans of growth. Some genera have a decided prostrate development which may or may not give rise to erect branches (*Pilinia*, *Stigeoclonium*). Others develop into erect thalli with little or no prostrate portions, but may have downward directed, rhizoidal branches (*Draparnaldia*). Reproduction is by zoospores and sexually by isogametes (mostly).

Stigeoclonium Kuetzing, 1843 (Plate IV, Fig. 59), is a heterotrichous genus in which the prostrate portion of the thallus, where growth occurs by division of apical cells, may be more developed than the erect growth. Plants are coated in a soft, inconspicuous mucilage. The habit of the erect growth is a branched filament of cylindrical or slightly swollen cells, the branches being mostly opposite or mostly alternate, according to species. The branches end in sharp points or taper to setae. The chloroplast is a parietal plate with a pyrenoid. Some species have downward growing branches with irregularly thickened walls.

The plants usually grow in flowing water and some can be used as indices of pollution. Commonly they form green fringes on stones or they may be solitary. They can be seen frequently on snail shells. Vegetative reproduction occurs commonly and easily by fragmentation. In asexual reproduction macrozoospores are produced singly. Isogametes

PLATE IV

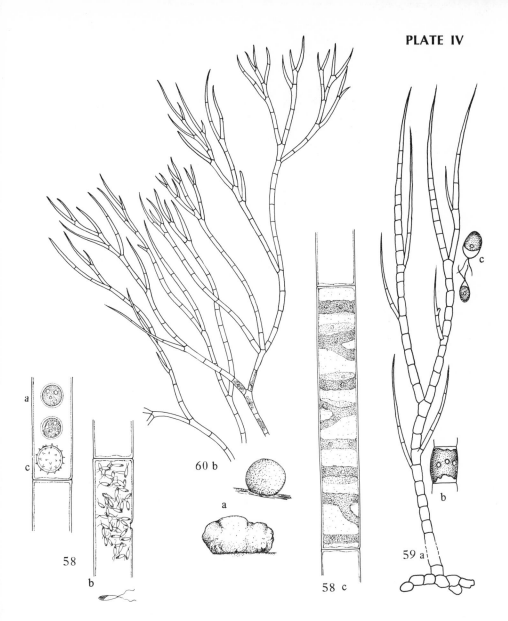

Fig. 58.   **Sphaeroplea annulina:** a, portion of cell with eggs and zygospore; b, portion of cell with antherozoids; c, vegetative cell
with ring-like chloroplasts

Fig. 59.   **Stigeoclonium** sp: a, filament with a portion of prostrate
thallus; b, cell with chloroplast; c, anisogametes

Fig. 60.   **Chaetophora pisciformis:** a, globular shaped thallus; b, portion of thallus showing branching habit of filaments; c,
colony of another species

PLATE IV

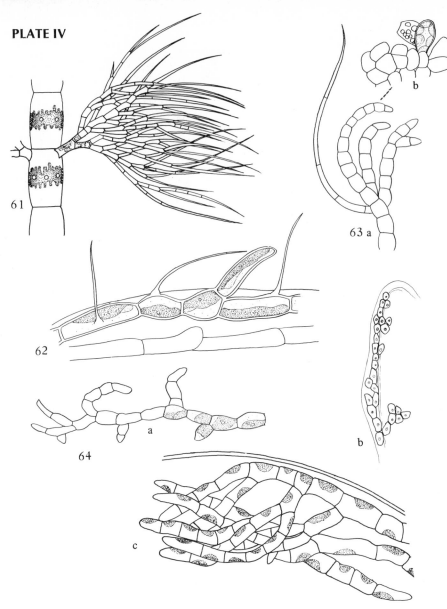

Fig. 61. **Draparnaldia glomerata,** portion of filament showing one branch fascicle

Fig. 62. **Bolbocoleon** sp, epiphytic on a marine alga

Fig. 63. **Trichodiscus elegans:** a, portion of thallus on **Azolla;** b, sporangia (redrawn from Bourrelly and Welsford)

Fig. 64. **Endoderma:** a, epiphytic on **Rhizoclonium;** b, endophytic in wall of **Cladophora;** c, **Endoderma (Entocladion) Codicola** in **Codium**

or anisogametes fuse with those from other filaments (heterothallic habit). Zygospores follow the usual plan of behavior in most species studied but in *S. subspinosum* the zygote forms a 2n plant, somewhat smaller than the haploid gametophyte. Hence there is an alternation of slightly dissimilar generations: meiosis occurs with spore formation rather than with zygote germination.

Chaetophora Schrank, 1783 (Plate IV, Fig. 60), is characterized by globular or arbuscular thalli composed of branched filaments enclosed in a firm mucilage so that plants retain their shape when removed from the water. According to species, globular or branched gelatinous strands are of macroscopic size and may be three to five mm. in diameter or up to five cm. long. Most species prefer hard, often cold water and occur more commonly in spring months in boreal latitudes. Cattail and reed stems are favorite habitats.

The basal prostrate portion of the thallus is but little-developed. The erect branches radiate from a common center, or, in one species, from a central cable of cylindrical cells. Typically the branches (often dichotomous) end in sharply pointed cells or in setae. In some species the branches are crowded or fasciculate at the periphery of the thallus. The chloroplast is a parietal, folded plate usually covering most of the cell wall. There is one pyrenoid (or more). Reproduction is by quadriflagellate zoospores and by isogametes.

Draparnaldia Bory, 1808 (Plate IV, Fig. 61), has an axis of relatively large, often barrel-shaped cells, with band-like chloroplasts, from which fascicles of branches arise. The branch cells are much smaller than those of the axis and have a parietal, plate-like chloroplast. The branches terminate in pointed cells or long, flagelliform setae. The plants are usually solitary and are embedded in a soft, amorphous mucilage. They often grow attached to sand or sticks in flowing, cold water. Reproduction is by quadriflagellate zoospores (produced singly in a cell) and by quadriflagellate isogametes which become amoeboid just before syngamy.

In the closely related genus, *Draparnaldiopsis*, at least one species (*D. indica*) has an isomorphic alternation of generations.

Trichodiscus Welsford, 1912 (Plate IV, Fig. 63), is a genus of mostly prostrate filaments, growing endophytic and epiphytic on the fern *Azolla*. It has tapering, upright, short branches which seldom rebranch and a few long cellular hairs. Reproduction is by isogametes formed in specialized, slightly enlarged cells on the upright branches, and by aplanospores.

FAMILY PROTODERMATACEAE

This family is suggested for those genera which tend to have no or only slightly tapering branches, which do not bear setae, and whose cells do not bear hairs. The thallus is mostly prostrate with few, if any, upright branches. Like the Chaetophoraceae the chloroplast is a parietal plate. Reproduction is by zoospores and rarely by isogametes. Here are included such genera as *Protoderma* Kuetzing, *Entocladia* Reinke (*Endoderma* Lag.; Plate IV, Fig. 64), *Dermatophyton* Peter, *Pseudendoclonium* Lambert, *Epibolium* Printz (*Pleurothamnion* Borzi), *Chlorotylium* Kuetz,[2] *Tumulofilum* Beger.

Endoderma Lagerheim, 1883 (*Entocladia* Reinke) (Plate IV, Fig. 64), consists of several species, both marine and fresh-water all of which are prostrate, branched filaments with only a few short branches, mostly pseudoparenchymatous. The chloroplast is a parietal plate. Growth is mostly by apical cells. Reproduction is by zoospores and by biflagellate isogametes. The filaments live within the wall of other algae, especially the thick-walled Cladophorales, or in shells of Mollusca where they form green, subsurface patches.

Protoderma Kuetzing, 1843 (Plate V, Fig. 66), forms circular or irregular patches on submersed plants, shells, and wood. The filaments are entirely prostrate, taper slightly at the apex, and cells are ulotrichoid in morphology. The thallus may be several cells deep in the center (pseudoparenchymatous) but monostromatic at the margin. Reproduction is by zoospores formed in the central cells of the thallus, or by aplanospores. Juvenile stages of *Stigeoclonium* may be confused with this genus.

Dermatophyton Peter, 1886, is a somewhat similar genus, growing epizoically on turtles. **Endophyton** Gard. (Pl. V, Fig. 65) occurs in red algae.

Pseudendoclonium Wille, 1900 (Plate V, Fig. 67), is an inconspicuous genus which forms a wood-encrusting or somewhat penetrating cushion of densely branched filaments, both erect and rhizoidal. The cells have a parietal, plate-like chloroplast with one pyrenoid. Reproduction is by quadriflagellate zoospores or aplanospores. The plants are found mostly on old wood along sea coasts.

Protococcus Agardh, 1824 (*Pleurococcus*, *Desmococcus*) (Plate V, Fig. 68), consists of cells which are solitary or clumped in gregarious masses. This anomalous and ubiquitous genus is given a place here because of the

---

[2] This is an artificial assignment, but consistency seems to preclude this genus from the Chaetophoraceae, where it is conventionally placed.

tendency of gregarious cells to form short, false filaments. This plant produces green coatings on moist tree trunks, boards, rocks, and other subaerial substrates. The cells have a massive, lobed, or plate-like chloroplast, with or without a pyrenoid. Reproduction is by cell division only, as far as known. The genus has been assigned variously, although it is usually placed in a family of its own (Protococcaceae). It is considered to be a palmelloid or reduced filamentous form.

Trichophilus Web. Van Bosse, 1887 (Plate V, Fig. 69), is a prostrate branched filament with no erect portions, growing among the hair scales of the sloth *Bradypus*. The branches taper slightly at the apex but there are no hairs or setae. Some cells become zoosporangia and give rise to quadriflagellate zoospores. Isogamete-formation is likely but questionable.

Order Coleochaetales

As recognized here this order is composed of genera in which cells have various types of bristles or hairs on the wall. The chloroplast is a parietal plate. The hairs arise either from the wall or from the protoplast and protrude through a pore in the wall. Some hairs have a sheathed base. Most of the plants included here are oogamous, with certain cells forming oogonia or antheridia. Plants are either unicellular, pseudofilamentous, or filamentous. In general they are prostrate or creeping. The two suggested families, Coleochaetaceae and Aphanochaetaceae, are usually regarded as belonging to the Ulotrichales, whereas many of the genera have been included in the Chaetophoraceae.

Family Aphanochaetaceae

In this family the plants are creeping filaments with few, if any, upright branches. Most forms are epiphytic or endophytic. The cells characteristically have the wall extended into a bristle or hair, often with a bulbous base. In some instances the hairs are terminal on the end of a branch. In this respect they show a chaetophoraceous attribute, but the hair is usually not an attenuated cell continuing the filament. Morphologically, such chaetophoraceous plants are more like some members of the Aphanochaetaceae. Some forms reproduce by anisogametes; others by egg and sperm. As interpreted here the following genera are included: *Aphanochaete* A. Braun, *Chaetonema* Nowak, *Thamniochaete* Gay, *Pseudoulvella* Wille, *Oligochaetophora* G. S. West, *Gonatoblaste* Huber, *Acrochaete* Pringsh., *Phaeophila* Hauck, *Pringsheimiella* ?, *Polychaetophora* W. et W. (*Diplochaete*), *Bolbocoleon* Pringsh.

Aphanochaete A. Braun, 1851 (Plate V, Fig. 70), is characterized by sparingly branched filaments of cylindrical or oval cells growing prostrate over larger fresh-water filamentous algae. One species forms loops like a measuring worm. The cell wall bears one or more bulbous-based, long hairs. There is a theory that such hairs are reduced and modified branches. There is a ulotrichoid chloroplast and pyrenoids. Reproduction is by quadriflagellate zoospores and by quadriflagellate anisogametes, both kinds being produced in cells of the same filament. The plus (female) gamete is produced singly in a swollen cell whereas the minus (male) gametes are developed singly or in pairs within small units resulting from division of terminal cells. The zygospore (red with oil) follows the usual behavior.

Chaetonema Nowakowski, 1876 (Plate V, Fig. 71), is a genus of few species with a habit much like that of *Aphanochaete*. The prostrate filament bears very short, upright branches, some of which terminate in a hair. The fact that this hair is a unicellular extension of the branch possibly relates this genus to Chaetophoraceae but the habit of growth and the oogamous sexual reproduction are unlike members of that family. The cells have a parietal chloroplast and a pyrenoid. Some cells may enlarge and form a zoosporangium in which four to ten zoospores are produced.

At the ends of branches a cell enlarges and becomes an oogonium, producing a single egg. Special small, barrel-shaped cells with practically no pigment divide their content to form eight sperm. Fertilization occurs when the egg protrudes from the apex of the oogonium, resulting in an oospore.

Acrochaete Pringsheim, 1862 (Plate V, Fig. 72), is an example of a genus which is mostly prostrate. The irregularly branched filaments commonly terminate in a hair, but these sometimes are few or absent. They grow endophytically in brown seaweeds. Asexual reproduction is by biflagellate zoospores produced in terminal cells; sexual reproduction is by biflagellate isogametes.

Phaeophila Hauck, 1876 (Plate V, Fig. 73), is a simple genus in which there is a slightly branched filament living as an endophyte in walls of marine algae or growing in shells of Mollusca. The cells, irregular in shape, bear one to several hairs which sometimes are curiously twisted at the base. Reproduction is similar to that of *Ectochaete*, but quadriflagellate motile elements are formed.

PLATE V

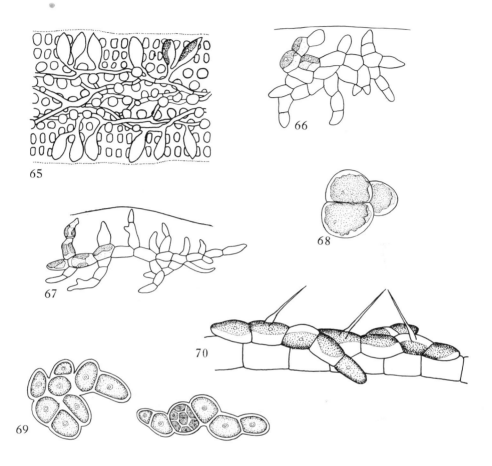

Fig. 65. **Endophyton ramosum,** portion of filaments with swollen tips, in medulla of a red alga

Fig. 66. **Protoderma viride,** epiphytic on an aquatic plant stem

Fig. 67. **Pseudendoclonium** sp, a filament from an encrusting thallus

Fig. 68. **Protococcus** sp, clump of cells from a subaerial stratum

Fig. 69. **Trichophilus Welcheri,** portion of pseudofilaments from a sloth hair

Fig. 70. **Aphanochaete repens,** epiphytic filament with bulbous hairs

PLATE V

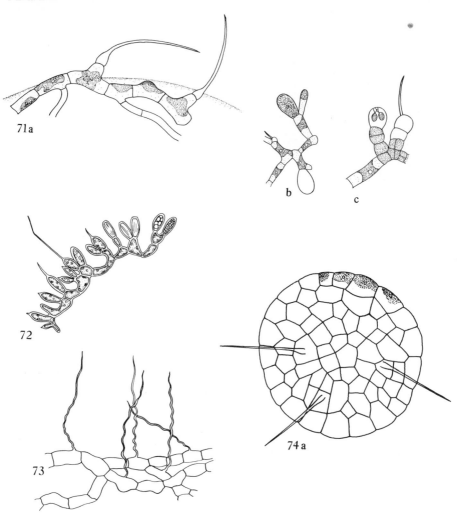

Fig. 71.   **Chaetonema irregulare:** a, vegetative filament epiphytic in mucilage of other algae; b, oogonia; c, antheridia (redrawn from Meyer)

Fig. 72.   **Acrochaete repens** (redrawn from Pringsheim)

Fig. 73.   **Phaeophila** sp, portion of branched thallus, endophytic in **Polysiphonia**

Fig. 74.   **Coleochaete orbicularis:** a, disc-like, prostrate thallus

PLATE V

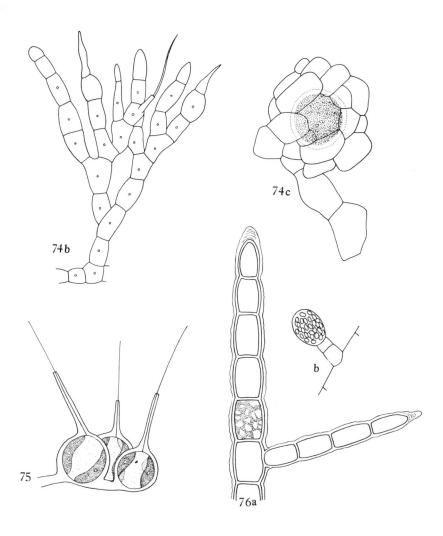

Fig. 74. **Coleochaete:** b, portion of erect thallus; c, zygospore with envelope of sterile filaments

Fig. 75. **Chaetosphaeridium globosum,** clump of cells with sheathed hairs

Fig. 76. **Trentepohlia aurea:** a, erect filament, showing branching habit; b, lateral sporangium

Bolbocoleon Pringsheim, 1862 (*Ectochaete* [Huber] Wille) (Plate IV, Fig. 62), is an example of an architecture in which the plant is mostly prostrate, with a few upright branches. Plants grow as epiphytes on marine algae. Certain small cells give rise to upright, elongate tapering setae, with a swollen base. There is a parietal or net-like chloroplast covering most of the cell wall. Reproduction is by zoospores. There is a question as to whether this genus can be separated from *Ectochaete* in which the hairs arise from the ends of ordinary vegetative cells.

FAMILY COLEOCHAETACEAE

In this family unicellular or branched filamentous plants have hairs which arise from the protoplast and protrude through a pore in the wall. In some forms the wall extends around the hair as a basal sheath. The chloroplast is parietal with one or more pyrenoids.

Coleochaete de Brébisson, 1844 (Plate V, Fig. 74), grows as partly prostrate, partly erect branched filaments or as entirely prostrate and disc-like thalli in which branches radiate from a common center and are closely adjoined. Some cells bear a seta which arises from a blepharoplast located just beneath a pore in the wall. The wall forms a basal sheath about the hair. There is a laminate, parietal chloroplast and one pyrenoid. The thalli are usually epiphytic but the disc-like plants grow on shells, glass, and other substrates. *Coleochaete scutata* commonly grows on the sides of laboratory aquaria, forming conspicuous but small, circular patches. These are favorite food of snails. One species, *C. nitellarum*, specifically grows under the wall of *Nitella*, with the setae extending through the host wall. The cells of this species are irregularly angular in shape and are arranged in likewise irregular filaments. Some species form upright filamentous tufts on the epidermis of aquatic plants.

Asexual reproduction is by zoospores produced singly in almost any cell. In sexual reproduction, which is oogamous, *Coleochaete* shows an advancement over other members of the order. The female sex organ is somewhat cone-shaped or flask-shaped, and appears at the margin of a colony, or among the internal cells. There is a neck-like extension called the *trichogyne* (as in the Rhodophyta). Within the oogonium a single egg occurs. The antheridia are formed by the binary division of a vegetative cell, also usually located at the ends of branches or at the margin of a thallus. Each cell produces a single biflagellate sperm. Because the branches continue to grow after the differentiation of sex organs these come to lie within the thallus rather than at the margin. The sperm unites with the oogonium at the trichogyne and the nucleus passes through to fertilize the egg. The zygote forms a thick wall (oospore) and then the oogonium becomes invested by proliferating filaments arising from the nearby vegetative cells. The whole, which is known as a *spermocarp*, becomes red in age and conspicuous in the thallus. Meiosis occurs with germination of the oospore to form as many as 32 biflagellate zoospores. The spermocarp undergoes a cleavage to allow zoospores to escape. It was in this genus that meiosis in the Chlorophyta was observed first (C. E. Allen, 1905).

Chaetosphaeridium Klebahn, 1892 (Plate V, Fig. 75), is an example of the one-celled expression of the Coleochaetaceae. Cells may be joined incidentally by basal, gelatinous tubes to form gregarious clumps, growing epiphytically on filamentous algae. The cells are globular, with a parietal chloroplast, and have a sheathed hair that arises from the cytoplasm. The only known methods of reproduction are by cell division (transversely) and by zoospores.

Order Trentepohliales

FAMILY TRENTEPOHLIACEAE

This order includes those plants which have branched, filamentous, often arbuscular thalli, the branches not tapering (or but very little) at the apex and without setae (see *Cephaleuros*, however) or wall hairs. Walls of cells are usually thick and sometimes lamellate. The chloroplast, while essentially parietal, is often net-like and sometimes massive. In habit of growth there is a decided distinction between a basal, prostate portion and an erect, freely branching portion. There are many epiphytic, endophytic, and parasitic species, and some are wood- or shell-boring. In several genera red carotenoid pigments are abundant, especially when plants are aerial or exposed to intense illumination.

Reproduction is by zoospores which are produced in enlarged (usually terminal) zoosporangia. The entire sporangia may be abscissed and carried away by the wind to germinate in a new habitat. In sexual reproduction isogametes are used, with the gametes produced in slightly swollen, zoosporangia-like cells.

Included in this order, with one family (*Trentepohliaceae*) and two or three tribes, are: *Trentepohlia* Martius, *Physolinum* Printz, *Gomontia* Born. et Flah., *Gongrosira* Chodat, *Ctenocladus* Borzi, *Cephaleuros* Kunze, *Stomatochroon* Palm, and *Phycopeltis* Millardet.

Trentepohlia Martius, 1817 (Plate V, Fig. 76), is a showy genus which forms bright orange, cottony growths in humid situations. Moist cliffs or exposed roots of trees on cliffs may be overgrown with this plant.

Plants are filamentous and erect, although much of the thallus may be prostrate. Some species are but very little branched whereas others have alternate or opposite branching. Cell walls are relatively thick and variously lamellate. Branching is often at right angles, with the branches arising from the midregion of the supporting cell. In some species the end of the filament bears a cap of pectose material which occurs in layers. The chloroplast, usually reddish with B-carotene, is somewhat massive and indistinctly shaped, or occurs as parietal bands or is disc-like, quite dissimilar from the typical chaetophoraceous chloroplast. Certain species enter into association with fungi to form the lichen *Coenogonium*. In this connection the lichen may involve only a few twisted fungal threads around the alga. In the tropics a lichenous growth is produced that appears as soft, cottony, lemon-yellow or orange-colored fans or shelving thalli on leaves or stems of higher plants.

Quadriflagellate zoospores are formed in slightly swollen sporangia which occur either intercalary or on stalks at the ends of branches, often terminating the filament. The stalked sporangia are abscissed and carried away by air currents to germinate in moist places, discharging a number of zoospores. Aplanospores may be produced also, and akinetes borne in chains are not infrequent.

Gamete-producing cells are likewise terminal or intercalary but these are not abscissed. Sex cells are biflagellate isogametes. The life cycle is of the usual ulotrichoid type, meiosis occurring with the germination of the zygospore.

Cephaleuros Kunze, 1829 (Plate VI, Fig. 77) is a pseudoparenchymatous thallus composed of an expanded mass of filaments which give rise to vertical branches, some of which are hair-like. This is a parasitic genus, growing just under the epidermis of leaves and fruits of higher plants. As a result, leaves of *Magnolia*, *Oleander*, banana, tea, or citrus fruits have grayish, discolored spots. The parasite is of considerable negative economic importance because of its capacity to ruin tea crops, especially in India and Ceylon. The alga attacks the young leaves which of course are the choicest for commercial tea. Whereas the alga does not injure citrus fruit it does produce objectionable discoloration and blotches.

The prostrate portion of the thallus is reddish from carotenoids (haematochrome). The upright branches protrude through the epidermis of the host. Asexual reproduction is by zoospores produced in stalked sporangia that develop at the tips of the protruding branches (hairs). Like *Trentepohlia* the zoosporangia are abscissed and produce zoospores in a moist habitat. Isogametes are produced in unspecialized but slightly swollen cells in the prostrate portion of the thallus.

Order Ulvales[3]

This is the "sea lettuce" order in which plants are an expanded sheet (sometimes narrow and ribbon-like) or a hollow tube with the walls one cell thick. Cells are quadrate and have a tendency to be arranged in quartets. The cells are ulotrichoid with a parietal chloroplast and a pyrenoid. Although developing primarily as a filament, cell division in two planes produces a double strand of cells. The two layers separate to form a tube. The tube splits in *Monostroma* so that a sheet type of growth is formed. Plants are attached by a multicellular, disc-like holdfast.

A few species occur in fresh or brackish, salt-marsh water. But mostly they are marine, with some species living unattached. In the ocean these plants are conspicuous on wharf pilings and rocks, especially in the intertidal zone. Inland plants live in flowing water, usually alpine or subalpine, or in brackish (hard) water.

Reproduction is by zoospores and iso- or anisogametes, whereas vegetative reproduction by fragmentation is common and efficient. There are two kinds of life histories: (1) meiosis, which occurs with zygospore germination to form haploid zoospores (ulotrichoid type); (2) an alternation of isomorphic generations in which the diploid has developed from the zygote, the haploid from a zoospore (see p. 43).

Family Ulvaceae

Monostroma Thuret, 1848 (Plate VI, Fig. 78), which is sometimes regarded as belonging to its own family, develops at first as a hollow sac that sooner or later splits to form a monostromatic sheet a few centimeters in width and length. In the water, plants appear as small pieces of lettuce leaves attached to rocks. There are both marine and fresh-water species, the latter occurring mostly in cold streams, which in the main means at high altitudes.

Iso- or anisogametes are produced, the plus and minus strains being formed on separate plants. The zygote swims for a time, becomes quiescent, and then enlarges decidedly, forming a sort of embryonic sporophyte, oval in shape. Here, as many as 32 quadriflagellate zoospores are produced by meiosis. The behavior of the zygote to form an intermediate growth before producing spores is the basis for some taxonomists having placed *Monostroma* in its own family. The zoospores in turn develop haploid gametophytes.

Hirose and Yoshida (1964) found that there are two kinds of life

[3] Gayral (1965) has suggested placing the Monostromaceae and Ulvaceae in the order Ulotrichales.

histories in *Monostroma*. One shows a zoospore-producing plant only. The other has an alternation of generations, diploid and haploid, with some species showing only a zygote as a diploid stage. In some species the alternation is of isomorphic generations, as in other Ulvales. This and other studies seem to indicate that the genus merits a complete revision.

Ulva (L.) J. Agardh, 1883 (Plate VI, Fig. 79), has leaf-like thalli, two cells thick, which at first develop as simple filaments. The leaf-like fronds are attached by a complex of coenocytic rhizoids extending from the lowermost cells of the thallus. Cells of the frond often tend to be arranged in quartets. *Ulva* grows in salt or brackish water, being worldwide in its distribution. It is often a dominant plant in the intertidal zone, and shows a selectivity for waters enriched by nitrogenous wastes.

Isogametes (from separate plants) unite to form zygotes which grow directly into diploid plants. These produce zoospores at maturity by meiosis, whole areas giving rise to spores simultaneously. The zoospores in turn produce haploid gametophytes, illustrating a type of life history in which there is an alternation of similar generations.

Enteromorpha Link, 1820 (Plate VI, Fig. 80), grows as hollow, intestiniform tubes, as much as 15 cm. or more in length. Species are both marine and fresh-water, especially in alkaline or basic streams. Reproduction and life history are similar to *Ulva*. The green alga *Collinsiella* is thought to be but a small, stunted gametophyte stage of *Enteromorpha*. Like the former *Ulva*, plants are abundant on wharf pilings and rocks in the intertidal zone, at the upper limits of the splash zone. The taxonomy of species in this genus is subject to revision following the culture studies of Bliding (1963).

FAMILY SCHIZOMERIDACEAE

This is a small family which includes but two genera, *Schizomeris* Kuetzing and *Trichosarcina* Nichols et Bold. These plants are *Ulothrix*-like in many respects and have been placed in the Ulotrichaceae in some systems of classification, partly because of the *Ulothrix* type of chloroplast when the plants are young, and because of the early ulotrichoid type of filament during growth.

Schizomeris Kuetzing, 1843 (Plate VI, Fig. 81), begins as a uniseriate, unbranched filament arising from a simple, disc-like holdfast. The cells at first are cylindrical and divided by transverse, ring-like wall formations. They soon become brick-like when successive divisions by vertical

PLATE VI

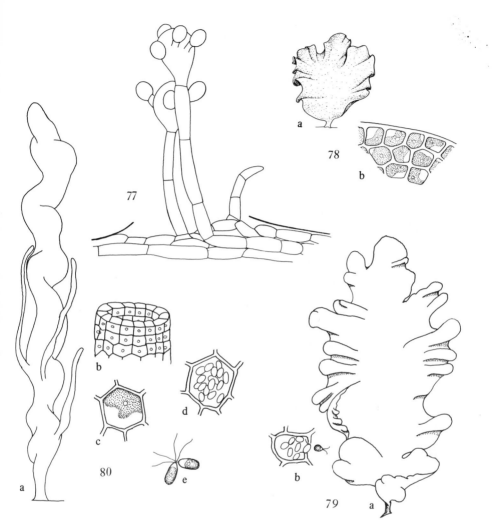

Fig. 77. **Cephaleuros virescens,** prostrate and erect portions of thallus endophytic (parasitic) in leaf of **Magnolia,** sporangia terminal

Fig. 78. **Monostroma** sp: a, habit of plant; b, marginal cells showing ulotrichoid chloroplast

Fig. 79. **Ulva latissima:** a, habit of plant; b, zoospore-formation

Fig. 80. **Enteromorpha** sp: a, habit of plant; b, diagram of section through thallus; c, cell with chloroplast; d, cell with zoospores; e, gametic union

PLATE VI

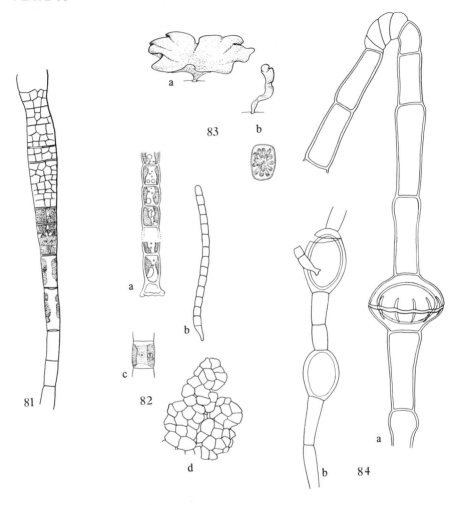

Fig. 81. **Schizomeris Leibleinii,** uniseriate and multiseriate portions of filament

Fig. 82. **Trichosarcina polymorpha:** a, filament with basal cell; b, habit of plant; c, cell in detail; d, palmelloid state (redrawn from Nichols and Bold)

Fig. 83. **Prasiola** sp: a, habit of thallus; b, cells with stellate chloroplast

Fig. 84. **Oedogonium** sp: a, macrandrous species; b, nannandrous species (dwarf male filaments)

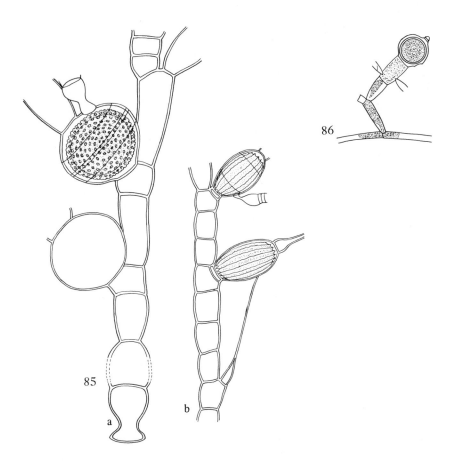

PLATE VI

Fig. 85.   **Bulbochaete:** two species with two types of oospore wall ornamentation; dwarf male plants epiphytic on oogonia

Fig. 86.   **Oedocladium Hazenii,** portion of filament with oogonium and antheridia (redrawn from Smith)

walls occur in the upper part of the thallus. The base remains uniseriate, the upper multiseriate and somewhat cylindrical. The chloroplast in the upper region becomes massive, usually with several pyrenoids.

Fragmentation is commonly used for vegetative reproduction. Quadri-flagellate zoospores are liberated from upper cells, either from a break-down of cell walls or by a terminal pore accompanied by a deterioration of the thallus internally, allowing spores to move apically.

There is a report that zoospores do not form the adult plant but germi-nate to produce short filaments that are gametophytic. The isogametes are reported to form a zygote that grows into a spore-producing thallus. Hence the life history is comparable to that of other Ulvales and dis-similar to any known for the Ulotrichaceae.

Plants are usually found in the tychoplankton or attached in shallow water, especially in water enriched with nitrogen wastes.

Trichosarcina Nichols et Bold, 1965 (Plate VI, Fig. 82), has ulotrichoid stages similar to *Hormidium*. But soon the filaments become multi-seriate and somewhat palmelloid thalli. This fragments into sarcina-like packets in the upper portions. The chloroplast is massive, with a single pyrenoid.

Reproduction by quadriflagellate zoospores is the only known method of reproduction in the type species, *T. polymorpha*. This plant was found in shallow pools in granitic rock. It has been suggested that this genus is synonymous with *Pseudendoclonium*.

Order Schizogonales

This is a small order in which plants are morphologically somewhat simi-lar to certain members of the Ulvales, but in which there are cytological and reproductive differences. Plants grow as multiseriate filaments or as attached, foliose, expanded fronds. Cells are semiquadrate and have axial, stellate chloroplasts. Like the Ulvales, cells are arranged in quartets, often with considerable space between the protoplasts. *Schizogonium* Kuetzing, 1843, grows as uni- or multiseriate threads, whereas **Prasiola** C. A. Agardh, 1821 (Plate VI, Fig. 83), appears as small, crinkled, lettuce-like fronds, usually gregarious. The latter is both aquatic and terrestrial, often growing in areas where there is nitrogenous waste. It is especially abundant in arctic, subaerial habitats. Some species are confined to swiftly flowing cold water such as found in the Rocky Mountains and the Andes. The plants are attached by rhizoidal outgrowths from the margin of the thallus. In at least one species reproduction is anisogamous, using non-motile larger gametes and smaller motile gametes, both of which are shed from the same plant. An interesting variation in the life cycle occurs wherein diploid cells of *P. stipitata* produce meiospores in the peripheral region of a thallus. These grow into small, leaf-like proliferations of the thallus, some of which in turn give rise to large gametes, others to small gametes; in both instances the gametes are motile. They unite to form a zygote that grows into a diploid plant. It has been noted that in vertical distribution along sea coasts, the diploid plants occur in the higher zones, while those that bear epiphytic gametophytes occur in a lower zone.

Order Oedogoniales

This strictly fresh-water and terrestrial order holds an isolated position, inasmuch as it has neither known ancestors nor descendants. Whereas the filaments with their basal-distal differentiation and holdfast are ulotrichoid, there are no features in common with any of the other orders of the Chlorophyta except that Oedogoniales do have a ulotrichoid type of life history. But the method of reproduction is quite unique, as is also the cytology and method of cell division. It is reasonable to assume that the order was derived from some ulotrichoid ancestral line, the representatives of which no longer exist as such. Similarly reasonable is an assumption that they may have developed directly from some motile unicell.

There is but one family with three genera. The filaments are branched in *Oedocladium* and *Bulbochaete*, but unbranched in *Oedogonium*, and most all species are attached, at least when young, by a special holdfast cell. In general, vegetative cells have polarity and usually are larger at the anterior end. In *Bulbochaete* cells bear bulbous-based, unicellular hairs that arise laterally near the anterior end. The chloroplast is a close or loose parietal network with narrow and padded portions enclosing pyrenoids. There is one nucleus.

Asexual reproduction is by zoospores formed singly in an unspecialized cell. Flagella are many, arranged in a ring around the anterior end (stephanokont) and arising from a double row of granules. Sexual reproduction is oogamous, with specialized sex organs, oogonium and antheridium, formed on the same or different filaments.

Oedogonium Link, 1820 (Plate VI, Fig. 84), is an unbranched, filamentous genus, attached (at least when young) by a holdfast cell. There is considerable variation in cell size, shape, and reproductive structures resulting in 400 or more recognized species. Plants grow as fuzzy fringes on grass and submerged wood, or, when mature, as yellowish-green floating mats. A few species are terrestrial, and, like *Oedocladium* spp, are common in the tropics.

Although somewhat cylindrical, the vegetative cells are enlarged anteriorly and sometimes are actually capitate. Some species have cells with undulate margins; some are hexagonal. The net-like chloroplast is often dense and may appear as broken, disc-shaped portions, obscured by the starch sheaths of the pyrenoids.

The cell wall is in three layers; an outer with chitin in combination with other substances; a middle layer of pectose; and an inner layer of cellulose, although it is claimed by some who have used the electron microscope that cellulose does not occur (see p. 39).

Cell division in Oedogonium is unique and results in a ring-like scar being formed near the anterior end of the cell. Cells in a filament, if they have divided, will have at least one of these rings or caps, or as many caps as the number of times that division has occurred. Cell division is initiated when a ring of hemicellulose develops inside the lateral walls just below the apical wall, so that it protrudes into the cell cavity. As the ring develops, or just prior to its formation, the nucleus migrates by some unknown means into the upper third of the cell where it prepares for mitosis. Meanwhile in the ring of cellulose, in a position where the ring adjoins the lateral wall, a fissure or invagination occurs so that the ring is practically split into two layers, one above the other. Then the cell wall, opposite the groove in the ring, splits so that a crack extends around the cell. By this time the nucleus has divided and this is quickly followed by transverse cleavage of the protoplast in the mid-region of the original cell. As this division is completed the two daughter protoplasts begin to elongate. When the upper protoplast extends itself the rings of cellulose in the ring expand and stretch, entering into the formation of a new cylinder of wall material. The new sleeve of wall material pushes up the anterior portion or the old cell wall, along with the original cross wall below which the transverse split occurred. Thus the upper protoplast comes to be enclosed by a new section and the old cap-like portion of cell wall, whereas the lower protoplast and one of the daughter nuclei is enclosed by the old mother cell wall entirely. A new cross wall is then laid down between the two protoplasts, quite independent of nuclear division.

Asexual reproduction is by relatively large zoospores, produced singly in an unspecialized cell. The flagellation, as previously indicated, is stephanokont. In sexual reproduction Oedogonium shows a great diversity of biologically intriguing habits, again illustrating the high refinements possessed by seemingly "simple" organisms. Any cell (except the basal cell) or a series of cells may enlarge greatly, accompanied by a concentration of food material (protein and oil) to form the female organ (oogonium) with a single egg. As the oogonium matures a pore (poriferous species) or a transverse slit (operculate species) is formed in the wall. In some species the cell immediately below the oogonium reacts to what may be regarded as a female hormone and enlarges without developing into a sex organ. This is known as the *suffultory* cell.

Either in the same filament (monoecious) or in different plants (dioecious) a vegetative cell divides to delimit one or a series of short compartment-like cells which serve as antheridia. Each cell forms one or two small sperms similar to the zoospores in flagellation. A sperm swims to the pore or operculum and the nucleus migrates to the egg nucleus. The zygote immediately forms a thick wall (usually of three layers). The oospore wall (at least one of the layers) is variously ornamented (sometimes smooth) with ribs, spines, flanges, areolae, etc., according to species. Upon germination four zoospores are produced by meiosis and if the species is dioecious two of these supposedly form male plants and two form female plants (macrandrous species).

A variation of this life history occurs in one group of species. A vegetative cell divides to form two somewhat rectangular cells in which medium-sized zoospores are produced singly. These spores swim for a time and then as if attracted by the female organ settle on the oogonium or on the suffultory cell below it, where they germinate to form small, few-celled dwarf filaments. The terminal or subterminal cell of such a filament becomes an antheridium which produces one (or two) sperm. Hence fertilization is easily and more surely achieved, the sperm being liberated in close proximity to the oogonium opening. The zoospores that produce the dwarf (*nannandrous*) male plants are called *andro-spores* and the cells that produce them *androsporangia*. If the androsporangia are borne in the same filament as the oogonia, the species is known as *gynandrosporous*. If *androspores* come from separate filaments the species is referred to as *idioandrosporous*. Species lacking androspores are called *macandrous*.

Bulbochaete Agardh, 1817 (Plate VI, Fig. 85), is a branched, filamentous, and attached genus, receiving its name from the bulbous-based hairs that develop laterally and anteriorly on many of the cells. Plants live in habitats similar to those of *Oedogonium*, especially on submerged aquatic plants and on overhanging grass leaves. Cells are subcylindric or pyriform. Reproduction is very similar to that in *Oedogonium*, but almost all species are nannandrous. One difference is the behavior of the suffultory cell, which undergoes a division as the oogonium matures, but does not enlarge. Cell division is peculiar and different from *Oedogon-ium*. Most elongation of the filament comes from successive divisions of the basal cell.

Oedocladium Stahl, 1891 (Plate VI, Fig. 86), is a branched, unattached, mostly terrestrial genus. Filaments are short and densely green, appearing much like patches of moss protonema. In their habit of growth some branches form rhizoids. Sexual reproduction is nannandrous. There may be many species of this genus but so far only about a dozen have been found.

Order Cladophorales (Cladophoraceae)

This is an order of both marine and fresh-water, mostly branched, coenocytic algae in which thick-walled cells have parietal, net-like or fragmented chloroplasts. There are many pyrenoids, and according to some cytologists these may lie between portions of the chloroplast as well as in the meshes. Some systems of classification place the order under the Siphonocladales, which are also coenocytic. Plants are coarse and wiry and attached, at least when young, by a holdfast cell or by rhizoidal outgrowths from cells in the lower part of the filament. Most members are attached to rocks, and are especially suited for flowing water. Some forms are known to be symbiotic with sponges in the sea.

Walls are relatively thick and lamellated, without an outer layer of mucilage. As mentioned elsewhere, plants in this order are heavily epiphytized because of the absence of the gelatinous layer. The wall contains cellulose-I and has a pattern of microfibrils lying in two or three directions, whereas most algae have randomly arranged polysaccharides in the wall.

In reproduction fragmentation is very much employed, some genera becoming free-floating and continuing to multiply indefinitely — often to the point of forming objectionable, tangled mats. Cell division occurs by cross septations forming in the mid-region, independent of nuclear division. In some, cell division occurs mostly in the apical units whereas in other species it is intercalary.

In asexual reproduction biflagellate zoospores are formed in unspecialized cells, these escaping through pores in the lateral walls. Sexual reproduction is isogamous, plants being either heterothallic or homothallic. The zygote follows one of two behaviors, as in the Ulvales. In some species a zygospore is formed and meiosis occurs when it germinates. In others, a diploid sporophyte generation is produced and reduction division occurs with the formation of zoospores in the outer cells of the branches. Thus, an alternation of isomorphic generations is followed.

Cladophora Kuetzing, 1843 (Plate VII, Fig. 87), includes both marine and fresh-water species. Some form orderly, branched, bush-like tufts; others, particularly in lakes, are very irregular in their plan of branching. *Cladophora glomerata*, a common fresh-water species, shows innumerable morphological variations in response to different habitat factors. In the ocean *Cladophora* is found mostly in the intertidal zone, and is often epiphytic on larger algae. Although all species seem to be attached at first, they commonly become free-floating, tangled ropes and are trouble makers. The Great Lakes support an abundant growth of *Cladophora glomerata* which, since 1960, has become increasingly obnoxious on bathing beaches and in boating areas. One species, *C. holsatica*, has been found capable of inhibiting the growth of mosquito larvae. This is a species which often grows as "*Cladophora*-balls" — the *Aegagropila* form that occurs in deep water as sponge-like thalli, often floating and eventually being washed up on shore. Another species in Japan's Lake Akan forms balls of impressive size and is of national interest. *Cladophora* is curiously rare in the tropics and subtropics.

Attachment of the *Cladophora* thallus is by rhizoidal outgrowths from the base of the plant, or from rhizoids growing down from lowermost cells of the filament, sometimes pushing down through the lamellae of the thick-walled basal cells. Upright branches are alternate, dichotomous, or trichotomous in arrangement. Actually branches develop near the apical end of a cell and then become elevated to a position at the cross wall to give the appearance of dichotomy.

The layered wall has microfibrils in spirals and these are interwoven between the lamellae. The fibrils of the lateral walls are continuous with those of the cross partition. From electron studies it is thought that the microfibrils are produced from the outer, peripheral region of the cytoplasm. When transverse septa are formed in cells, the division begins in the outermost layers of the wall.

As described for the family, asexual reproduction is by biflagellate zoospores; sexual reproduction by isogametes. Marine species and at least one (perhaps other) fresh-water species have an alternation of isomorphic generations, the haploid nuclei having 11 chromosomes and the diploid 22 (cf. *Cladphora clavuligera*).

Rhizoclonium Kuetzing, 1843 (Plate VII, Fig. 88), is an inelegant, coarse, wiry filament, mostly unattached and mostly unbranched. Like *Cladophora* the walls are thick and often lamellate, sometimes completely covered by epiphytic diatoms. Branching, when it occurs, is very irregular and there is no arbuscular plan of growth. Some species have short, rhizoidal branches. Plants often form streaming masses, or hanks, in flowing water, or are attached to rocks in the tide pool zone of the seashore. Some species live on mud flats and in tidal marshes. Like *Cladophora*, some species form floating, tangled mats. Some species can also be confused with certain sparsely branched forms of that genus.

The cytology is very similar to that of *Cladophora*, and there is likewise a mucilage-free cell wall. The number of chromosomes in the haploid plant varies from 12 to 48. The diploid phase of *R. hierogly-*

phicum has been reported as 24 and also as 36, suggesting polyploidy. Reproduction is similar to one group of species in *Cladophora* in which meiosis occurs with the germination of the zygospore. Whereas isogametes are commonly used, *R. lubricum* is anisogamous.

Pithophora Wittrock, 1877 (Plate VII, Fig. 89), is a distinctive, mostly tropical and subtropical genus, quickly identified, at least when mature, by the cask-like akinetes which alternate with vegetative cells, or which may occur in series. The cell walls are thick, but only those of the akinetes are lamellate. Branching is alternate or opposite and in some species there are branches of the second or third order. There is a general tendency to show an arbuscular type of thallus. Sometimes rhizoids develop at the branch tips. So far, zoospores and gametes have not been reported for *Pithophora*. The thick-walled akinetes are highly successful in multiplying the plant. Upon germinating the akinete is divided by a cross partition, apparently independent of any nuclear division. One of the two cells thus formed puts out a rhizoid, whereas a new filament is initiated by the other.

Pithophora is useful in aquaria as an oxygenator, although the growth may become overly abundant. Some species are infamous for their ability to interfere with fish nurse pond operation.

Basicladia Hoff. et Tilden, 1930 (Plate VII, Fig. 90), is another coarse filament with few, if any, branches which occur only at the extreme base of the plant (rarely somewhat above). Species (of which only four are known) are almost entirely confined to an epizoic existence on the backs of the snapping turtle, or on other turtles with roughened and grooved carapaces. Here they form veritable gardens and account for the name "moss back" given to turtles. Occasionally the plants are found on rough stones or bricks, or snail shells. Cytologically *Basicladia* is similar to *Cladophora*. Lower cells in the filament are extremely long, while higher cells are shorter. These latter may swell slightly and produce swarms of zoospores. A typical lateral pore occurs in the wall for their escape. Probably gametes also are formed but the life cycle has not been completely followed.

Chaetomorpha Kuetzing, 1845 (Plate VII, Fig. 91), is a coarse, unbranched marine filament growing attached to rocks and corals. Occasionally *C. linum* is found in fresh and brackish water. Cytologically the genus is similar to other Cladophorales but there is a greater abundance of carotenes and xanthophylls, in addition to chlorophyll-*a* and -*b*. Plants form tangled tufts much like *Cladophora*. In the filament, lower

PLATE VII

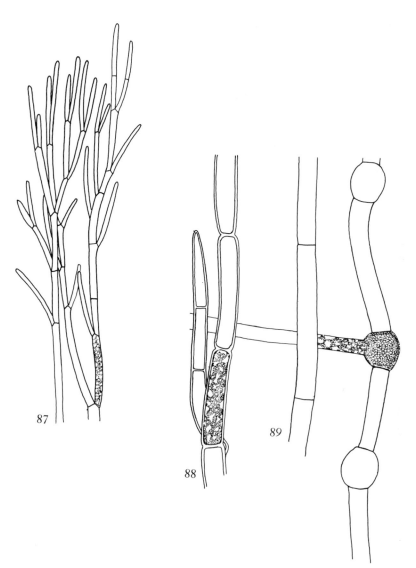

Fig. 87.   **Cladophora glomerata,** apical portion of thallus

Fig. 88.   **Rhizoclonium Hookeri,** portion of filament with reticulate chloroplast

Fig. 89.   **Pithophora varia,** branching habit with akinete

PLATE VII

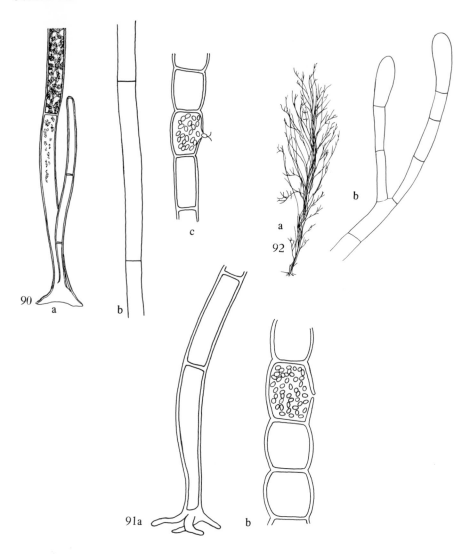

Fig. 90. **Basicladia chelonum:** a, basal portion of filament showing habit of branching; b, upper cells of filament; c, sporangium with escape pore

Fig. 91. **Chaetomorpha area:** a, base of filament; b, upper cells with sporangium

Fig. 92. **Spongomorpha** sp: a, habit of plant; b, terminus of one branch

PLATE VII

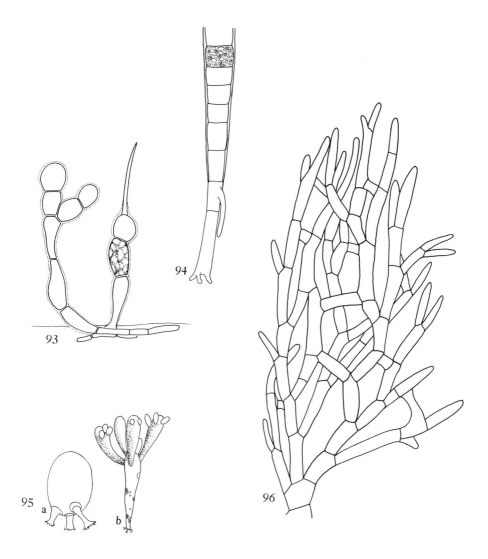

Fig. 93.   **Wittrockiella paradoxa:** filaments from soil; sporangia terminal and subterminal

Fig. 94.   **Urospora** sp, base of filament

Fig. 95.   **Valonia** spp: a, **V. ventricosa** (after Boergesen); b, **V, urticularis** after Schmitz)

Fig. 96.   **Microdictyon mutabile,** branching habit

P. H. WELSHIMER MEMORIAL LIBRARY
MILLIGAN COLLEGE, TENN. 37682

cells have a habit of extending downward into the cell below. Electron microscopy shows the same cross patterns of cellulose-I fibrils. The outermost layers of the walls are cemented by a sort of "encrustment." In *Chaetomorpha media*, for example, the nucleus has 18 chromosomes in the n-number and 36 in the diploid, but it is thought that there is much polyploidy. The definite polarity of the cells is determined by the behavior of the zoospores which germinate after becoming attached, anterior end downward. The fibrils in the wall of the germling are at first transverse and then parallel with the longitudinal axis of the new cells.

In reproduction *Chaetomorpha* is similar to *Cladophora*, having biflagellate zoospores and gametes which escape through lateral wall pores. The life history involves an alternation of isomorphic generations, with the two phases sometimes occurring at different seasons.

In the Philippine Islands commercially-grown fish are fed for a time in tanks containing coarse growths of *Chaetomorpha*.

Spongomorpha Kuetzing, 1843 (Plate VII, Fig. 92), is like a much-branched and usually tufted *Cladophora*, with several axes twisted together. By some, *Spongomorpha* is regarded as a subgenus of *Cladophora*. By others, *Spongomorpha*, *Urospora*, and *Acrosiphonia* are considered as members of a new family Acrosiphoniaceae. Plants grow on rocky shores and in tide pools in northern and colder waters where they are attached by a profuse rhizoid development. These rhizoidal growths serve to clump many strands together. In growth, cell division takes place mostly in apical cells, the branches becoming hooked and interlocked.

Reproduction includes the use of akinetes which may form in clusters at the ends of rhizoids. Asexual reproduction is by biflagellate zoospores in seriately arranged sporangia. Sexual reproduction is by isogametes. In one species at least, *S. coalita*, there appears to be an alternation of dissimilar generations, the sporophyte being a small, filamentous plant growing as an endophyte and previously described as *Codiolum petrocelidis*. The life history is subject to further investigation.

Wittrockiella Wille, 1909 (Plate VII, Fig. 93), is a soil alga growing in brackish water and swamps. The filaments are little-branched, short, erect, and covered with a firm, tough mucilage. Downward growing branches form rhizoids. The cells enlarge upward, eventually forming aplanospores. The terminal cell may form an akinete, which has a thick, lamellate wall. The upper cells of vegetative branches are yellowish with haematochrome and bear a terminal hair which is an outgrowth from an extension of inner lamellae. The hair pushes through the outer layers of the wall which form a sheath around the base.

This is a somewhat anomalous genus, having many nuclei and chloroplasts like Cladophorales, the haematochrome and habit of the Trentepohliaceae, and the hair of the Coleochaetaceae.

Urospora Areschoug, 1866 (Plate VII, Fig. 94), a marine genus, is similar to *Chaetomorpha* (an unbranched filament), but cells have a much greater diameter and are much shorter. The cells may have but one pyrenoid. Filaments enlarge toward the anterior end. Their habitat is rocks and wood in the intertidal zone, and they are widely distributed. This genus occurs in the Antarctic along with *Monostroma* and coralline algae.

Reproduction is asexual by quadriflagellate zoospores produced in very large numbers. The spores are radially arranged in the sporangium before assuming motility. In some species at least the swarming zoospores, before escaping, become flattened and expanded posteriorly, preliminary to the formation of a holdfast. Sexual reproduction is anisogamous, the male being colorless. Curiously the pigment spot is posterior. The life cycle involves a diploid zygote that may form a "*Codiolum*" stage — an elongate, one-celled embryonic phase — before carrying out meiosis to form zoospores. The gametophytes produced by zoospores are heterothallic.

Order Siphonocladales

The composition of this order must be determined arbitrarily. Members have some characteristics suggesting affinities with Cladophorales and Ulotrichales, whereas they also have features in common with the Siphonales and Dasycladales. Accordingly, the limitations of all these orders long have been subject to differing opinion as to which characteristics are important in separating and/or grouping coenocytic genera of the green algae.

As conceived here this order contains coenocytic genera which have a few septations that mark off rhizoidal attaching "cells" and occasionally erect segments. Plants are vesicular or sac-like, or are branched strands which become net-like by the interjoining of branches. The vesicles contain large vacuoles, with the cytoplasm peripheral and net-like. The chloroplasts are numerous within the cytoplasm and accordingly are reticular in arrangement. In appearance the chloroplast is mesh-like. Most chloroplasts have a pyrenoid. There are many nuclei which divide amitotically.

The formation of septations is unique. An area of the peripheral cytoplasm becomes concentrated and then undergoes a cleavage-like separation from the bulk. This becomes cut off by a wall and the segregated portion enlarges or elongates. This type of unit multiplication is known as *segregative cell division*.

Some members are lime-encrusted. In general the life cycle involves a macroscopic, diploid plant that gives rise meiotically to haploid gametes. This habit of omitting a haploid, gametophyte generation is found in the Siphonales also.

FAMILY VALONIACEAE

Members of this family are marine, tropical, or subtropical and consist of relatively large vesicles which may be solitary, clustered, or gregariously grouped to form a cushion. The thalli are apparently one-celled but there are, however, numerous cells formed just within the membrane. These cells are scattered and are not arranged to form a compact or continuous layer. The thallus is coenocytic, and is attached basally by rhizoidal outgrowths. Reproduction is isogamous. The best-known genera are *Valonia* (large globular vesicles) and *Dictyosphaeria* (a cushion of vesicles).

Valonia Ginnani, 1757 (Plate VII, Fig. 95), includes plants which are globular, sausage-shaped, or club-shaped, as much as four centimeters in diameter. (The latter is the largest of all cells, but is a coenocytic unit.) There are many attaching rhizoids, and in some growth habits new vesicles may form at the base of the old thallus. These in turn throw out rhizoids, thus building an elaborate thallus. Vesicles have scattered small cells within the membrane, as described for the family.

Besides vegetative proliferation reproduction in *Valonia* is by meiotic divisions. The entire protoplast forms haploid, biflagellate isogametes. Also diploid zoospores are produced without reduction division. Motile elements escape through the many pores which appear in the wall of the vesicle at maturity. The zygote and the zoospores develop directly into a new thallus.

Because of its large size specimens of *Valonia* have been favorite subjects for physiological research and many behaviors and responses of protoplasm have been learned. The vacuoles of *Valonia* are known to collect nitrates as much as 2000 times the content in the surrounding medium.

FAMILY ANADYOMENACEAE

In this coenocytic family the fronds are much-branched and rather delicate, some forming networks by the interjoining of lobes. The life history is significantly similar to that of the Cladophorales. Genera are tropical or subtropical.

Microdictyon Decaisne, 1839 (Plate VII, Fig. 96), a tropical marine genus of macroscopic size, illustrates the tendency to form branched filaments. There is a semblance of a main axis consisting of coenocytic, subcylindrical units. But the axis is soon lost in growth because the spur-like, opposite branches become interconnected and attached to other branches by pads called *tenaculae*. Some species are less net-like and resemble *Cladophora*.

Reproduction is by zoospores and isogametes and the life history involves two isomorphic generations.

Anadyomene Lamouroux, 1812 (Plate VIII, Fig. 97), is characterized by larger, club-shaped vesicles in a filamentous series giving rise to other filaments in fan-shaped fashion, several such filaments of vesicles arising from the apex of larger cells. The spaces between the branches are filled with smaller unicellular laterals forming a sort of cortex. The branches become adjoined by rings of cellulose. The whole presents a somewhat flattened expanse. Reproduction is by zoospores formed in the small lateral units of the thallus.

FAMILY SIPHONOCLADACEAE

Cladophoropsis Boergesen, 1905 (Plate VIII, Fig. 98), has rather loose tufts of irregularly branched filaments, with the thallus composed of cylinders of slightly inflated vesicles. The branches do not have a cross wall at their plane of origin; rather when present, it lies some distance above. The pigments include β-carotene but not siphonoxanthin or siphonine, the latter pigments being characteristic of the Siphonales. Haploid gametes fuse to form a diploid zygote which produces a diploid gametophyte again. It appears clear now that *Cladophoropsis* is not to be separated from *Spongocladia* Areschoug.

FAMILY BOODLEACEAE

Boodlea Murray, 1889 (Plate VIII, Fig. 99), is much like *Cladophoropsis*, and is often included in the same tropical family. The branches are more numerous, are opposite or whorled, and are so interconnected with *haptera* as to form cushion-like tufts. Reproduction is by biflagellate or quadriflagellate swarmers produced in unmodified lateral cells of the branches, escaping through a pore in the wall. As in other related genera the gametophyte is diploid and there is no sporophyte generation known.

Order Dasycladales

This is another tropical order in which there are very elaborate if not exotic thalli, some of which are encrusted with lime. There are stalked, circular discs or saucers, stalked penicillate tufts, delicate feathery plumes, all of macroscopic size. The general plan of architecture is an axis with variously arranged whorls of lateral segments, some of which are fertile. The development of the thallus in reference to the initial nucleus of the zygote is so unique (see below) that the order is well-defined. It is a very ancient order as shown by casts of calcareous fronds occurring in Ordovician limestone.

FAMILY DASYCLADACEAE

Acetabularia Lamouroux, 1816 (Plate VIII, Fig. 100), is a gracefully stalked, saucer-like disc with the romantic common name of Mermaid's Wineglass. It may be as much as ten cm. tall, growing on shells and coral. At least one species has been reported to be decidedly phototropic, bending the stalk in the direction of light. This elongate tube and its branches begins with the germination of a zygote. The initial tube with the zygote nucleus shows basal-distal differentiation. From one end the rhizoids develop, from the other a vertical elongating axial vesicle. The nucleus does not divide, oddly enough, until the plant is completely mature. A whorl of lateral, sterile, hair-like lobes develops immediately below the apex of the developing vertical vesicle. These are shed as successive whorls of hairs are formed, these also being cast off as the axis continues to elongate. Finally a whorl of rays is formed at the apex. These are known as a *fertile disc* because the rays are elements in which reproductive cysts eventually are cut out. The fertile rays may be closely adjoined to form a compact disc, or may freely radiate. Occasionally two such discs of rays develop. Arising from the center of the disc at the apex of the axis there may be a circle of vertically extended, branched *sterile hairs*. These arise from a ring of knobs that develop at the base of the fertile rays. In some species there is a ring of these same lobes immediately below the fertile disc. These circles of knobs are referred to as *corona superior* and *corona inferior*. By this time the diploid nucleus, which has enlarged tremendously, undergoes rapid amitotic as well as mitotic division. The daughter nuclei migrate up into the fertile rays. Within the rays the protoplast undergoes cleavages, cutting out uninucleate portions that

PLATE VIII

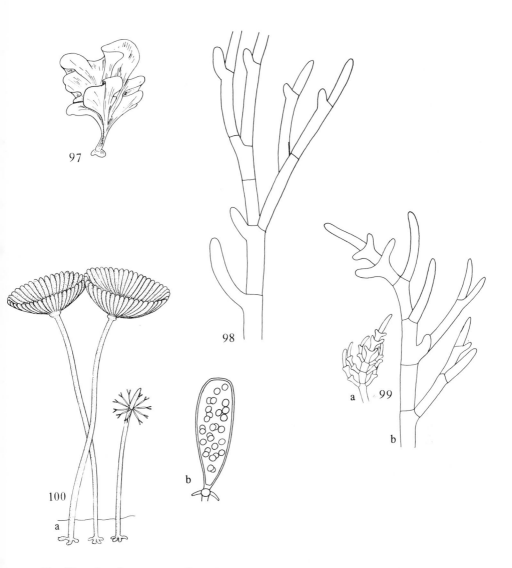

Fig. 97. **Anadyomene stellata,** habit of plant

Fig. 98. **Cladophoropsis** sp, tip of filament showing branching habit

Fig. 99. **Boodlea siamensis:** a, habit of plant (redrawn from Boergesen); b, portion of branch

Fig. 100. **Acetabularia mediterranea:** a, young and mature thalli; b, gametangium (sporangium with cysts)

PLATE VIII

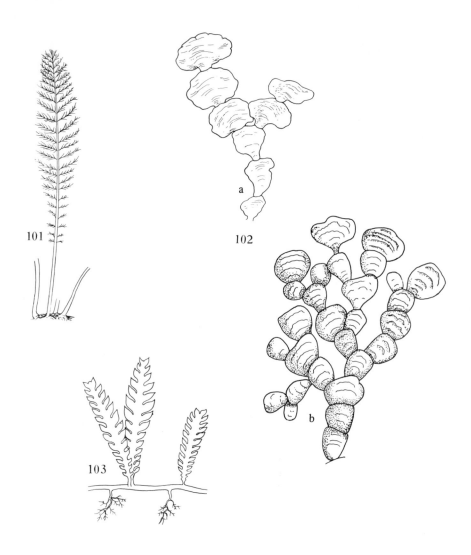

Fig. 101. **Batophora Oerstedi** (?)

Fig. 102. **Halimeda** sp, portions of thalli

Fig. 103. **Caulerpa** sp, showing downward-growing rhizoidal branches

PLATE VIII

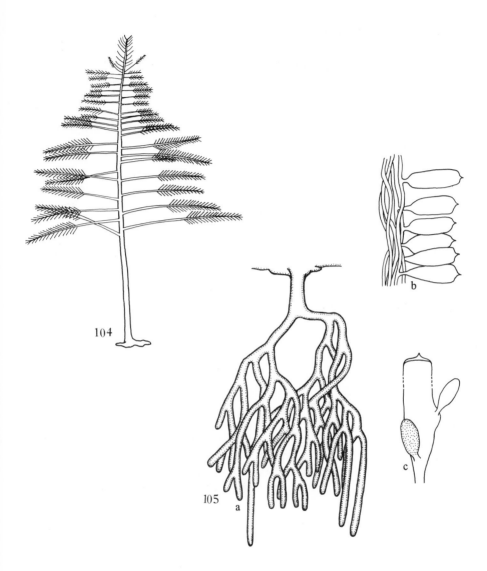

Fig. 104. **Bryopsis plumosa**

Fig. 105. **Codium** sp: a, habit of pendulous plant; b, portion of thallus at surface; c, gametangia on terminal vesicle

become enclosed by a thick wall and so form numerous cysts. The cyst wall has a definitely-formed cap-like lid. Within the cyst, either soon or after several months dormancy, the nuclei multiply, finally dividing meiotically. Around these nuclei isogametes are organized and these are released by the lifting off of the cyst lid. The uniting gametes may be derived from the same fertile disc. The clumping of gametes occurs as (+) and (−) unite.

The life history therefore involves solely a diploid gametophyte, the only haploid cells being the gametes.

Batophora J. Agardh, 1854 (Plate VIII, Fig. 101), grows as a cluster of green, feathery fronds in which there are whorls of short branches rather remotely arranged on the main axes. The primary branches are re-divided and are dichotomously or trichotomously forked. When mature, clusters or whorls of enlarged, globular gametangia develop in the region of the ultimate divisions. The plants are uncalcified and the wall, like several other genera in this order, contains mannose. *Batophora* is similar to *Dasycladus* Agardh, 1827, but in the latter genus the whorls of branches are much closer together, and the gametangia are borne on the inner side of the branch vesicles rather than outwardly.

Order Siphonales

Except for a very few species, this order is tropical marine, and includes macroscopic plants. Basically the thalli are complexes of coenocytic, siphonous filaments involving rhizoidal branches, horizontal prostrate portions, and upright, highly branched fronds. Because there are no cross walls the entire plant is essentially one-celled. It is remarkable that a cell can assume the enormous variety of forms (about 400 species) that comprise this order. A few forms, oddly enough, are endophytic in the leaves of higher plants and some are epiphytes on red algae (the green alga *Derbesia*, e.g.).

The pigments are peculiar in this order of the Chlorophyta because included in most forms are siphonoxanthin and siphonein. Astoxanthin is lacking in the Siphonales. There are numerous disc-like or spindle-shaped chloroplasts and of course many nuclei which apparently are always diploid. The chloroplasts lie in a peripheral film of cytoplasm around a central vacuole. A few forms are calcium-encrusted (e.g., **Halimeda,** Plate VIII, Fig. 102) and like the Dasycladales the order is represented in the Ordovician and early Cretaceous.

The order is thought by some to be polyphyletic. Certainly the fresh-water, oogamous Dichotomosiphonaceae does not seem to be closely related to other members which are anisogamous. Yet in other respects *Dichoto-mosiphon* has definite Siphonales characters.

Reproduction is commonly and efficiently vegetative by fragmentation.

Another way is by internally cutting out segments of the protoplast and forming walls to produce aplanospores, a type of segregative cell division described by Boergesen. In the rhizoidal portion vesicles may form in a linear series. Asexual reproduction by zoospores is rare or lacking. When segments are specialized as gametangia in sexual reproduction they become cut off by a cross wall.

FAMILY CAULERPACEAE

This family (with only one genus, Caulerpa) has long, stolon-like, prostrate strands from which erect fronds arise, and downward-projecting rhizoidal extensions. Reproduction is largely by fragmentation and proliferation but iso- or anisogametes are formed in sexual reproduction. Gametes are produced by meiosis generally in the segments of the erect filaments and sometimes in the horizontal stolons.

Caulerpa Lamouroux, 1809 (Plate VIII, Fig. 103), is a marine, subtropical genus that inhabits the littoral zone on rocks and corals, or grows on mangroves, as well as in benthic habitats to a depth of 250 feet. The numerous species (many ornate) show a remarkable variation in the morphology of the erect, plume-like portions of the thallus. The plant body is not composed of involved and intertwining filaments but of a single, elongated (usually branched) vesicle. Commonly the erect portion takes the form of a flattened feather. Pigments include an abundance of A-carotene but no siphonein nor siphonoxanthin.

Support for the upright growth is provided by internal, lateral extensions of the wall to form rods or tongues known as trabeculae. These also occur in the stolon. The trabeculae arise from structures along the wall called micromeres. Besides giving support the trabeculae are thought to aid in conduction and absorption. The trabeculae may become detached from the wall.

As mentioned, vegetative multiplication is by fragmentation and proliferation. Sexual reproduction occurs when there is meiosis of some of the nuclei in certain areas within the erect portion of the thallus. Most species are heterothallic. Anisogametes are formed by these haploid nuclei and in this area pores appear in the wall. The gametes lie in a network at first and then escape through the pores in huge numbers, uniting to form zygotes. The female is about three times the diameter of the male. Like the Volvocales, the gametes have a red eye-spot and a parietal chloroplast. In some species the entire plant becomes gamete-producing.

The life history, lacking a sporophyte generation, is similar to that of the Siphonocladales. In Bali and throughout the Polynesian Islands, this genus is a favorite food.

Family Bryopsidaceae

Bryopsis Lamouroux, 1809 (Plate VIII, Fig. 104), has the same general architecture as *Caulerpa*, and like that genus has a tropical distribution. One species, *B. plumosa*, occurs along the north Atlantic coast of North America. The thallus is more delicate than that of *Caulerpa* and the upright portion is a flattened pinnate "tree." The upright stem of the "tree" is naked of small branches at the base, as are also the lower parts of the primary branches. The branches are either bilateral or radial and bear a distinct constriction at the basal point of origin. Like *Caulerpa*, vegetative reproduction is accomplished by fragmentation and proliferation. Special branches become walled off to serve as utricle-like gametangia.

After meiosis biflagellate anisogametes are formed and these escape through a gelatinization and breakdown of the apex. Plants are always dioecious. The diploid zygote develops into a diploid gametophyte again.

Family Codiaceae

Codium Stackhouse, 1797 (Plate VIII, Fig. 105), has a dichotomously branched, strand-like growth of spongy texture. Some species form a macroscopic growth that may be a foot or more in length (*C. magnum* up to eight meters) and that resembles a hank of branched, green macaroni. Other forms are globular cushions. Plants grow in the intertidal or sublittoral zone in both cold and warm water, being common along the Pacific coast of North America, for example. Architecturally there is a prostrate portion with numerous rhizoidal outgrowths. Growing, erect, coenocytic filaments, much entwined, form axial cables. From these cables out-turned swollen and club-shaped branches form a compact "cortex" or palisade. The swollen branches are called utricles. There are two groups of species in *Codium*, those with utricles bearing internal wall thickenings at the apex, and those without. Outwardly the utricles have a short, sharp point, giving them a superficial resemblance to an old-fashioned electric light bulb. Within the utricles are disc-like chloroplasts (lacking pyrenoids) which are crowded near the apex. There are many diploid nuclei. There are no true cross walls but in the cables there are ingrowths which form septa.

On the utricles small club-shaped lobes develop as "thumbs" and are walled off by a cross partition. These function as gametangia and produce either male or female anisogametes. Species are either dioecious or monoecious. The male gametangia are brown with many more gametes than the female, which are dark green. The discharge of gametes in some detail has been described for at least one species. In *Codium fragile* the internal layers of the gametangium wall soften and swell when wetted by a returning tide. The apical cap splits and opens as a lid and through the opening a large mass of mucilage is extruded. Running lengthwise through the center of the mass and continuous with the cavity of the gametangium is a narrow canal. Through this the gametes make their escape, becoming aggregated at the open end. Flagella do not develop until gametes have been extruded. The zygote germinates to form a diploid gametophyte immediately by developing an elongate vesicle which eventually forms differentiated branches (rhizoids and vertical filaments).

FAMILY DICHOTOMOSIPHONACEAE

Dichotomosiphon Ernst, 1902 (Plate IX, Fig. 106), forms a mat of dark green filaments. They may grow in shallow water a few feet in depth, in subaerial habitats around springs, or in benthic situations to a depth of 40 feet or more. The filaments are characteristically dichotomously branched and are distinctly constricted at the plane of branching. There are spindle-shaped chloroplasts in the peripheral cytoplasm which lack pyrenoids.

The filaments show some differentiation, there being downward growing colorless rhizoidal branches, tangled, elongated filaments, and upward or outward extended sex-organ-bearing branches. At the tip of these latter branches are abstricted short, hooked, cylindrical, antheridial branches and one or two oogonial branches. Near the tip of the antheridial branch a transverse wall delimits an antheridial cell. Here, around each nucleus, a biflagellate sperm is formed. At the end of the oogonial branch the tip is delimited by a cross wall and the resulting cell enlarges greatly. This is the oogonium, containing a single egg in which one nucleus persists as the female. The oogonium becomes bright yellow and large enough to be seen easily with the unaided eye. The life history of *Dichotomosiphon* is not completely known. It is assumed that the thallus is diploid and that meiosis occurs with gamete-formation. Asexual reproduction occurs by large akinetes which form in a chain whereby segments of a filament become constricted and rounded off, finally being separated by cross partitions.

Dichotomosiphon tuberosus has been known to be highly troublesome in the Great Lakes area, where it forms tangled clots caught on fishing nets. The clots hold moisture when the nets are spread out to dry and permit bacterial and fungal decay of the meshes.

Family Phyllosiphonaceae

This family includes highly branched, tubular plants which grow within other plants and animals. As far as known, reproduction is always by aplanospores.

Ostreobium Bornet et Flahault, 1889 (Plate IX, Fig. 108), grow in the shells of oysters and other Mollusca. The filaments are narrow and entangled, creeping beneath the surface of shells. The filaments have tuberous inflations here and there. Reproduction is by aplanospores.

Phyllosiphon Kühn, 1878 (Plate IX, Fig. 109), has relatively stout, irregularly branched filaments among the leaf tissues of higher plants belonging to the Araceae. Leaves of the host have discolored, yellowish blotches because of orange-colored globules of oil that collect in the host cells in response to the irritation of the parasite. Eventually host cells in the vicinity of the infesting algae lose their chlorophyll. Reproduction is by means of numerous aplanospores formed throughout the filament.

Although this genus is reported to produce starch, some students claim that only oil is formed, and this, in addition to the pigment composition, are considered justification for removing it to the Heterosiphonales in the Chrysophyta. If this were done, another family name would need to be established for the chlorophycean genera remaining in the family.

Order Derbesiales

Family Derbesiaceae

This is a monogeneric family including *Derbesia* of subtropical waters. This plant is the sporophyte stage of a plant which has been known previously as *Halicystis*. In some systems of classification the latter name is retained and placed in the Halicystidaceae.

Derbesia Solier, 1847 (Plate IX, Fig. 107), is a sparsely branched, cylindrical strand, composed of complexes of siphonous filaments. These arise from a prostrate rhizomatous growth, each filament having a cross partition at its base. The tubes contain numerous fusiform chloroplasts with two or three pyrenoids.

Oval sporangia, which are lateral on the filaments, are cut off by a cross wall. In these, zoospores with truncate apices are formed. They have a circle of flagella that arise from a double row of blepharoplasts. The spores develop into relatively large vesicles (*Halicystis* stage) that

PLATE IX

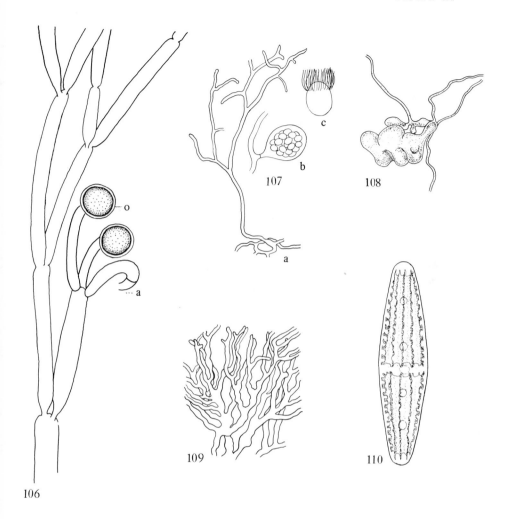

Fig. 106. **Dichotomosiphon tuberosus,** portion of filament with oogonia and antheridium

Fig. 107. **Derbesia** sp: a, habit of portion of thallus; b, sporangium; c, zoospore

Fig. 108. **Ostreobium,** portion of filamentous habit within mollusk shell (redrawn in part from Taylor)

Fig. 109. **Phyllosiphon Arisari,** diagram of coenocytic threads within leaf of **Arisaema**

Fig. 110. **Netrium** sp

PLATE IX

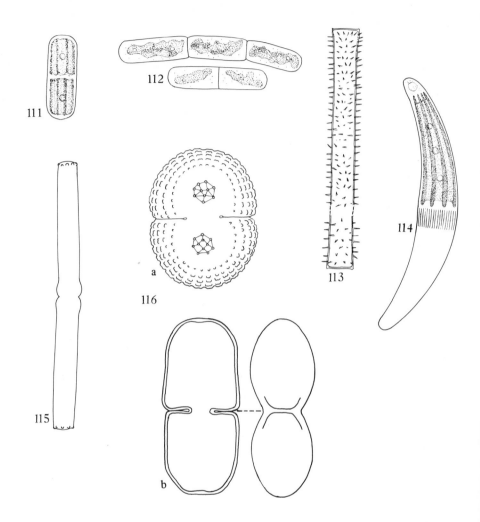

Fig. 111. **Cylindrocystis** sp

Fig. 112. **Ancylonema Nordenskioldi**

Fig. 113. **Gonatozygon pilosum**

Fig. 114. **Closterium** sp

Fig. 115. **Pleurotaenium Ehrenbergii**

Fig. 116. a, **Cosmarium quadrifarium** var.; b, a smooth-walled species

PLATE IX

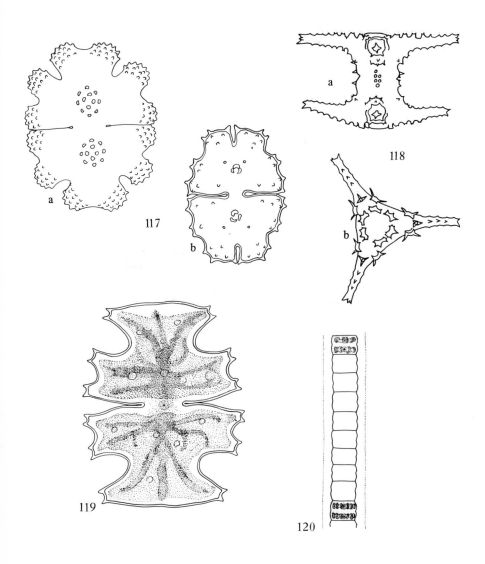

Fig. 117. **Euastrum** spp

Fig. 118. **Staurastrum:** a, "front" view; b, polar view

Fig. 119. **Micrasterias depauperata** var.

Fig. 120. **Hyalotheca dissiliens**

arise from rhizoidal growths on (mostly) calcareous Rhodophyta. These coenocytes (up to three cm. in diameter) have a large vacuole and a parietal cytoplasm in which there are numerous chloroplasts. In the upper region of the vesicle a thin, membranous septation is formed that cuts off an apical segment. In this area biflagellate anisogametes are produced. The zygote germinates directly to form the sporophyte.

Not all species of *Derbesia* have been found to possess a gametophyte stage. It is assumed at present that meiosis occurs in the sporangium.

Subphylum Conjugatae (Conjugales)

This group of the Chlorophyta is so distinct that it merits a category equal to the Chlorophyceae and the Charophyceae. Conventionally, this group, characterized by their conjugation type of sexual reproduction, has been given an Order status (Zygnematales or Conjugales) under the Chlorophyceae. The Conjugatae comprise the largest group of the Chlorophyta in numbers of species, and is very well-defined because of their reproduction and chloroplast morphology. Within the Conjugatae, which is strictly fresh-water in distribution, are filamentous, solitary, and (rarely) colonial plants. Conjugation, the characteristic which unites these diverse forms, is accomplished by *contents* of unspecialized vegetative cells (acting as gametangia) assuming the role of gametes (+) and (−), uniting when gametangial cells become yoked (Latin: *conjugo*). There are no motile cells in the Conjugatae, the gametes moving toward one another by an amoeboid type of action.

Chloroplasts in the Conjugatae are large, few in number within a cell, and, with rare exceptions, contain large pyrenoids. The detailed morphology of the chloroplast, which may be a broad plate, a ribbon, an axial star, or a ridged column, is different from all other algae. The nucleus is large and centrally located. Many of the Conjugatae have unusually large numbers of chromosomes. The wall of two or three layers has a mucilaginous outer covering. In the majority of the Desmidiales (one of the two component orders) the wall is in two sections which adjoin the mid-region, thus forming two "semicells," with the protoplast correspondingly divided.

There are no truly branched plants in the Conjugatae, and practically all are tychoplanktonic, living as solitary cells, floating, or occurring as filamentous mats or green "clouds," or as gelatinous masses. Some desmids are euplanktonic and one (*Oocardium*) is colony-forming, inhabiting tubes in calcareous encrustations.

Whereas the morphology of Conjugatae members has a helpful place in their classification and systematic arrangement, the details of their sexual reproduction are fundamentally important and serve as a basis for grouping or separating families and genera. Earlier systems of classification did not recognize either the morphology and the position of the zygospore in reference to the gametangia, or the developments during zygospore germination. This is partly because of the paucity of zygospores formed by desmids in nature. At present, and especially following the work of Okada (1953), two orders are recognized: Desmidiales and Zygnematales. The first includes five families: Gonatozygaceae and Mesotaeniaceae, which comprise what have been called the Saccoderm Desmids (cells with simple, one-piece walls); Cosmariaceae, Hyalothecaceae, and Closteriaceae, which constitute the Placoderm Desmids (cells with a complex wall, the membrane in two sections). The Zygnematales include the Mougeotiaceae and Zygnemataceae (see Table 2.2). The Desmidiales are mostly unicellular (a few filamentous genera) and have the cell wall and cell contents mostly divided into two symmetrical parts. The Zygnematales are all filamentous and have plain walls, with neither the walls nor the cell contents symmetrically divided.

SACCODERM DESMIDS: FAMILY MESOTAENIACEAE

This is a family of desmid-like cells whose length is at least twice the diameter. They are elongate-oval, cucumber-shaped, or cylindrical. Plants are unicellular or incidentally filamentous as a result of daughter cells remaining adjoined after division. The wall is one continuous piece and there are no mucilage pores, punctations, nor (except rarely) any external ornamentations. As in most other Chlorophyta the wall is in two layers, the inner being cellulose and the outer pectose and mucilaginous. The chloroplast (one to three or four in a cell) takes the form of band, axial rods, or ribbons. Multiplication is by vegetative cell division which occurs by a median cross wall following nuclear division and the transverse division of the chloroplast. The two daughter cells elongate to an adult size.

Conjugation occurs by two cells (plus and minus) becoming invested by a common mucilage. Usually the cells put out papillae that make contact and form an interconnecting (conjugation) tube. In most instances union of the two cell contents is accomplished by amoeboid movement of the two gametes toward one another. The gametangia are undivided and the resulting zygospore is formed either between the two cells, or partly within and between the cells (see Text Figure 2.1).

The zygote immediately becomes a zygospore with a thick, three-layered wall. Upon germination four haploid nuclei are produced by meiosis (sometimes two large and two small). This is followed by divisions of the zygospore protoplast which may result in either two or four daughter protoplasts which form as many new cells. The variations in this process are too numerous to be outlined here.

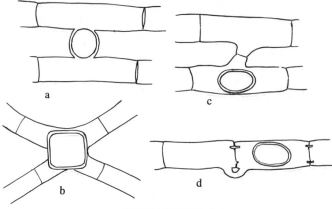

TEXT FIGURE 2.1

Types of conjugation and zygospore-formation in the Zygnematales. a, *Mougeotia*, zygospore formed between two gametangia; b, *Mougeotia*, zygospore formed within both gametangia and tube; c, *Spirogyra*, scalariform conjugation, zygospore formed within female gametangium; d, *Spirogyra*, lateral conjugation, zygospore formed in female gametangium.

Netrium Naegeli, 1849 (Plate IX, Fig. 110), is a common oval or "water-melon"-shaped cell, sometimes subcylindrical, in which there are two or four axial chloroplasts with radiate ridges. Like some of the Placoderm desmids certain species of *Netrium* have terminal vacuoles containing vibrating granules of gypsum. The central nucleus is large and conspicuous. Two cells conjugate by a wide tube and the zygospore forms within the tube and extends into both gametangia. Two new cells are produced from zygospore germination. *Netrium* is found within a great range of pH, although it is usually abundant in desmid habitats where the medium is acid.

Cylindrocystis Meneghini, 1838 (Plate IX, Fig. 111), shows cells which are short-cylindric and sometimes constricted in the midregion. The poles are broadly rounded, and the wall is smooth and in one section. Each "half" of the cell contains a stellate chloroplast, or an axial pad with radiating plates, and a pyrenoid. Reproduction is similar to that of *Netrium*. Species of this genus are widely distributed and are adjusted to a great pH range. They commonly occur on moist soil, among mosses, and on dripping cliffs.

Ancylonema Berggren, 1870 (Plate IX, Fig. 112), from the Arctic, is the only one in the family which forms short filaments. The cells are sausage-shaped with a plate-like chloroplast and two pyrenoids.

FAMILY GONATOZYGACEAE

This family is composed of cylindrical cells, either solitary or in readily dissociated filaments. The cells are not divided and the walls are in three layers. The wall is predominantly smooth, with some evidence of sharp granules or spines. When filamentous the cells dissociate before reproduction and conjugation occurs between individuals. The zygospore is formed between the two gametangia and within the tube. Chloroplasts are ribbon-like.

Gonatozygon De Bary, 1896 (Plate IX, Fig. 113), is characterized by cylindrical cells which are slightly inflated at the poles. The wall bears short spines or spine-like granules. The chloroplast is ribbon-like and convolute, extending from one pole to the other, or interrupted medianly where the nucleus is located. In conjugation, plus and minus cells come into juxtaposition and a connecting tube is formed between the two. The contents of the cell migrate into the tube when fusion occurs to form a zygospore with a three-layered wall. Upon meiosis, either two or four segments of the protoplast are formed and these initiate the production of as many cells.

PLACODERM FAMILIES

The other families of the Desmidiales — Closteriaceae, Cosmariaceae, and Hyalothecaceae — constitute the Placoderm or true Desmids. Conventionally these families are grouped together as the Desmidiaceae (see Table 2.2). They include the majority of the Conjugatae (about 11,000 species and varieties) and some of the most microscopically beautiful cells known. There are mostly unicellular genera in the desmids, though one or two are colonial and a few filamentous (cf. *Onychonema*, Plate X, Fig. 122; *Desmidium*, Plate X, Fig. 121). Filamentous forms are especially common in the tropics.

The wall is in two sections, adjoined at the midregion where there usually is a shallow (*Pleurotaenium, Hyalotheca* [Plate IX, Fig. 120], *Desmidium*) or deep (*Cosmarium, Euastrum, Staurastrum*; Plate IX, Figs. 116-119) median constriction. The incision is known as the *sinus*, and the narrow section joining the two cell halves (semicells) is called the *isthmus*.

Placoderm cells (Plate IX, Figs. 115-116) appear decidedly different in front, side, and top views. The same cell may be circular, subquadrate, or radiate in "front" view, but oval, round, or thin and disc-like when seen from the end or side. If the cell is not divided into two semicells by a median constriction (*Closterium*), the contents are so divided. Iron may become deposited in the cell wall, either homogeneously or in bands. The

TABLE 2.2

I. ORDER DESMIDIALES
  A. Family Mesotaeniaceae
  Zygospore within gametangia or between and adjoining them
    1. Tribe Mesotaenieae
        a. *Ancylonema*
        b. *Cylindrocystis*
        c. *Mesotaenium*
        d. *Netrium*
    2. Tribe Spirotaenieae
        a. *Spirotaenia*

  B. Family Gonatozygaceae
    1. Tribe Gonatozygeae
        a. *Genicularia*
        b. *Gonatozygon*

  C. Family Closteriaceae
  Zygospore formed variously, between and separate from the gametangia, or within both and adjoining them
    1. Tribe Penieae
        a. *Penium*
    2. Tribe Closterieae
        a. *Closterium*
        b. *Roya*

  D. Family Cosmariaceae
  Zygospore formed external to gametangia and not adjoining them
    1. Tribe Docideae
        a. *Docidium*
        b. *Pleurotaenium*
        c. *Triploceras*
        d. *Triplastrum*
    2. Tribe Euastreae
        a. *Euastrum*
        b. *Ichthyocercus*
        c. *Ichthyodontum*
        d. *Micrasterias*
        e. *Tetmemorus*
    3. Tribe Cosmarieae
        a. *Actinotaenium*
        b. *Allorgia*
        c. *Amscottia*
        d. *Arthrodesmus*
        e. *Cosmarium*
        f. *Cosmocladium*
        g. *Dysphinctium*
        h. *Euastridium*
        i. *Oocardium*

122

      j. *Staurastrum*
      k. *Staurodesmus*
      l. *Xanthidium*

   4. Tribe Sphaerozosmeae
      a. *Onychonema*
      b. *Sphaerozosma*
      c. *Teilingia*

E. Family Hyalothecaceae

Zygospore formed in one gametangium only; within gametangia and adjoining them; formed external to gametangia.

   1. Tribe Hyalotheceae
      a. *Groenbladia*
      b. *Hyalotheca*
      c. *Spondylosium*

   2. Tribe Bambusineae (Gymnozygeae)
      a. *Bambusina*
      b. *Desmidium*
      c. *Phymatodocis*
      d. *Streptonema*

II. ORDER ZYGNEMATALES

Zygospore formed in one gametangium only, or in tube between them; or within tube and in both gametangia.

A. Family Mougeotiaceae

   1. Tribe Mougeotieae
      a. *Mougeotia*
      b. *Pleurodiscus* (?)
      c. *Mougeotiopsis*

   2. Tribe Zygogonieae
      a. *Gonatonema*
      b. *Zygogonium*

B. Family Zygnemataceae

   1. Tribe Zygnemeae
      a. *Debarya*
      b. *Temnogametum*
      c. *Zygnema*
      d. *Zygnemopsis*

   2. Tribe Spirogyreae
      a. *Entransia* (?)
      b. *Sirogonium*
      c. *Sirocladium*
      d. *Spirogyra*

[4] Adapted in part from Okada (1953).

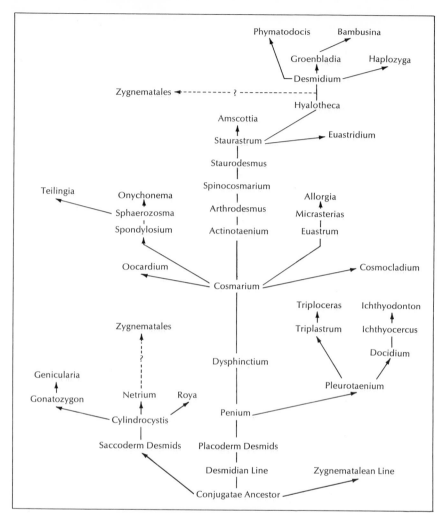

CHART 2.2   Suggested Phylogenetic Arrangement of the Desmids
in Relation to the Zygnematales[5]

wall has an inner layer of cellulose, a layer of cellulose and pectin, and an
outer layer of mucilaginous pectin. The wall is further characterized by
having minute and simple, or large and specialized, pores through which
mucilage is secreted. The pectin mucilage from the fine pores often forms
radiating "needles" as it hardens. These needles are sometimes mistaken
for spines. Mucilage secretion is related to the ability of many desmids
to propel themselves in gliding, sometimes with jerky movements, inter-

[5] Based primarily on morphology.

estingly enough in the direction of light. There may be some connection between the red-ray absorption maxima of chlorophyll-a and the movement of desmids in response to light. Externally the wall may be smooth or variously ornamented with granules, verrucae, and spines. The form and pattern of arrangement of these wall features are specific.

Internally, there are one, two, or four chloroplasts in each semicell. These are mostly axial, but if four or more in number they are parietal. In some genera the chloroplasts show a remarkable ability to shift their position in the cell.

The cytoplasm is actively streaming in some genera and these usually possess polar vacuoles in which granules of metabolic by-products (gypsum) collect. These by-products exhibit Brownian movement.

In cell division there is a variety of techniques employed. In those cells which have a median incision (forming semicells) the isthmus elongates slightly, followed by mitosis of the centrally located nucleus. Then a transverse wall forms across the isthmus (see Text Figure 2.3). The first septum is of pectin material. A cellulose layer is then constructed of cords of cellulose fibrils, which determine the pattern of striations in the wall of the adult cell. The permanent cellulose begins to develop just beneath the cords. The isthmus portion enlarges and gradually assumes the shape of the mature semicell. The new sinus forms in the plane of the original sinus. Finally the two new semicells separate at the apical walls, although sometimes cells remain attached, thus forming pseudofilaments.

In those plants which do not have a median incision (*Closterium*, e.g.) the first indication of cell division is the transverse cleavage of each chloroplast. The nucleus divides and each daughter nucleus migrates to the position of chloroplast cleavage. These positions become the midregions of the two new cells. Then a cross wall forms at the midregion of the old cell. The lateral wall on either side of this cross wall then elongates and builds a new cell half that assumes the same conical shape as the original. Thus, when formed, the new cells have walls which consist of one half the old cell wall and one pole formed of new cell wall material. In some species a new wall section or cylinder is laid down be-

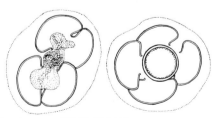

TEXT FIGURE 2.2

Zygospore-formation in a placoderm desmid.

TEXT FIGURE 2.3

Cell division and
new semi cell
formation in a
placoderm desmid.

tween the newly formed polar cones and the mid-region of the old cell where the two wall pieces come together. This new section or sleeve is called a *girdle*. The new sections are demarked by transverse lines and at the mid-region of a **Closterium** cell there are as many transverse lines as there have been cell divisions (see Plate IX, Fig. 114).

Sexual reproduction occurs as described for the subphylum. Gametes are released by the separation of the two conjugating cells at their midregions or by a connecting tube. The zygospores may be formed so that they are partly enclosed by the old parent cell walls, or between the conjugating cells. In filamentous forms conjugation tubes are used as in the Zygnemataceae. Walls of zygospores (sometimes smooth) are variously decorated with spines, horns, or branched, arm-like processes. The chemistry of the wall is such that zygospores are easily fossilized or remain in a subfossil condition, as shown by their frequent appearances in bog borings (see Text Figure 2.2).

Parthenospores occur in some species. They have the same wall markings as zygospores of the same species but are produced when a heavy wall is formed around one of the gametes. A parthenospore germinates by forming four nuclei, but only one is used to produce a new cell. The zygospore likewise forms four nuclei by meiosis and from these one or four new plants develop.

Culture studies have shown the existence of clones within a species which have varying chromosome numbers. It is also known that there are plus and minus strains within a species which determine the possibility of sexual reproduction. Accordingly, zygospore formation in the one-celled desmids is relatively rare because the opportunities for sexually compatible cells to come in contact are infrequent. Zygospore formation in filamentous desmids can be somewhat more frequent. Depending upon species, conjugation may even take place between sister cells of recent cell division.

The desmids are well-known inhabitors of acid or soft-water situations, such as *Sphagnum* bogs, or shallow-water habitats where there is a concentration of organic acids. Accordingly, they constitute dependable index organisms of water with neutral reaction or low pH, the optimum range seeming to be between pH 5.4 and 6.8. In general, desmids are abundant in waters where the ratio between calcium and potassium is relatively low. We are not certain whether calcium itself or in combination is an *inhibitor* to desmids or whether calcareous (hard) waters *lack* certain elements (perhaps trace elements) which are essential for desmids.

There are about 35 genera which conventionally are grouped in three tribes as determined by their general architecture and cell-proportions:

the Penieae, the Closterieae, and the Cosmarieae. (See Table 2.2 which presents the system recommended in 1953 by Okada.)

Permeability, by using vital stains, indicates that there are probably two types of desmid wall. In one group vital dyes are taken up and the sap is stained. In another group, the dye appears as blue-green globules in the cytoplasm.

Although the family is well-defined and natural, it seems clear that many of the genera are artificially constructed and represent lines of converging evolution. Chart 2.2 shows the suggested interrelationships of the genera in the Mesotaeniaceae and the Desmidiaceae.

Desmids are worldwide in their distribution. Whereas many species are semi-ubiquitous, there are combinations of taxa which show geographical isolations. Thus, there is a group in tropical South America, an association in North Africa, one in tropical Asia and the Indies, another in New Zealand and Australia, etc.

Desmids have proven to be popular subjects for experimentation in the behavior of anucleate cells; in their response to all manner of alterations in the chemistry of the medium; and in genetics and hybridization.

FAMILY ZYGNEMATACEAE

This is a family of about ten genera, all of which are truly filamentous, with cylindrical cells that have no pores in the wall nor external markings. There is no basal-distal differentiation; and except for some occasional and incidental rhizoidal outgrowths, they are unbranched. The chloroplasts, as mentioned, are few, large, and often ornate, being spiral ribbons, axial plates, or stellate masses. The pyrenoids (lacking in *Mougeotiopsis*) are large. The nucleus is usually large and cradled in cytoplasmic strands in the center of the cell. Most genera form floating or partly submersed mats or "clouds" of filaments in pure growths. *Zygogonium* forms wefts of yellowish-green filaments on soil and over dripping rocks.

Conjugation is usually accomplished by tubes between cells of filaments, or by geniculations of filaments which bring cells into contact (scalariform conjugation), the contents of one cell passing to the other by amoeboid action. In some species conjugation occurs between cells of the same filament (lateral). In such instances a tube develops around the cross wall between two cells and the contents of one (male) passes through the tube to fuse with the contents (and nucleus) of the female. It is thought that the chloroplasts of the male gamete distintegrate whereas those of the female persist and are retained in the formation of the zygospore. In some genera the empty gametangia become filled with pectic substances (e.g., *Debarya*).

The zygospores of the Zygnemataceae, which can be either round, oval, or quadrangular, have three-layered walls. There is an inner layer of cellulose, a middle layer of cellulose with chitin, and an outer layer with pectin predominating. The outer and middle layers may be smooth, or ornamented with scrobiculations or reticulations. Germination has been outlined above.

Spirogyra Link, 1820 (Plate X, Fig. 123), is the commonest genus in the family with about 300 species. Although worldwide in distribution, *Spirogyra* is curiously rare (relatively) in the Tropics. The chloroplasts which are spiral ribbons vary in number from one to as many as 15 and may be loosely or tightly coiled. The three-layered cross wall shows a middle lamella of pectose bounded on either side by layers of pectin. Reproduction is either scalariform or lateral, and occurs at different times of the year according to species. Zygospores form in the female gametangium. In a few species the male filament is slightly smaller than the female. The retention of one gamete and the motility of another illustrates a type of anisogamy.

Subphylum Charophyceae (Charophyta)

In the past this fresh-water subphylum (or Class) of the Chlorophyta has been subject to varying dispositions according to changing ideas of the times. They were once considered as a group of ferns; at another as a separate phylum of green plants. At present they hold a place as a subdivision of the green algae. Certainly they have many green algal characteristics, at the same time possessing unique features of their own. Like some other algal groups, the Charales, a very ancient one as shown by their fossil history, have no known ancestors nor any descendants. They are the most advanced of all the green algae in many respects and the largest in size of any of the fresh-water Chlorophyta, in some habitats reaching the length of a meter or more. Although distribution varies from lake to lake, some species do show zonations according to depth; a few species of *Nitella* and *Tolypella* grow well at 25-40 feet.

The plants are erect filaments with whorls of branches of limited growth arising from nodal cells of the main filament. There are occasionally branches of unlimited growth arising from the same node, and there are rhizoidal, anchoring branches which in some species produce special reproductive buds or *bulbils*. These are much-used by diving birds for food.

Growth is apical by a meristematic cell which divides repeatedly by transverse walls. The lower cell so formed then divides transversely to form an upper, *nodal* cell, and a lower, *internodal* cell which elongates greatly, as much as ten centimeters. The nodal cell undergoes several vertical divisions to form a nodal zone and it is from these cells that branches, both vegetative and reproductive, are formed. The branches develop by the same apical cell behavior. The sex organ branches develop

PLATE X

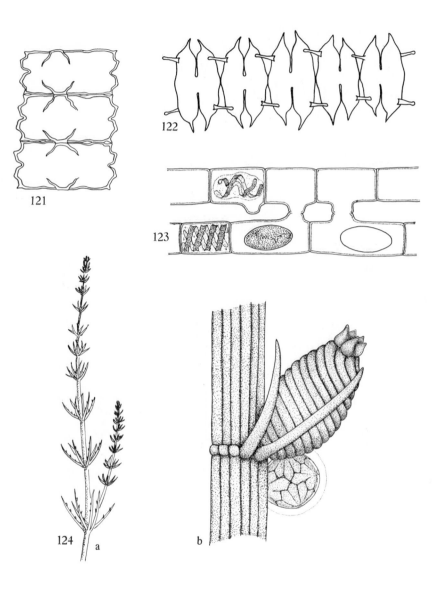

Fig. 121. **Desmidium Swartzii**

Fig. 122. **Onychonema laeve** var.

Fig. 123. **Spirogyra:** conjugation; zygospore immature

Fig. 124. **Chara** sp: a, habit of plant portion; b, node of "leaf" with
nucule (oogonium) above and spherule (antheridium) below

PLATE X

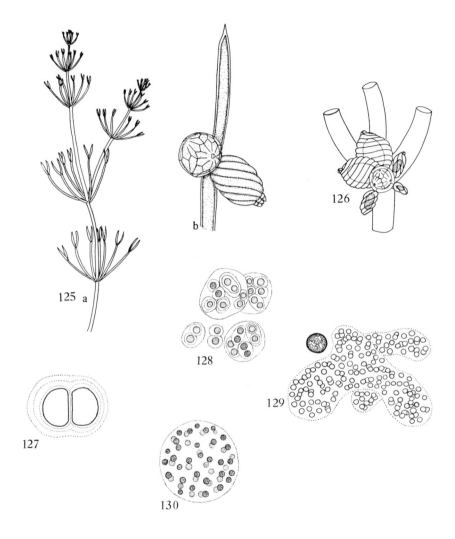

Fig. 125. **Nitella** sp: a, habit of plant portion; b, node with sex organs, the nucule below the spherule

Fig. 126. **Tolypella** sp, cluster of sex organs (redrawn from Corillion)

Fig. 127. **Chroococcus turgidus**

Fig. 128. **Gloeocapsa** sp

Fig. 129. **Microcystis aeruginosa**

Fig. 130. **Aphanocapsa Grevillei**

PLATE X

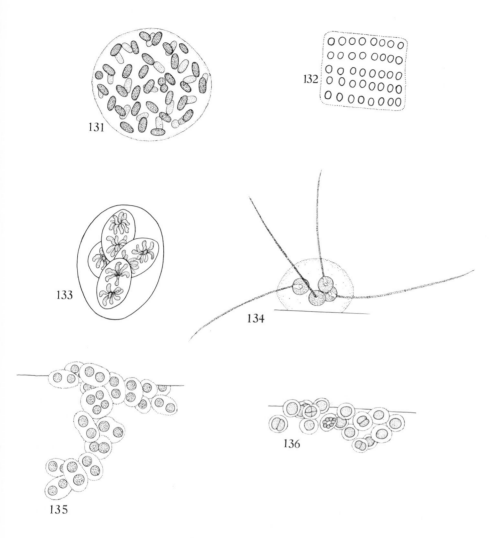

Fig. 131. **Aphanothece stagnina**

Fig. 132. **Merismopedia tenuissima**

Fig. 133. **Glaucocystis Nostochinearum**

Fig. 134. **Gloeochaete Wittrockiana**

Fig. 135. **Entophysalis** sp, epiphytic

Fig. 136. **Xenococcus** sp, epiphytic

from the same node as the vegetative branches, or from the nodes in the branches which also give rise to bracts.

The large cells of Charales contain numerous oval, disc-like chloroplasts which exhibit active cyclosis. There are many nuclei which multiply amitotically.

Most of the species of the genus *Chara* (as well as of genera other than *Nitella*) are encrusted with lime. The lime presumably results from photosynthesis, wherein carbon dioxide is taken from bicarbonates, causing insoluble calcium carbonate to form. Because the amount of lime deposited is appreciable, and because the process may continue in a particular habitat over many thousands of years, considerable amounts of lime (marl and other calcareous substances) accumulate in lake bottoms (see p. 372). In suitable places it is profitable to recover these deposits for commercial purposes (soil reconditioning, cement manufacturing).

Whereas *Chara* is especially selective of hard water situations, *Nitella* in the tribe Nitelleae prefers soft, sometimes darkly stained, water. *Tolypella* (Plate X, Fig. 126), a close relative of *Nitella*, on the other hand, seems to be found only in hardwater lakes. A very few species of *Chara* and *Nitella* have been found in brackish waters near sea coasts.

In addition to the use of bulbils, vegetative reproduction can occur by rhizoidal or stoloniferous proliferation. There are no zoospores formed in the Charales. Sexual reproduction is oogamous, with gametes produced in highly specialized branches. These develop in such a way as to produce a *nucule* (oogonium) or a *globule* (antheridium). In the node of a branch an "initial" cell divides to form a lower (*stalk* or *pedicel*) and an upper or outer meristematic (*apical* cell). The latter forms four and then eight cells. These eight cells at the end of the pedicel each divide twice to form eight radiately arranged series of three cells each. The cell nearest the pedicel (the inner cell of each series) is the initiator of antheridial filaments; the middle cell elongates greatly and forms a club-shaped, columnar cell called a *manubrium*; and the outer cell broadens and flattens to form a *shield* cell. The broadened shield cell adjoins by its margins other shield cells so that a shell is formed around the whole internal complex. The globular structure has been referred to in the past as an antheridium. Each of the inner cells (of the original row of three) divides to form six cells, and these may redivide. The many cells in these heads then divide two or four times to cut off "*antheridial initials*" — so-called because they form long filaments of small cubical cells. In each of these a biflagellate antherozoid is formed, each cell actually being an *antheridium*.

On the same node or on the node of another plant an initial cell forms a row of three cells, the apical one being an oogonium initial cell. This cell first elongates and then divides to form a *stalk* cell and an *oogonium* (terminal). The contents of the oogonium constitute a single egg. The median cell of the row of three divides vertically and forms five *sheath cells* (tube cells). These elongate as the oogonium develops and twist spirally around the female organ. These cells cut off one or two cells at their tip so that surmounting the oogonium is a cluster known as the corona. The sheath cells separate slightly at the base of the corona when the oogonium is mature, thus permitting the entrance of the antherozoid. The nucule then consists of an oogonium, its stalk cell, and the sheathing cells (composed of tube cells and the corona).

The zygote forms a thick wall which takes on the spiral grooves and ridges determined by the sheath cells. The latter break down as the oospore matures and their outer walls are sloughed off, leaving the inner walls as ridges. The zygospore germinates with meiotic division. One of the four nuclei initiates the development of a new gametophyte by producing a protonemal, embryonic filament that continues to develop by means of an apical cell.

In the classification of the single order (Charales) one family is recognized (Characeae) with two tribes, the Chareae and Nitelleae.

Family Characeae: Chareae

Chara Valliant, 1719 (Plate X, Fig. 124), is characterized, in practically all species, by having the axial filament overgrown by columnar or corticating cells which develop (like the branches) from nodal cells. In addition short, thorn-like cells, or stipules, may develop from the node. The globule develops below a bract at a node which puts it below the nucule. The crown of the nucule, as previously described, consists of five cells which characterizes the tribe. Plants are either monoecious or dioecious. *Chara* is coarsely covered with lime and most species have a disagreeable skunk or onion odor caused by sulphurated compounds. Included in this tribe also are *Nitellopsis* Hy, 1889 (oogonia and antheridia developed from different node cells); *Lamprothamnus* Groves, 1916 (oogonia below the antheridia); *Lychnothamnus* (Rupr.) Leonh., 1862 (with antheridia beside the oogonium). Ophel regards the latter genus to be undistinguishable taxonomically from the former.

Family Characeae: Nitelleae

Nitella Agardh, 1824 (Plate X, Fig. 125), is more delicate in habit of growth, greener because there is no lime deposit, and not ill-smelling. The branches are di- or trichotomous at the tips, and the filaments are not corticated as in *Chara*. The globules are borne on a pedicle at a furcation of a branch, whereas the nucule is located laterally and below the furcation. Characteristic of the tribe there are ten cells in the corona, the five cells at the tip of the tube cells being divided by a transverse wall. Another genus in the tribe is **Tolypella** (A. Br.) Leonh., 1863 (Plate X, Fig. 126), one in which reproductive organs occur in dense "cabbage heads" of short branches.

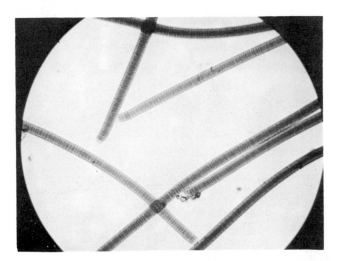

a
b

a. Oscillatoria princeps x 100; b. Gloeocapsa
sp showing laminated sheaths x 400. (Wards
Natural Science Establishment)

Phylum Cyanophyta

The plants that comprise this Phylum are predominantly fresh-water, but there are many marine and brackish species. They often attract attention because of the dense "blooms" that some of the planktonic forms develop in lakes and ponds, especially during warm months of the year. The Cyanophyta are thought to be the most ancient of all chlorophyll-bearing organisms on earth; impressions in rock of the Archaeozoic era (more than two billion years old) strongly resemble the shape that blue-green algae would make. Many are remarkable in their ability to adjust to high temperatures (hot springs) and to low temperatures of polar regions. Probably because of their gelatinous sheath, at least in part, they can withstand long periods of desiccation. The compactness of protein molecules and their bonds in the protoplasm also aid cells in withstanding extremes. Some of the characteristics possessed by blue-green algae are so much like those of bacteria that one older system of classification (recently revived) grouped them under the Schizophyta (Fission Plants). Although possessing a simple and conservative morphology the Cyanophyta also show, in contrast, a highly refined physiology and a complex metabolism, making them biologically interesting and economically important.

Architecturally blue-green algae may be solitary or incidentally clumped cells, round or oval (*Synechococcus, Chroococcus*); globular or plate-like colonies of cells (few to thousands) enclosed in mucilage. The form taken by perhaps the majority of cyanophytes is that of a thread of cells (a *trichome*) in which there is no division of labor. There are, however, unbranched filaments in which there is differentiation of some cells to form *heterocysts* (enlarged cells with homogeneous content; (Plate XI, Fig. 144), and other cells to form *akinetes* (spores; Plate XI, Fig. 146). Trichomes may or may not have a *sheath*. Filaments may have false branches (Plate XI, Fig. 150) whereas true branching (Plate XI, Fig. 152) occurs in a few genera. Such filaments may be uniaxial or multiaxial. Another type is the trichome which tapers from base to apex, usually from a basal heterocyst. This type may form complex colonies by having many such trichomes aggregated within a common mucilage.

Heterocysts are formed by metamorphosis of a vegetative cell located either intercalary or terminal in a trichome. There is a second wall layer, layed down internal to the original cell membrane. A pore is left at either pole where the heterocyst adjoins other cells in the trichome, thus permitting an intercellular connection. As the heterocyst matures and the wall is completed these pores become plugged with mucilage and the plugs show clearly as shining nodules when the plant is viewed microscopically. The contents of the heterocyst become homogeneous and there are chemical changes in nucleic acids as other material is synthesized. The cell often appears empty. The electron microscope has revealed that the protoplast of a heterocyst has more complexities, however, than have been seen by the light microscope. In a few species the heterocyst becomes a reproductive body and germinates by forming endospores (Plate XI, Fig. 146) which in turn develop new filaments. Otherwise, the heterocyst, because it is a weak link in the trichome, helps to multiply the plant by facilitating fragmentation.

Cytology

PIGMENTS

Pigmentation of course constitutes one of the primary characteristics of the Cyanophyta. There is chlorophyll-a (but not chlorophyll-b), phycocyanin-r, phycocyanin-c, phycoerythrin-c B-carotene, and as many as eight xanthophylls (allophycocyanin, zeaxanthin, mycoxanthophyll, asteroxanthin, and lutein; (see p. 26). The variations in the relative abundance of these pigments, in various combinations, result in many hues — olivegreen, gray-green, yellow-brown, or purplish. *Phormidium persicinum* is reddish-purple, a marine species which can grow as deep as 20 meters even in high latitudes. It is poorly-developed in shallow water where light is more intense. The same species, when grown in different wave lengths, shows significant variations in pigment composition. This has given rise to a theory of complementary chromatic adaptation. It is thought that the color of the pigment is complementary to the color quality of light waves reaching the plant (according to observations made on a number of blue-green and red algal species). This type of adaptation is known as the Gaidukov phenomenon. Pigments are located partly in the cell's peripheral region (the chromoplasm), there being no chloroplast. Electron microscopy shows the pigments to occur in lamellae, however, and not in solution. According to some studies the lamellae are not enclosed by a membrane as are the pigment-bearing bodies of other algae. It has been estimated that more than one-half of light absorption in the cyanophyte cell is by the phycocyanin fraction.

Cell Wall

The cell wall consists of an inner, thin, cellulose layer, a median pectic layer, and an outer mucilage layer. Electron microscopy shows the inner membrane itself to be composed of three layers, bearing upon and probably continuous with the cytoplasm. The outer film of mucilage acts advantageously by sloughing off parasites, and in retaining water by absorption, useful during periods of desiccation. The copious mucilage which characterizes the blue-greens has earned for them the previously used name of Myxophyceae (slime algae). In colonial forms the secretion from many cells results in a common gelatinous sheath. This may be lamellated or stratified in filamentous forms especially, and sometimes pigmented: cf. scytonemin in *Scytonema*, or fuxorhodin and fuxochlorin in *Calothrix*.

Cytoplasm

There may or may not be a plasma membrane. The cytoplasm occurs as chromoplasm (peripheral) and as a central "body" (centroplasm). The chromoplasm, at least in some plants examined, occurs in a network. The central body contains less pigment, but usually harbors nuclear granules, there being no organized nucleus with nuclear membrane and nucleolus. The nuclear material also may be arranged in a loose reticulum and includes fibrils in which DNA and RNA are present. In some forms the chromatin is located in the chromoplasm, but in others the threads of nuclear material or chromonemata are distributed throughout (Shinke and Ueda, 1956).

There are no true vacuoles but there may be pseudovacuoles (pockets of gas). These provide buoyancy in many of the planktonic species. The appearance of pseudovacuoles has been explained by a change in physiology resulting from oxygen deficiency at lake bottoms, but this is not borne out by observations on the behavior of plankters. At least in many instances bloom-producing plankters with pseudovacuoles rise to the surface and then become scattered in relation to light, warmth, and gas-expansion. The pseudovacuoles refract light so that cells appear purplish, brown, or even black under the microscope. When considered in its entirety the blue-green algal cell is suggestively similar to a chloroplast.

Food Storage

Contained within the chromoplasm and sometimes among the lamellae are granules of various food storage substances such as glycogen (cyanophyte starch) and cyanophycin (protein). The carbohydrate trehalose may also be found. Oil droplets occur in some species, as well as lipids, the predominating being sulpholipid. In at least one analysis it was found that 8% of the dry weight of the plant is composed of nitrogen.

REPRODUCTION

Reproduction in the Cyanophyta is primarily by binary fission. Growth in multicellular plants occurs by both apical and intercalary cell division. Fragmentation occurs commonly and very successfully. In one group (Chamaesiphonales) the protoplast becomes divided into many naked spores (endospores), a type of aplanospore. In "higher" blue-green algae, a vegetative cell can become concentrated with nutritive material, accompanied by the formation of a thick wall, thus forming an *akinete*. Occasionally a short section of a filament will become invested by a common, thick membrane to form a *hormospore*. Sexual reproduction does not occur, nor are there any motile spores or other type of swimming cells.

Habitats

In their adjustments to or "selection" of habitats blue-green algae display considerable versatility (possibly related to their long geological history). They may be eu- or tychoplanktonic in both fresh and marine waters, sometimes forming profuse and conspicuous growths of "bloom" proportions. As such, cyanophytes all too often induce a chain of biological upsets involving death of fish and other animals. The extrametabolites of a few species are toxic or at least inhibitory. As mentioned elsewhere, planktonic species are almost invariably those with pseudovacuoles. Not a few cyanophytes are benthic (on sticks, stones, reeds) in shallow water or down to depths of 100 feet. Often mat-forming, bottom growths become loosened through gas-accumulation and are buoyed to the surface with portions of the substrate sludge, thereby forming unsightly clots. Moist rocks and dripping cliffs invariably have gelatinous films and mucilaginous clumps (*Nostoc*, *Scytonema*, *Gloeocapsa*), and exposed surfaces are sometimes brightly colored by such algal growths. The supralittoral and upper intertidal zones of sea coasts are characterized by a blue-green flora (*Rivularia*, *Stigonema*), and blue-greens are usually the dominants in the algal floras of tidal marshes and mud flats. Except possibly for diatoms, blue-greens are the most abundant algae living on and under soil surfaces, including desert soils. Because of adjustability to light intensities blue-greens can occupy walls of caves and other situations which are dimly illuminated. At least 152 genera are well-adapted for life in hot springs and geysers where temperatures may be as high as 75 or 82°C. (see p. 327). Blue-greens exhibit an unusual tendency toward various kinds of symbiotism; as endophytes in *Gunnera* leaves and stems, roots of *Cycas* and clover (*Trifolium*), thalli of liverworts and *Azolla, Richelia,* in frustules of *Rhizosolenia* (diatom); endozoically in the digestive tract of mammals, including Man; commensally with fungi to form lichens (see p. 324). Some colony-forming blue-greens cause lime to be deposited and they become the nuclei for calcareous concretions (ooliths) which occur as "fossils."

Movement

Although non-motile, many filamentous blue-green algae do possess the ability to move. This is especially noticeable in such genera as *Oscillatoria, Schizothrix,* and *Spirulina, Arthrospira.* The movement is accomplished by the secretion of mucilage against substrates (in the former genera), and by the physical changes which occur in the extruded mucilage. The general effect is that of propulsion, with a forward and backward gliding movement, or the rotation of the forward end of a trichome. A streaming of mucilage up and down the exterior of an *Oscillatoria* trichome has been demonstrated and this induces filament movement in opposite directions. It is interesting that some Cyanophyta are responsive to weak light in their movement, but not to intense illumination. Different species react to different ranges of wave lengths. By experimentation it has been shown that response to light is to those wave lengths which are absorbed by the carotenoid and the phycobilin pigments.

Nitrogen-Fixation

An interesting aspect of cyanophyte physiology is the ability of several forms to fix atmospheric nitrogen (see p. 336). The amount of N fixed is about 1.2% of the weight of the sugar used. In this respect blue-greens are similar to the bacteria and are unique among the algae, for in no other phyla are there forms which have this capacity. At least 20 species are nitrogen-fixers, mostly in the genera *Anabaena, Nostoc,* and *Cylindrospermum.* Some species of *Scytonema* and *Mastigocladus* are nitrogen-fixers also. Thus the soil-inhabiting species take their place among the bacteria as important soil conditioners. Wanataba in India found that in controlled growth, *Tolypothrix tenuis* could fix nitrogen at the rate of 2000 lbs. per acre per year, thus potentially increasing rice production by about 20%.

Nitrogen-fixers have been found symbiotic with lichens wherein extracellular nitrogenous products are contributed to the fungi; also to host plants in such liverworts as *Blasia* and *Anthoceros* which blue-greens endophytize.

It has been determined, at least in some species, that glutamic acid is the intermediary by which nitrogen is assimilated into cyanophyte metabolism. When nitrogen-fixation occurs simultaneously with the photosynthetic process the fixation makes use of H as a donor. In culture it has been shown also that some cyanophytes can fix N in darkness if supplied with sugar.

Representative Orders

Of the many systems of classification[1] to which blue-green algae have been subjected, the simplest is one which recognizes one Class, Myxophyceae, and three Orders: Chroococcales, Chamaesiphonales, and Hormogonales, or Oscillatoriales. The latter name conforms to the rules of botanical nomenclature, but places many families together which, according to some students, should be placed in separate orders as treated herein. One helpful system of classification recognizes more orders and places them under two tribes: Coccogoneae (unicellular and colonial) and Hormogoneae (filamentous). Ecological studies and taxonomic surveys show that species vary decidedly in various habitats; also that generic distinctions break down. Hence the systematics of the Cyanophyta is subject to reinterpretation.

Tribe Coccogoneae: Order Chroococcales

This is an artificial assemblage of one-celled or colonial blue-green algae which reproduce solely by fission. Cells are mostly spherical or oval, but there are rod-shaped forms (*Aphanothece, Chroothece*). Most genera are colonial, with many individuals enclosed in a common mucilage. Whereas many are benthic or are on subaerial strata, the majority are planktonic and some are bloom-producers.

Family Chroococcaceae

Chroococcus Naegeli, 1849 (Plate X, Fig. 127), is a genus with many species of round or spheroidal cells, occasionally solitary but mostly forming families of from four to 16 individuals. The cells are surrounded by mucilage which in a few instances is lamellate. This type of plant is the simplest expression morphologically of any chlorophyll-bearing organisms (except for chlorophyll-bearing or green bacteria). *Chroococcus limneticus* is a common euplankter whereas *C. turgidus*, a relatively large species, is tychoplanktonic, especially in desmid habitats.

Gloeocapsa Kuetzing, 1843 (Plate X, Fig. 128), is a genus of mostly subaerial plants in which *Chroococcus*-like cells occur in extensive gelatinous

---

[1] See Drouet and Daily, 1956; Drouet, 1968.

masses, the cells being arranged in "families." The sheaths are concentrically lamellate around one, two, four, or eight cells. The distinction between this genus and *Chroococcus* is feeble and is made mostly upon the size of the plant mass and the numerous lamellate sheaths in the former. The thalli are marine or fresh-water, often subaerial on wet rocks, or on soil, and in many instances are a brightly colored yellowish, brown, or violet.

Microcystis Kuetzing, 1833, emend. Elenkin, 1924 (Plate X, Fig. 129), consists of hundred or thousands of small, marble-like cells grouped in a common mucilaginous matrix. The colony may be round and definite in shape or irregular and sometimes clathrate, depending upon the species. Most species are euplanktonic and are aided by pseudovacuoles. One or two species live loosely on the bottom. As a plankter *Microcystis* is infamous because of the ability of at least some species to produce toxins which are lethal to animals and birds that consume water where dense blooms deteriorate. Further, the death of large masses of vegetation and the subsequent decomposition by bacteria leads to oxygen-depletion and the suffocation of fish and other animals. The extrametabolites produced by *Microcystis* seem to inhibit the development of many other blue-green algae because there is a somewhat regular sequence of species appearing in a body of water. *Microcystis* is the subject of considerable research in efforts to identify and analyze toxins (see p. 363).

Aphanocapsa Naegeli, 1849 (Plate X, Fig. 130), is very much like *Microcystis*, but cells, often in pairs, are evenly and sometimes remotely spaced within the colonial mucilage. Cells have no pseudovacuoles, are usually bright or pale blue-green in color. The sheath is wide and colorless, and the globular colony is rather regularly shaped.

Aphanothece Naegeli, 1849 (Plate X, Fig. 131) is similar to *Microcystis* except that cells are elongate or rod-shaped (sometimes bacilliform). Cells are often crowded within a firm mucilage. Some colonies occur as olive-green masses three to five centimeters in diameter. These often are carried into shallow water and onto beaches where they are mistaken sometimes for colonies of the genus *Nostoc*.

Merismopedia Meyen, 1839 (Plate X, Fig. 132) consists of round or oval cells arranged in rectilinear series to form rectangular plates, usually with a wide gelatinous sheath. Cell division takes place in two directions in one plane to form the colonies which in some species may in-include many hundreds of cells (but usually 16 to 64). Species are tychoplanktonic. *M. tenuissima* is almost invariably found in desmid habitats.

Glaucocystis Itzigshon, 1854 (Plate X, Fig. 133) is an oddity of the plant world, as is *Gloeochaete* Lagerheim. It consists of two plants, involving blue-green protoplasts growing endophytically in the colorless cells of another alga, *Oocystis*. The latter has round or oval cells, two or four together, enclosed in an old mother cell wall. The cells contain vermiform or lumpy blue-green protoplasts which are organized around one or two centers in a radiate fashion. Electron microscopy has shown the cyanophyte protoplasts (or cyanelles) to be different from other blue-green endophytes in colorless algae. For example the protoplasts have no bounding membrane or wall. It has been suggested that *Glaucocystis* be retained as a name for the duplex organism (as for lichen "genera") but that *Skujapelta* be applied to the blue-green cells (*S. nuda*) for *Glaucocystis nostochinearum* endophytes. There are few "species" of *Glaucocystis*, and plants are rather rare but widely distributed. There is some evidence that the host organism is a flagellate.

Gloeochaete Lagerheim, 1883 (Plate X, Fig. 134) is regarded as a colorless tetrasporalean (Chlorophyta) plant with a parietal, cyanophyte protoplast. The cells are in clumps of four, enclosed in mucilage through which long, gelatinous hairs extend. In this genus reproduction occurs by flagellated, volvocoid zoospores. Starch accumulates as a reserve food.

These anomalous plants have been given some attention but their true composition and status remain enigmatic.

FAMILY ENTOPHYSALIDACEAE

In this family coccoid individuals form false, filamentous arrangements, at least in part extending from a horizontal stratum of cells in mucilage.

Entophysalis Kuetzing, 1843 (Plate X, Fig. 135), is mostly marine. Spherical cells form palmelloid masses from which pseudofilamentous strands extend somewhat vertically. The cells are mostly in pairs, each pair enclosed by definite mucilage.

Order Chamaesiphonales

This order is composed of marine and fresh-water forms which are peculiar in their use of endospores (see p. 32) for reproduction. The plants also reproduce by fission. They may be solitary (rarely) or gregarious. Sometimes cushion-like, parenchymatous, or pseudofilamentous growths are formed. Plants are attached, sometimes epiphytic or creeping within shells of Mollusca, sometimes endophytic in large marine algae. A few species are confined to waters and margins of hot springs and geysers. Drouet and Daily (1956) have disavowed the genera in this order and recognize only one genus, *Entophysalis*, which other taxonomists treat as a member of the Chroococcales.

FAMILY PLEUROCAPSACEAE

Xenococcus Thuret, 1880 (Plate X, Fig. 136), is characterized by globular cells rather indefinitely arranged in a one- or few-layered stratum on the walls of other algae (marine or fresh-water). Each cell has a mucilaginous sheath. There may be a common gelatinous investment of the entire thallus. All cells are capable of undergoing internal cleavage of the protoplast to form numerous endospores which drift away, after dissolution of the cell wall, to form new growths.

FAMILY DERMOCARPACEAE

Dermocarpa Crouan, 1858 (Plate XI, Fig. 137), has pyriform cells compactly arranged to form an epiphytic cushion with both an individual and a colonial sheath. In at least one species, however, the cells are solitary. Plants are both marine and fresh-water, mostly growing as epiphytes. Enlarged cells within the thallus act as endosporangia.

FAMILY CHAMAESIPHONACEAE

Chamaesiphon Braun et Grunow, 1865 (Plate XI, Fig. 138), are solitary or gregarious, club-shaped or cylindrical cells, attached by a narrowed base to submerged plants and filamentous algae (especially Cladophorales). The cells have a thin sheath which eventually opens at the apex. The protoplast successively cuts off endospores at the apex and these drift away, become adherent, and germinate to form new individuals. A patch of these plants will show many stages of development, from recently attached endospores to mature, tubular individuals.

Tribe Hormogoneae: Order Oscillatoriales

These are the multicellular and filamentous cyanophytes in which a thread of undifferentiated cells may or may not be enclosed by a sheath. There are no branches. In some plants there may be more than one trichome in the sheath (*Microcoleus*). Plants may be solitary or adherent to form mucilaginous skeins or mats which are attached at first and become free-floating. Many species are planktonic (*Trichodesmium, Lyngbya*, some *Oscillatoria*). *Trichodesmium* grows abundantly in the Red Sea and, because of its light-refracting pseudovacuoles, gives that body of water its name. Not a few are inhabitors of damp soil or other aerial substrates where they form brown, black, or blue-green films or velvety expanses. One genus, *Porphyrosiphon*, forms orange-red or blood-red patches of considerable extent on barren soil.

FAMILY OSCILLATORIACEAE

Oscillatoria Vaucher, 1803 (Plate XI, Fig. 139), has trichomes which are solitary or matted together and may be straight and rigid or twisted, curved, and entangled. They are slightly differentiated at the anterior end and show a definite polarity, for in many species there is a tapering toward the apex, and the apical cell may carry a thickened membrane (*calyptra*), or it may be swollen (*capitate*). There is an inconspicuous mucilaginous envelope which does not show as a definite sheath. The cells are mostly shorter than wide, and the cross walls are often marked by rows of granules (cyanophycin?). The contents may include pseudovacuoles, especially in the planktonic species such as *O. rubescens*, which often forms dense blooms that turn the water red because of light refraction.

Oscillatoria takes its name from the active movement that the trichomes exhibit — a gliding, sliding, as well as rotating movement (see p. 139). A cluster of *Oscillatoria* trichomes placed in a laboratory vessel will slide and slither across the substrate and up onto the sides of the jar, carrying water by capillary action.

Reproduction is by cell division and by fragmentation, the latter being accomplished by *necridia*. These constitute an inexpensive and rapid way to bring about fragmentation. A cell here and there in the trichome will die, providing a weak link in the thread. The space becomes filled with mucilage and there is a swelling and then a breakdown in the necridium so that short sections of the trichome are released. By fission these short sections develop into full-length plants.

Trichodesmium Ehrenberg, 1830 (Plate XI, Fig. 140), includes a well-known species, the *Oscillatoria*-like *T. erythraeum*, which has pseudovacuoles that are light-refractive. This species appears intermittently in the Red Sea, producing such a dense growth as to color the water. The plant actually develops as a benthic form at great depths and then becomes free-floating. This is the plant which also colors the

PLATE XI

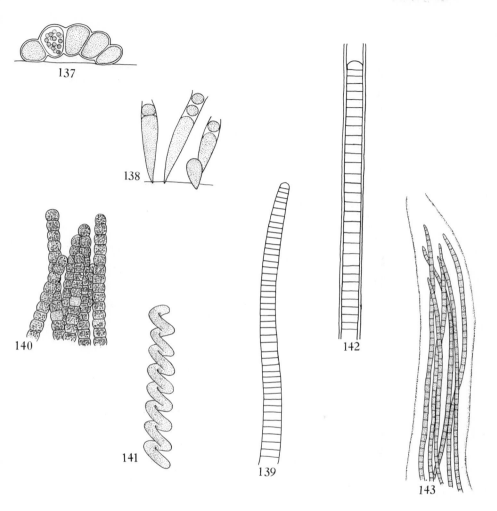

Fig. 137. **Dermocarpa pacifica:** epiphytic; endospore-formation (re-drawn from Smith)

Fig. 138. **Chamaesiphon incrustans,** forming endospores

Fig. 139. **Oscillatoria nigra**

Fig. 140. **Trichodesmium lacustre,** fascicle of trichomes (redrawn from Smith)

Fig. 141. **Spirulina princeps**

Fig. 142. **Lyngbya** sp

Fig. 143. **Microcoleus** sp

PLATE XI

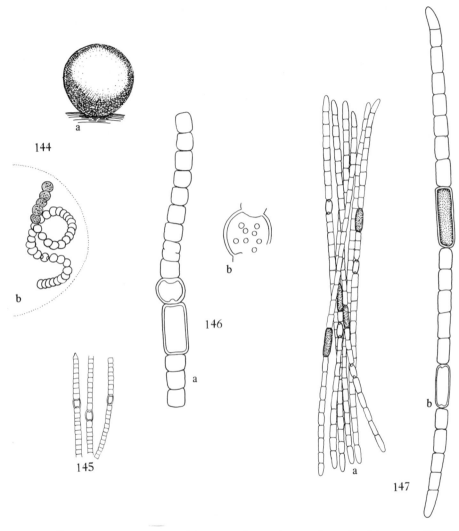

Fig. 144. **Nostoc** sp: a, Nostoc colony; b, portion of trichome with akinetes

Fig. 145. **Hormothamnion enteromorphoides** (redrawn from Taylor)

Fig. 146. **Anabaena** sp: a, trichome; b, germination of akinete with endospores

Fig. 147. **Aphanizomenon flos-aquae:** a, flake of trichomes; b, single trichome with akinete and heterocyst

PLATE XI

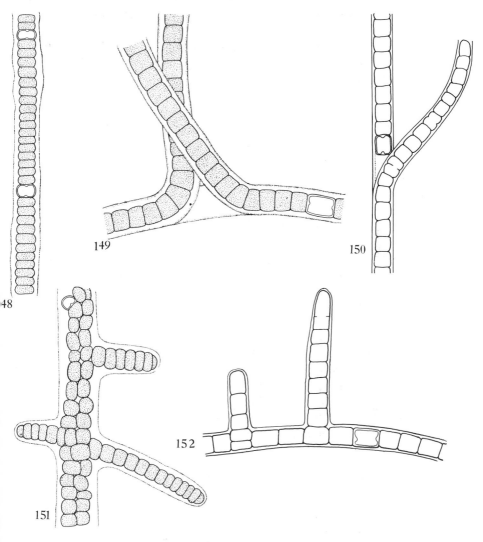

Fig. 148. **Nodularia spumigena**

Fig. 149. **Scytonema** sp

Fig. 150. **Tolypothrix** sp

Fig. 151. **Stigonema ocellatum**

Fig. 152. **Hapalosiphon pumilus**

Vermilion Sea of Mexico (Gulf of California). One species from the famous Sargasso Sea has been shown to be a nitrogen-fixer.

Spirulina Turpin, 1827 (Plate XI, Fig. 141), is an oddity in which a trichome is formed by a single, spirally twisted cell. The cell is cylindrical and the spiral may be close or loose, according to species. The cells are very active in their movement in a back and forth cork-screw motion. A close relative is *Arthrospira*, which is a longer trichome and multicellular. Plants are either fresh-water or brackish, often densely entangled and occurring with *Oscillatoria*.

Lyngbya Agardh, 1824 (Plate XI, Fig. 142), is very similar to *Oscillatoria* but has a definite, sometimes lamellate sheath which extends beyond the apex of the trichome. Some students disregard the sheath of this and other genera and favor the lumping of these in one genus. Plants are marine or fresh-water and usually solitary, but may be incidentally clustered. One species is spirally coiled, planktonic in fresh water, and may form growths of bloom proportions in favorable habitats. A few species are epiphytic and are twisted around a host filamentous alga, or lie parallel with the substrate.

Microcoleus Desmaziers, 1823 (Plate XI, Fig. 143), has a wide gelatinous sheath enclosing many *Oscillatoria*-like trichomes which are gradually tapered to their apices, ending in blunt points. The trichomes under proper conditions exhibit great movement, sliding and gliding back and forth over one another through the sheath, and sometimes emerging from it. Plants occur as blue-green strands on damp soil, or on tidal flats, moist meadows, etc.

Order Nostocales

FAMILY NOSTOCACEAE

In this family the trichomes show some differentiation, certain cells forming heterocysts, others akinetes. A definite sheath is present in some, but all are encased in mucilage in one form or another. The cells are globular, barrel-shaped, or sub-cylindric. In a few forms there are pseudo-vacuoles (*Aphanizomenon*, *Anabaena* spp). Some genera have a few planktonic species, but mostly plants occur in gelatinous, sedentary masses (definite or indefinite in shape), or in skeins.

Nostoc Vaucher, 1803 (Plate XI, Fig. 144), has globular, bead-like cells arranged in much-tangled trichomes, many of these enclosed in a copious gelatinous matrix which is bounded externally by a pellicle-like membrane. The colonies may be microscopic, pea-size, walnut-size, or as much as eight centimeters in diameter. The olive-green or blue-green colonies may be smooth or warty. One species, N. *commune*, forms leathery or rubbery sheets on damp soil and is very common in the Arctic and in alpine meadows. Another species, N. *parmeloides*, forms small, shelving growths on the down-stream side of stones immersed in cold water. Invariably these colonies harbor the larva of a midge fly. A chief characteristic of *Nostoc* is the formation of akinetes in long series; sometimes an entire trichome will be converted. In the Orient the large colonies of a terrestrial species long have been gathered for food.

Hormothamnion Grunow, 1867 (Plate XI, Fig. 145), is a subtropical, mostly marine genus in which sub-cylindrical or barrel-shaped cells form trichomes that are enclosed in a thin sheath. Many such filaments, enclosed in a soft mucilage, have a horizontal basal portion from which long, slender strands extend vertically.

Anabaena Bory, 1822 (Plate XI, Fig. 146), are solitary and euplanktonic, or occur as many plants embedded in a soft matrix, forming gelatinous masses on substrates, or intermingled with other algae. Cells are spherical, barrel-shaped, or sub-cylindric and the trichomes are straight, regularly coiled, or entangled. Heterocysts are conspicuous and akinetes are large, solitary, two, or several together. Some species have pseudovacuoles and are highly buoyant.

A number of planktonic species are of considerable interest because of their toxin-secreting capacity. They share a distinction along with *Microcystis* of being the most poisonous of all the blue-green algae (see p. 362). They often occur in water blooms and play a role in the many disturbances resulting from unbalanced conditions in lakes and reservoirs.

Aphanizomenon Morren, 1838 (Plate XI, Fig. 147), occurs as many trichomes together and parallel in bundles, all embedded in a common, indistinct mucilage. The cells are cylindrical or sub-cylindrical, each trichome including one heterocyst and one cylindrical (often large) akinete located in the mid-region. The akinetes germinate by producing endospores. These in turn form new trichomes by germinating in *situ*, which explains the bundled arrangement.

The cells contain pseudovacuoles so that the bundles float high in the water, thus forming conspicuous blooms — rather like lawn mower clippings which have been dumped into a lake. Because these profuse growths float high in the water they become crowded at the surface and die in the intense light. As the cells immediately deteriorate, their cell contents are released, thus discoloring the water and producing nauseating odors when their proteins decompose. Besides being a pest in water supplies, there is some evidence that *Aphanizomenon* also may produce lethal toxins. This genus is well-known to the sanitary engineer because of the troubles it causes and because of the amounts of copper sulphate needed to keep the plant under control in reservoirs. Seven species of this water-pest have been described and in culture ten strains of the common *A. flos-aquae* have been identified.

Nodularia Mertens, 1822 (Plate XI, Fig. 148), is a fresh-water, marine, and brackish water genus in which trichomes are solitary and enclosed in a gelatinous sheath. The cells, akinetes, and heterocysts are much compressed in the longitudinal axis so that they are wider than they are long, almost disc-shaped. Akinetes occur singly or in a series of five or more. Plants are tychoplanktonic in lakes and pools, or terrestrial; seldom, if ever, do they grow in pure stands or in abundance. This genus has the distinction of being the first to have been reported as producing toxic blooms (Australia).

Order Scytonematales

FAMILY SCYTONEMATACEAE

Trichomes in this family have relatively wide sheaths, the filaments possessing false branching. The false branch forms where a cell has died and collapsed, or where there is a heterocyst or a series of them. The cells adjoining the weakened joint in the trichome continue to divide and in so doing form a lateral extension, an out-turned development of the axial filament. In some species both cells adjacent to the heterocyst or dead cell continue to divide so that a pair of branches develop at one point. As the trichomes develop laterally the sheaths are also constructed. *Plectonema*, with a scytonemaceous type of branching, has no heterocysts. Plants have either round, oval, or quadrate heterocysts. Akinetes are lacking in most genera, rare in others. Vegetative cells are mostly quadrate, or slightly longer than they are broad; in the branches, these cells are definitely longer than they are broad.

Scytonema Agardh, 1824 (Plate XI, Fig. 149), is predominantly a fresh-water and subaerial genus, but has been reported from brackish situations. False branches arise almost always in pairs and some distance from a heterocyst. The sheaths are usually firm and thick, often lamellate and colored with a pigment known as scytonemin. The sheaths of some species have diverging or wing-like lamellae (oblique); in others they are parallel. The plants usually occur in mats or tufts in subaerial habitats where they form tawny or chocolate-brown expanses.

Tolypothrix Kuetzing, 1843 (Plate XI, Fig. 150), differs chiefly from *Scytonema* by having false branches which are solitary and arise just below a heterocyst or a chain of them. The sheath is narrower and the lamellae, if present at all, are not divergent. These plants often form floating, cottony, olive-green, or tawny tufts.

Order Stigonematales

FAMILY STIGONEMATACEAE

In this family (which is both marine and fresh-water) the trichomes exhibit true branching; i.e., branches formed by the lateral (vertical) division of cells. Filaments are either uniseriate or multiseriate, the heterocysts either intercalary or cut off laterally from a vegetative cell. These heterocysts can sometimes be discerned only with difficulty because they are on the upper side of a cell as viewed through the microscope. Plants are sedentary, aquatic, or subaerial. Some genera are thermal (*Thalophila*, *Albrightia*). In one genus (*Mastigocladus*) some species grow in shells of Mollusca or corals.

Stigonema Agardh, 1824 (Plate XI, Fig. 151), is characterized by filaments of round or oval cells which are multiseriate, although branches may be uniseriate. The sheaths are usually wide, gelatinous, and colored yellow or brown. Especially in some species there are also sheaths surrounding individual cells. In some forms plants are almost palmelloid and the linear arrangement is nearly lost. Heterocysts are rare and are seen with difficulty. Cell walls may have pores (pit connections) through which protoplasmic strands pass. This is a characteristic found also in the Florideae of the Rhodophyta.

Stigonema is more often found in subaerial habitats, especially on dripping rocks. Some species occur on submersed reeds in desmid habitats.

Hapalosiphon Naegeli, 1849 (Plate XI, Fig. 152), is uniseriate, has a close, firm sheath and intercalary heterocysts. The branches usually arise unilaterially. Cells are quadrate or sub-cylindric and do not have interconnections. Akinetes are produced either singly or in a long series.

Plants often form compact, tangled tufts on aquatic plants, especially in acid habitats.

Order Rivulariales

FAMILY RIVULARIACEAE

This marine and fresh-water family is unique because all members have trichomes which taper from base to apex. Usually there is a heterocyst at the basal end and, in some, an adjacent akinete. The filament includes a definitive sheath in which there may be more than one trichome (*Dichothrix*). Filaments may be solitary or many within a colonial mucilage, which may be hard and rubbery (*Rivularia*), or relatively soft (*Gloeotrichia*).

Calothrix Agardh, 1824 (Plate XII, Fig. 153), represents those genera in which the filaments are usually solitary, or are sometimes clustered a few together in star-shaped clumps. In marine habitats especially, the plants may be aggregated to form encrusting expanses or patches of tufts. The trichomes taper from a basal heterocyst to either a long, fine, or a blunt point. The sheath, which sometimes does not enclose the terminal heterocyst, extends beyond the apex of the trichome, often flaring at the summit. The cells are usually wider than they are long, sometimes decidedly disc-like. In some species an akinete adjoins the basal heterocyst when plants are mature. The filaments are adjoined to various substrates, with the lower part lying parallel for a short distance and then rising vertically (*C. parietana*, e.g.).

In marine situations *Calothrix* occupies a position in the splash zone (just above high tide level), as well as being a member of a supratidal association. In polluted waters it often is found in the katharobic zone, along with *Stigeoclonium*. The latter, however, often occurs in water bearing greater loads of organic matter (the mesosaprobic and oligosaprobic zones).

Rivularia Roth, emend. Agardh, 1812 (Plate XII, Fig. 154), is characterized by compactly arranged filaments in firm, often hard mucilage, tending to be radiate but often so densely arranged as to appear parallel. The colonies appear as sedentary, hard, black or greenish balls on wood, rock, algae, and substrates in tidal marshes. In some areas *Rivularia* is perennial on seacoasts; frequently, however, it is seasonal, being absent in winter. Some species have aggregates of colonies to form macroscopic expanses, especially in marine habitats where they grow just below the splash zone. The filaments have their individual sheaths, but they are confluent and all are embedded in a common mucilaginous matrix. Colonies may show false branching of trichomes with successive "generations" of branchings forming concentric zones determined by the location of the basal heterocysts of the new trichomes. Some species are lime-encrusted and form calcareous patches on submersed logs, or on rocks in hard-water streams. In some species calcium is deposited within the colony. This genus is differentiated from Gloeotrichia especially by the fact that akinetes are never formed.

Gloeotrichia J. G. Agardh, 1842 (Plate XII, Fig. 155), resembles Rivularia, although the colonial mucilage is less firm; the filaments are more radiate within the more globose colony, and plants bear akinetes adjacent to the basal heterocysts when mature. Colonies are epiphytic on aquatic plants and larger algae where they form globular, gelatinous masses, gray-green or blackish in color. In favorable habitats they may be extremely abundant and completely coat such plants as Myriophyllum. One species, G. natans, begins as an attached, soft, gelatinous mass, then becomes free-floating as brownish, expanded masses at the water surface. By this time the plants have developed elongate, cylindrical akinetes. Another species is planktonic and sometimes forms dense blooms during warm periods. The colonies appear as minute, globular "tapioca" grains, occurring at the surface like "pea soup." This species, G. echinulata is known to cause severe skin irritation among bathers, producing a rash much like that caused by the well-known "swimmers' itch" cercariae.

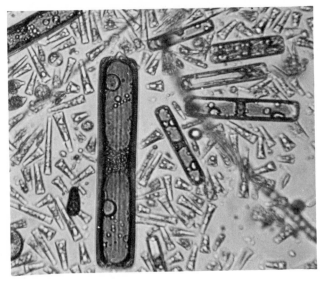

a. *Chrysosphaerella.*
(Wards Natural Science
Establishment); b. Fresh
water diatoms. (Hugh
Spencer)

Phylum Chrysophyta

These are the yellow-green or golden-yellow algae, a division which includes almost altogether microscopic but diversified plants, and one which is subject to repeated if not continuous taxonomic rearrangement. Conventionally, it comprises three quite different major subphyla or "Classes" which have been brought together with seeming justification because of a few fundamental characteristics they share in common. These three are: Xanthophyceae (Heterokontae); Bacillariophyceae (Diatoms); Chrysophyceae (Golden-Yellow Algae). In addition some systems of classification recognize the Coccolithophoridae and Silicoflagellatae (Silicoflagellineae) as separate groups; otherwise they are included in the Chrysophyceae. The characters which unite these three groups are not held completely in common throughout, but because these classes do possess various combinations of the characters, they appear to have a not too far removed common ancestor.

First, there is a similar if not identical pigmentation, both in kind and in relative abundance. Pigments include chlorophyll-a and, in some, -e, diadinoxanthin, diatoxanthin, B-carotene, lutein, fucoxanthin. The distribution of these among the several classes will be outlined in appropriate places below.

A second common character (or nearly so) is the cell wall. Although somewhat variable in composition it frequently is siliceous. It may consist of siliceous scales with or without bristles (Mallomonas, Plate XII, Fig. 169), or be composed of practically pure silica (Diatoms). Generally and basically the wall substance is predominantly pectin and galacturonic residues. In some there is a small amount of cellulose; in others the wall is impregnated with calcium. Another wall feature is the frequent occurrence of two sections, overlapping in the mid-region of the cell.

Further there is a similarity in the stored food; fats and oils (common to many) and carbohydrate-like leucosin (in some), as well as chrysolaminarin. In culture it has been shown that *Vaucheria* (Plate XII, Fig. 167, Xanthophyceae) can produce both starch and oil. Some of the flagellated members of the Chrysophyta are known to feed phagotrophically, especially those which have a *haptonema*, a flagellum often used for anchorage (see below).

The flagellation too is variable but in general there are two heterokont flagella (one simple, one pleuronematic; see definitions, p. 24). They are apical or subapical. In some forms there is a third "flagellum," the haptonema. This may be long or short and inconspicuous, and is sometimes coiled.

The pigments are enclosed in chloroplasts of miscellaneous shapes: bands, oval discs, plates, stellate discs. Pyrenoids may occur but these are seldom found and, if so, they are external to the chloroplast.

In some Chrysophyta there is a red eye-spot, or a black or red oil spot, the significance of which is not understood.

Reproductive methods vary from group to group. Vegetative reproduction, by cell division and fragmentation, is commonly employed. Asexual reproduction is by various spores: aplanospores, autospores, or zoospores, and by a unique type, the *statospore*. The latter is formed by an inner portion of the cell's protoplast becoming segregated from the peripheral part. A wall (sometimes two-parted) is then formed about the inner, delimited portion, and this may be smooth or specifically decorated. In some statospores this wall has a pore. In *Chromulina* (Plate XII, Fig. 168), for example, the protoplasm external to the spore wall migrates to the pore and passes through and fuses with the spore protoplasm, after which a plug is built into the opening. Upon germination either plastic, amoeba-like spores or biflagellate zoospores are formed from the statospore. Akinetes occur in a few genera, especially the filamentous. Sexual reproduction is isogamous or anisogamous, although in some diatoms and in the Heterosiphonales oogamy occurs (*Vaucheria*). Also in a few genera such as *Chrysolykos*, *Kephyrion*, and some *Mallomonas*, there is a special isogamous type of conjugation.

Some groups (Xanthophyceae and Chrysophyceae) are mostly fresh-water, but the diatoms are abundant also in the oceans, as are the Silicoflagellata and Coccolithophoridae. Almost all forms are microscopic. In architecture the yellow-green algae show all plant body-types found in the Chlorophyta: motile and non-motile unicells, colonies (motile and non-motile), branched and unbranched filaments, coenocytic siphons. None, however, attain the degree of complexity found in the green, red, and brown algae. Plants are either attached or planktonic and may appear in profuse growths approaching bloom proportions.

Subphylum Xanthophyceae

This yellow-green algal group is known also as the Heterokontae because there are two structurally different flagella (or sometimes but one flagellum), rather than flagella of equal length and morphology which in general characterize the Isokontae of the Chlorophyta. Zoospores of *Botrydiopsis* have one long pleuronematic and a short, simple flagellum.

Within this group are motile and non-motile forms, mostly fresh-water but many marine. Xanthophyll and B-carotene often mask chlorophyll-a and chlorophyll-c, but some members are densely green (*Botrydium*, *Vaucheria*, e.g.). The pigments are included in parietal plate-like or disc-shaped chloroplasts which may vary from one to many (especially in the Heterosiphonales). Pyrenoids, occurring infrequently, usually free from the chloroplast, are not surrounded by a starch sheath. Food accumulates as leucosin or as oil, the former thought to be a carbohydrate which appears as a shining, white solid. This substance, when in some quantity, gives the xanthophycean cell a metallic lustre.

Cells are either uninucleate or coenocytic, as in the Heterosiphonales. The cell wall is basically pectose (sometimes with pectic acid), but often is largely cellulose (according to some interpretations). As mentioned, some silica may appear in the walls as impregnations. In several genera the wall is in two sections, equal or unequal in size, adjoined (usually in the mid-region) so that one part overlaps the other (*Ophiocytium*, e.g.). These overlapping sections often are clearly evident at the ends of filamentous forms after fragmentation (*Tribonema*). The cells dissociate at the mid-region rather than at the cross walls, resulting in H-shaped sections.

Order Rhizochloridales

These organisms have amoeboid, i.e., plasmodial, protoplasts which have pseudopodia. Some are free-living; others are encased in a lorica which is attached to a substrate.

FAMILY STIPITOCOCCACEAE

Stipitococcus West et West, 1898 (Plate XII, Fig. 156), grows within a curiously shaped lorica at the end of a long, needle-like stipe, attached to filamentous algae. The shape and the habits invite speculation. The lorica is oval, round, or pitcher-shaped and has an apical opening. The protoplast has one or several yellowish chloroplasts. There are one or two pseudopodia extending through the lorica opening, but they are sometimes difficult to discern.

As far as known, reproduction is solely by zoospores. The protoplast may put out a pair of heterokont flagella and metamorphose to form a single zoospore, or it may divide, producing two zoospores which swim from the lorica.

For some unknown reason *Stipitococcus* seems to be limited in its distribution as an epiphyte to members of the Zygnematales. This suggests that the outer sheath of these algae must contain some nutrient or growth stimulator especially favorable for the germination of zoospores.

Order Heterocapsales

This order includes those forms in which oval or pyriform cells are embedded in a gelatinous matrix. The mucilage may be amorphous, or organized as branching stalks. Cells retain the ability to divide by mitosis to form new individuals, in which respect the order is comparable to the Tetrasporales in the Chlorophyta. Like those forms also, some members of the Heterocapsales have an eye-spot and contractile vacuoles. Stored food occurs as drops of oil and as leucosin. Reproduction is by zoospores.

Family Chlorosaccaceae

Gloeochloris Pascher, 1932 (Plate XII, Fig. 157), is characterized by four or five parietal chloroplasts irregularly arranged in mucilage. Plants occur as yellowish-green, globular, mucilaginous masses attached to aquatic plants. They are rarely found free-floating. Some species are described as having contractile vacuoles and an eye-spot, suggestive of a motile ancestor.

Order Heterococcales

In this order a miscellany of forms are grouped which (in the main) have lost the ability to divide vegetatively. They form autospores or divide otherwise internally. The order is comparable to the Chlorococcales of the Chlorophyta and like the latter may reproduce also by zoospores. Plants are unicellular, colonial, or pseudofilamentous (rarely). Practically all are tychoplanktonic; a few forms are sedentary.

Family Pleurochloridaceae

This is a large family of variously shaped unicells, with smooth or ornamented cell walls. Most are fresh-water, though there are examples of marine forms.

PLATE XII

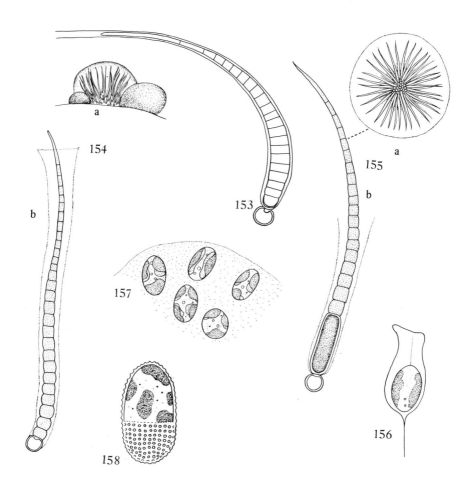

Fig. 153. **Calothrix** sp

Fig. 154. **Rivularia** sp: a, colony, diagram of trichome arrangement; b, trichome

Fig. 155. **Gloeotrichia echinulata:** a, diagram of trichome arrangement; b, trichome with akinete

Fig. 156. **Stipitococcus urceolatus,** epiphytic on filamentous alga

Fig. 157. **Gloeochloris Smithiana,** few cells with a gelatinous sheath

Fig. 158. **Chlorallanthus oblongus**

PLATE XII

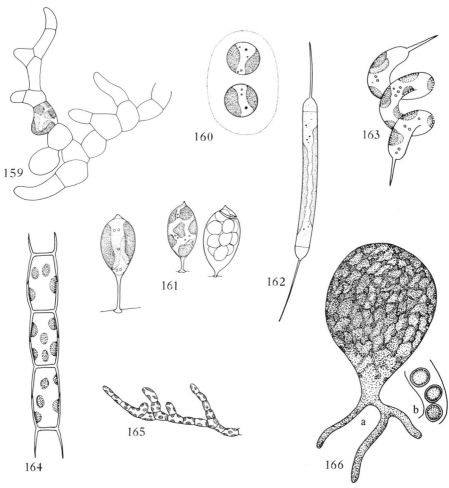

Fig. 159. **Heterococcus caespitosus** (redrawn from Bourrelly)

Fig. 160. **Chlorobotrys regularis**

Fig. 161. **Characiopsis pyriformis**

Fig. 162. **Centritractus belanophorus**

Fig. 163. **Ophiocytium capitulum**

Fig. 164. **Tribonema utriculosum**

Fig. 165. **Monocilia viridis** (redrawn from Gerneck)

Fig. 166. **Botrydium granulatum:** a, habit; b, hypnospores in rhizoidal portion

PLATE XII

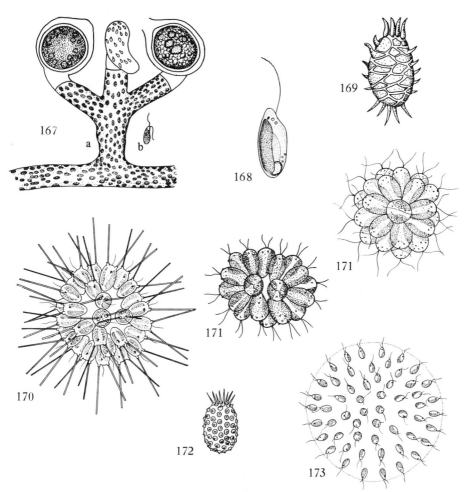

Fig. 167. **Vaucheria geminata:** a, portion of filament with oogonia and antheridium

Fig. 168. **Chromulina** sp

Fig. 169. **Mallomonas pseudocoronata**

Fig. 170. **Chrysosphaerella longispina**

Fig. 171. **Synura uvella**

Fig. 172. **Acanthoica Schilleri,** showing coccoliths (redrawn from Conrad)

Fig. 173. **Uroglenopsis americana**

Chlorallanthus Pascher, 1930 (Plate XII, Fig. 158), is a genus of oval or cylindrical cells that have walls ornamented with scrobiculate depressions arranged in rectilinear series. The scrobiculations are sometimes shallow and difficult to see. There are several disc-like chloroplasts as well as oil bodies and leucosin. Reproduction is by zoospores and autospores, with the wall separating into two equal parts to release the spores. The distribution and occurrence seem to be related to conditions found in soft-water bogs.

FAMILY GLOEOBOTRYDIACEAE

In this family cells are arranged in gelatinous, free-floating (usually) colonies. The colonial mucilage may have lamellations. Sexual reproduction is unknown, but zoospores or autospores are used.

Chlorobotrys Bohlin, 1901 (Plate XII, Fig. 160), is perhaps the most common genus in the family, usually tychoplanktonic in soft-water, desmid bogs. It is quickly identified because there is always a pair of globular cells within a wide, gelatinous sheath. There are many polygonal chloroplasts, oil droplets, and, questionably, a red eye-spot in each cell. Reproduction is by two or four autospores from each cell, these in turn becoming enclosed in pairs within a gelatinous sheath. Hypnospores also have been reported.

FAMILY CHARACIOPSIDACEAE

This family includes one-celled plants of various and bizarre shapes which are always epiphytic (at least when developing), attached by a long or short stalk that is actually a basal extension of the cell wall. Species of some genera become free-floating in age. As in many other families in this order reproduction is solely by zoospores and autospores.

Characiopsis Borzi, 1895 (Plate XII, Fig. 161), is a replica of *Characium* in the Chlorophyta in respect to shape and habit. Cells are cylindrical, oval, or fusiform and are usually attached by a slender stipe and an adhesive (iron-impregnated) disc. The yellowish-green chloroplasts, seen as parietal plates, vary from one to several. Oil globules and leucosin granules are usually detectable. Like the Chlorococcales, there may be as many as 64 nuclei in the cell. Reproduction is by heterokont zoospores and aplanospores which escape by the breakdown of the cell wall.

Family Centritractaceae

This family of unicells is characterized by having the cell wall in two sections, one of which overlaps the other in the mid-region. Plants are varied in form, mostly sausage-shaped, and are planktonic. They contain several chloroplasts, a single nucleus, and reproduce by autospores and heterokont zoospores.

Centritractus Lemmermann, 1900 (Plate XII, Fig. 162), is characterized either by straight and cylindrical cells with narrowed apices, or by cells which are fusiform in outline. In both instances there is a long straight spine at each pole. The cell wall sections are usually conspicuous, overlapping in the mid-region. The chloroplasts (usually two) are parietal plates. This genus has been found in soft-water habitats, often with Ophiocytium, and should be compared with that genus. The method of reproduction is as yet unknown.

Family Chlorotheciaceae

This family also has cells with two-parted walls but the wall construction differs from the former family, the two sections being of different lengths. Plants are solitary or colonial, free-floating or attached. The cells have two to many chloroplasts. Reproduction is by zoospores or autospores.

Ophiocytium Naegeli, 1849 (Plate XII, Fig. 163), is perhaps the most common genus in the family, if not in the order, with several species occurring in bogs and other acid situations (primarily). Cells are cylindrical and curved or variously coiled, with rounded poles which may or may not bear a spine. The wall is in two sections, one forming a "cap" over the other. In some species a spine serves as an attaching stalk. A stalked colony of individuals is formed in O. arbuscula, constructed by zoospores coming to rest and germinating on the rim of the mother cell.

The chloroplasts are many, parietal plates, regularly arranged and nearly encircling the cell. Unlike Centritractus there are several nuclei. Reproduction is mainly by heterokont zoospores. These escape when the cap-like upper section of the wall lifts away. If zoospores fail to leave the cell they become autospores. These cells have a very resistant material in the wall permitting them to remain for indefinite times in the tychoplankton. As a result they are more often found as dead and empty coiled tubes than with choroloplasts.

Ophiocytium as a genus is highly selective of habitat. It is noteworthy that water suitable for one species is suitable for several, and a habitat invariably will have a number of species. Furthermore it will support many other xanthophycean genera such as *Perone*, *Trachychloron*, and *Chlorothecium* (at least in central North America habitats).

Order Heterotrichales

This is the order to which all cellular, filamentous heterokonts belong. The filaments may be branched (*Monocilia*, Plate XII, Fig. 165) or unbranched. Their counterpart in the Chlorophyta is the Order Ulotrichales or Chaetophorales. Characteristically reproduction is asexual by aplanospores and zoospores, and sexual by isogametes.

FAMILY TRIBONEMATACEAE

In this family cylindrical or slightly swollen cells form unbranched filaments, the cells containing from two to many parietal, disc-like or plate-like chloroplasts and leucosin. Chlorophyll is in small quantity and the color is pale, yellowish-green. The walls have two sections which overlap in the midregion, with H-shaped sections being formed when the filaments fragment. Plants are attached by a short stipe and adhesive disc when in the germling stage, but soon become free-floating. Aplanospores are commonly used in reproduction but occasionally isogametes are formed. Zoospores of the heterokont type are formed singly in a cell.

Tribonema Derbes et Solier, 1856 (Plate XII, Fig. 164), consists of pale green filaments, forming cloudy, submersed growths which often appear as though dead. The cells vary in shape from short and box-like to elongate cylinders. In some species the lateral walls are slightly convex. Chloroplasts may be few to as many as 32, rarely more. In some species they are folded within the wall. The walls are relatively thin and the joint in the mid-region where the two parts overlap is indistinct. The H-shaped structures can be seen, however, at the ends of the filaments.

Vegetative reproduction by fragmentation is freely used. Asexual reproduction is by solitary aplanospores or zoospores. The aplanospore wall is bi-valved, the valves separating at the time of germination. The zoospores with heterokont flagellation produce an attached, tubular germling which is anchored by a thickened disc. After the germling has undergone a few transverse wall formations the young filament of cells breaks away. Sexual reproduction is isogamous, but almost anisogamous because, according to early observations, one gamete loses its flagella and becomes stationary prior to the approach of the male (?) gamete.

FAMILY MONOCILIACEAE

Monocilia Gerneck, 1907 (Plate XII, Fig. 165), possibly synonymous with **Heterococcus** (Plate XII, Fig. 159), is in its own family. There are short, unbranched filaments with scarcely any basal-distal differentiation.

Order Heterosiphonales

These are the siphonaceous, coenocytic members of the Chrysophyta, comparable to the Siphonales of the Chlorophyta. They are few in number, but occur in both marine and fresh-water habitats. One genus, however, is terrestrial, growing on moist soil. They are all filamentous or saccate, have many discoid chloroplasts within a reticular cytoplasm, and accumulate food as oil (or possibly as starch also in *Vaucheria*). Asexual reproduction is by aplanospores or zoospores, whereas sexual is isogamous, anisogamous, or oogamous.

FAMILY BOTRYDIACEAE

Botrydium Wallroth, 1815 (Plate XII, Fig. 166), has as a thallus a globular vesicle growing on moist soil, with rhizoidal, subterranean extensions. They occur gregariously on mud, especially along river banks where water has receded, sometimes forming a continuous expanse covering many square yards.

The vesicles are coenocytic and have numerous chloroplasts in a network of cytoplasm. Chlorophyll predominates and the plants are densely green. Pyrenoids are reported, but oil and not starch is the food reserve.

In the subterranean rhizoidal branches thick-walled aplanospores (hypnospores) may be produced in large numbers, as well as in the vesicle. It appears that sexual reproduction is used when the plants are somewhat desiccated and then become flooded. The entire content of the vesicle becomes divided into numerous biflagellate swarmers. These have been regarded as zoospores but some observations have shown that they behave as iso- and/or anisogametes. Apparently meiosis occurs with the formation of gametes and the zygote grows immediately into a new vesicle. This plant should be compared with the chlorophyte genus *Protosiphon* which often grows in the same habitat.

FAMILY VAUCHERIACEAE

In this filamentous family there are two genera recognized, *Vaucheriopsis* and **Vaucheria** De Candolle (Plate XII, Fig. 167), which is a much-branched, filamentous coenocyte. The thallus consists of a mat of these filaments, some of which are colorless, rhizoidal branches. Others are densely green and vegetative, and some are reproductive. The wall has an outer layer of pectose and an inner one of cellulose (supposedly). Plants grow in either fresh or salt water, in tidal flats and on moist soil where they form green, velvety expanses. In flowing water, green, streaming hanks are formed on stones. When immersed, the plant grows with many erect branches in penicillate tufts. Some species are known to thrive and reproduce within pockets of winter ice.

Once considered a member of the Chlorophyta, the genus is now well-situated in the Chrysophyta because of the oil food reserve and the heterokont flagellation of reproductive elements. The short flagellum of the male gamete is pleuronematic. Asexual reproduction occurs when the tip of a branch enlarges, the contents become condensed, and the apex is cut off by a cross wall as a zoosporangium. Within, the multinucleate content metamorhposes to form a single large zoospore (synzoospore). There is a pair of heterokont flagella, almost equal in length, for each of the many nuclei in the spore. The zoospore escapes and grows directly into a new thallus. If the spore does not become motile it forms a large aplanospore.

Sexual reproduction is oogamous. The position and shape of the sex organs are used as a basis for grouping the many species into Sections. Plants are mostly monoecious but some are dioecious. Sex organs are located either sessile on the main filament or at the end of special branches. The oogonia and antheridia may be on the same or on different stalks. The oogonium — tumid, round or oval — has a wall with a wide pore when mature, and is cut off from the stalk or main filament by a cross wall. The contents constitute a single egg in which all nuclei but one degenerate.

The antheridium is a hooked cylinder, cut off by a cross wall from the stalk or main filament (according to species). It is usually curved in such a position that the apex opens toward the oogonium pore. Very many biflagellate antherozoids are produced in an antheridium, these escaping through the apical pore(s). They have one short pleuronematic and one long, simple flagellum. The zygote develops an oospore wall and becomes dormant. Unlike the Siphonales reduction division apparently occurs with zygospore germination. Hence the life history is similar to that of the majority of green algae. Because of its oogamous reproduction the retention of *Vaucheria* in the Chrysophyta, therefore, might be considered inconsistent.

Subphylum Chrysophyceae

This highly diversified subphylum (or Class), in which members have various combinations of the phylum characteristics, is differentiated rather hazily by pigment composition and by the almost total lack of strictly plant-like organisms. Most of the forms, both unicellular and colonial, are motile (isokont and heterokont) and protozoan-like in some of their cytological characters. Cells have one or two golden-yellow or brownish chloroplasts which sometimes have pyrenoids. Pigments are chlorophyll-a and an abundance of B-carotene, fucoxanthin, and lutein. Stored food is mostly leucosin, although oil and chrysolaminarin occur in some. A few forms have a holozoic type of nutrition. An elaborate vacuolar system occurs in a number of species, reflecting their protozoan nature. Along with a few volvocoid characters, possessed by some, is a red eye-spot.

The architecture within the group varies to include motile and non-motile unicellular genera, and single-celled amoeboid forms; or palmelloid, filamentous, branched and unbranched, and colonial-glomerate (palmelloid or in chains) forms. The rhizopodal tendency, lacking in the Chlorophyta, is well-developed in this subphylum.

Reproduction by cell division is used throughout. In a few instances there are zoospores, or naked, amoeboid spores, and commonly there are statospores. Sexual reproduction is rare and is always isogamous. Chrysophyte spores, e.g., *Cysta* spp., are known from Miocene diatomite. It is thought that meiosis occurs with gamete-formation and that the vegetative plant therefore is diploid.

Members of the Chrysophyceae are both fresh-water and marine, especially some of the flagellated unicells. A number of genera occur in arctic and subarctic habitats, and in cold water of alpine regions. It is noteworthy that many chrysophycean and bacillariophycean species are highly successful in the cold water of the Arctic where illumination is often much reduced or critically periodic. This is in keeping with the general observation that algae with an abundance of yellow and orange pigments are apparently adapted to life in dimly lighted (and frigid) habitats that are unsuitable for most of the other algal groups.

The Class is variously treated systematically and is repeatedly rearranged. A system that has not been used but which may be adopted (in part at least) more generally is one proposed by Bourrelly (1954). In this scheme the Chrysophyceae are elevated to the status of a phylum (Chrysophyta) but with the diatoms and the yellow-green algae treated as separate phyla also. In his scheme Bourrelly recognizes five orders and their respective families, each named after a genus in accordance with the International Rules of Nomenclature. The composition of respective families is subject to speculation and will vary as more research on life histories and cytology is completed. The morphological architecture displayed by the Chryso-phyceae shows close parallelism with the developmental trends in the Chlorophyta and the Xanthophyceae.

It is appropriate to describe briefly a few representative genera.

Order Chrysomonadales (Chromulinales)

This is an artificial order which at present is undergoing taxonomic revi-sion. It is convenient only for grouping the motile forms. Mobile unicells have one or two flagella, with rhizopodal stages transitory. In some there is a haptonema. Colonial forms also occur. Not a few forms have an ex-ternal shell (lorica) and in several there is a rigid periplast (as in the euglenoids) which, however, may have siliceous scales or rods. The stato-spore type of cyst is used in many forms.

FAMILY CHROMULINACEAE

This is a family of one-celled swimmers, either with or without a lorica. There is a single flagellum, apparently always of the simple type, and one or two thin chloroplasts.

Chromulina Cienkowski, 1870 (Plate XII, Fig. 168), has subspherical or broadly oval cells with one flagellum and one or two thin, broad, parietal chloroplasts. In some species at least there is a second, much reduced flagellum (haptonema) within the cell. There is a pyrenoid, usually an eye-spot, and vacuoles at the flagella base. Although there is no wall, the membrane has three distinct layers. This membrane, which is ex-tended into the flagellar sheath, is pliable, and cells often show amoeboid protrusions. Leucosin is the principal stored food product.

Occasionally the cells become amoeboid. Reproduction is by cell divis-ion while the organism remains motile. Smooth-walled statospores are known in some species (see p. 33). These organisms are tychoplank-tonic in lakes as well as euplanktonic in rivers (often in winter). They occur also in brackish water, and probably in marine as well.

FAMILY MALLOMONADACEAE

This unique family is one which has uniflagellated cells with siliceous scales in or covering the wall, or siliceous rods in the wall. Organisms are either solitary or colonial. Reproduction is by cell division, by zoospores, and by the characteristic cysts.

Mallomonas Perty, 1832 (Plate XII, Fig. 169), is characterized by oval or elliptical cells which have a periplast completely overlain with siliceous, overlapping, perforated scales, some of which bear long siliceous needles. Yellowish or brown because of iron deposits, the scales are specifically different and are highly ornamented, as shown by the electron microscope. The spines arise from a rounded apex of the scale.

There is one pleuronematic flagellum and one or two golden-yellow or light brown chloroplasts. A second, reduced flagellum is sometimes discernible, and is regarded as a photoreceptor. Some species of *Mallomonas* are colorless.

Reproduction is vegetative by frequent cell division, asexual by zoospores which soon become sedentary and secrete a mucilaginous sheath, or rarely by isogametes. From such a stage there is a metamorphosis, and the motile condition of the mature individual is resumed. In some species statospores are used. These differ in shape and appearance from the parent cell periplast which persists after the statospore and its plug are mature.

Mallomonas has been a favorite subject for electron microscopy, which can show the refined differences in scales, and needles. Such ultramicroscopic features both confirm and negate previous classification of some taxa.

Species are euplanktonic in both hard-water (especially) and in soft-water lakes, though they seldom occur in abundance. They are common in the diatom-cyanophyte type of lake. Some species seem to prefer cold water, and are thus common in subarctic and arctic lakes and beneath ice. At least 15 species are known to exist in North America.

Chrysosphaerella Lauterborn (Plate XII, Fig. 170), is a curious colonial genus in which oval, uniflagellate cells have a pair of collars at the anterior end from which long, cylindrical siliceous rods arise. Cells have two laminate chloroplasts and an eye-spot. These globular colonies are uncommonly found but the genus is widely distributed as a plankter.

FAMILY SYNURACEAE

This family includes colonial genera which have two flagella of equal length. Like the previously described family, cells have a periplast but no cell wall. There are siliceous scales embedded in the periplast in the anterior region of the cell.

Synura Ehrenberg, 1838 (Plate XII, Fig. 171), is characterized by cells which are pyriform or elongate-pyriform in shape, radiately arranged in globular or oblate-spheroidal colonies. The cells are adjoined at the interior of the colony by mucilaginous stalks. There are two laminate, usually golden-brown chloroplasts. The siliceous scales are significantly similar in morphology to those of *Mallomonas*. Typically there are vacuoles at the base of the two pleuronematic flagella of equal length. Vlk, however, reports (1931) one pleuronematic and one simple flagellum. The flagellum attachment is reported to involve fibrous "roots" at the base. Depending on the physiological condition, there is a prominent posterior granule of leucosin.

Cell division occurs within the colony, or a cell may liberate itself and then divide to form a small colony. There is an unusual fragmentation of the colony which is accomplished by the cells rearranging themselves to form two radiate clusters that eventually separate. Like so many other genera, an amoeboid protoplast may escape from the periplast and then metamorphose to form a biflagellate zoospore.

Synura is euplanktonic and occasionally occurs in such numbers as to produce objectionable tastes and odors in reservoir waters. It occurs in a wide range of habitats, from soft to hard water. In northern, temperate latitudes *Synura* appears early in the spring immediately following an intensification of light. Occasionally *Synura* appears with diatoms throughout the winter, often with a dominant "bloom" of *Dinobryon* spp.

Family Coccolithophoridaceae
(Coccolithineae of the Haptophyceae)

This is a unique family of intriguing organisms (sometimes placed in a class of its own) in which motile cells have an outer, separate membrane that is profusely beset with buttons (discs or rings) of a calcareous compound, thought possibly to be formed by the Golgi apparatus. These buttons are called *coccoliths* (**Acanthoica**; Plate XII, Fig. 172). There are three classes of these. In one the holococcoliths are crystals of calcite in the outer layer of the cell envelope, and are revealed only by the electron microscope. Another type is the heterococcoliths, which are complexes of plates or bands and which may occur in two shapes on the same organism. Some of these bear spines and are visible by the light microscope. In one genus there is a third type of coccolith, the pentalith (*Braarudosphaera*). These three types of membrane structures provide features of some taxonomic value. It is interesting that the coccoliths are shed as new ones are formed internally to take their place.

The cells have two types of flagella of equal length and two broad, parietal chloroplasts. As in many motile Chrysophyta, there is a vacuole system. In reproduction, cells may divide either in the motile or non-motile condition. The protoplast divides first (longitudinally), followed by a cleavage of the membrane to form two new cells. In marine genera the protoplast divides to form zoospores which escape by an opening in the envelope at the anterior end; or the cleavage may be unequal, the larger protoplast retained in the old envelope and the smaller escaping. Gametes with eye-spots are reported for some genera. Division of the zygote immediately after fusion is meiotic.

From culture studies it has been learned that motile cells with a haptonema can become non-motile and may become attached by that flagellum. In this state a cell may divide to form sedentary palmelloid or pseudofilamentous growths, and in some instances cells develop coccoliths different from those of the motile phase. These growths resemble forms that have been given other generic names. Further studies may show that many plants will need to be reclassified after study with the electron microscope.

The members of this family are mostly marine, but at least two genera (*Hymenomonas* Stein, 1878; *Pontosphaera* Lohman, 1902, sometimes included in the former) occur in fresh water of North America. In plankton hauls Coccolithophorids constitute as much as 45% of the bulk in temperate waters and at least in some sections are important in the food chain. In marine deposits fossil remains of the coccoliths occur in abundance from as far back in geologic time as the Paleozoic and Jurassic, and especially from the calcareous deposits of the Cretaceous.

FAMILY OCHROMONADACEAE

This family includes both unicellular (*Ochromonas*) and colonial (*Uroglenopsis*) genera, which are motile by unequal (heterokont) flagella. In some there is a lorica.

Uroglenopsis Lemmermann, 1894 (Plate XII, Fig. 173), is a fresh-water, motile, spherical colony containing hundreds of ovate cells, arranged at the periphery of a mucilaginous envelope. The cells usually have a single parietal chloroplast and a red eye-spot. Oil collects as a food reserve.

Reproduction is by cell division and by statospores which have prominent, tube-like plugs. The common species *U. americana* is frequently present in habitats which also support *Dinobryon* spp. In the Arctic *Uroglenopsis* may be the dominant plankter in tundra lakes. Characteristically, the entire colony of many hundreds of cells may convert to statospores simultaneously.

Dinobryon Ehrenberg, 1835 (Plate XIII, Fig. 174), is characterized by the chrysophycean protoplast being contained in a cone-shaped, colorless lorica. Although solitary cells may occur, they are mostly arranged in forked chains, one or two cones fitted into the open end of another. The protoplast is ovoid or fusiform, and has one or two parietal, yellowish chloroplasts and an eye-spot. Leucosin occurs in the basal part of the protoplast. There are two heterokont flagella.

Dinobryon uses several reproductive techniques. Commonly the protoplast divides, and one of the new portions comes to rest at the lip of the parent lorica. Both divided and undivided protoplasts may escape and become quiescent, then continue to divide to form palmelloid masses. Statospores also occur. Sometimes these contain two nuclei, the significance of which is not understood.

Dinobryon, like a few genera well-supplied with yellow and carotenoid pigments, is relatively abundant in arctic waters. The genus is widely distributed over the world. It is frequently abundant in hard-water plankton, and common in the tychoplankton of pools. The loricas occur empty in preserved collections, and often in living samples, because of the readiness with which the protoplasts escape from the loricas. Taxonomy is based upon the shape and arrangement of the loricas, which are specifically different.

Family Prymnesiaceae

This family recently has been assigned to a separate class, the Haptophyceae, to include those flagellates which possess a haptonema, a modified organ, either long or short. In at least some forms the haptonema acts as a tactile or attaching organ. The Orders Prymnesiales and Isochrysidales are recognized as constituting the Haptophyceae.

The family Prymnesiaceae is distinctive in having three flagella — the haptonema and two additional simple ones. The haptonema extends directly forward for attachment, while the other two equal flagella are locomotory. *Prymnesium* (marine), which has been especially troublesome in the fish culture ponds of Israel, produces a toxin. The cells are ellipsoidal or narrowly oval. There are two parietal chloroplasts and a vacuolar system.

Prymnesium has been the subject of considerable research in respect to the nature of its toxins, and for studies of algal nutrition. The lethal toxin is proteinaceous, acid-labile, thermostable, and non-dialyzable.

Chrysochromulina Lackey, 1939 (Plate XIII, Fig. 175), has circular, but dorsiventrally flattened, cells with three flagella, one of which is a long

PLATE XIII

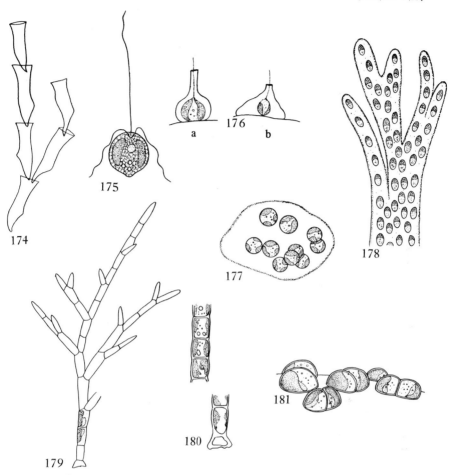

Fig. 174. **Dinobryon cylindricum**

Fig. 175. **Chrysochromulina parva** (redrawn from Lackey)

Fig. 176. **Lagynion:** a, **L. ampullaceum;** b, **L. Scherfellii**

Fig. 177. **Chrysocapsa planctonica**

Fig. 178. **Hydrurus foetidus,** apex of colony strand

Fig. 179. **Phaeothamnion confervicola**

Fig. 180. **Nematochrysis sessilis** (redrawn from Pascher)

Fig. 181. **Epichrysis** sp

PLATE XIII

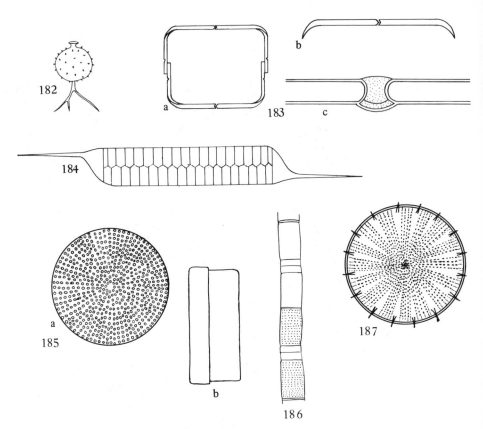

Fig. 182. **Chrysostrella furcata,** cyst

Fig. 183. Diatom diagrams: a, cross section of frustule, epitheca, and hypotheca, showing girdle bands; b, wall of epivalve showing raphe in section (upper and lower fissures); c, sagittal section along raphe; outer fissure (upper) and inner fissure (lower) extending to central nodule, showing canal connecting upper and inner fissures at the central nodule, and the canal extending below the central nodule which connects the inner fissure of one raphe with that of the raphe on the opposite side of the central nodule

Fig. 184. **Rhizosolenia** sp

Fig. 185. **Coscinodiscus perforatus:** a, valve view; b, girdle view

Fig. 186. **Melosira** sp, portion of filament

Fig. 187. **Stephanodiscus** sp

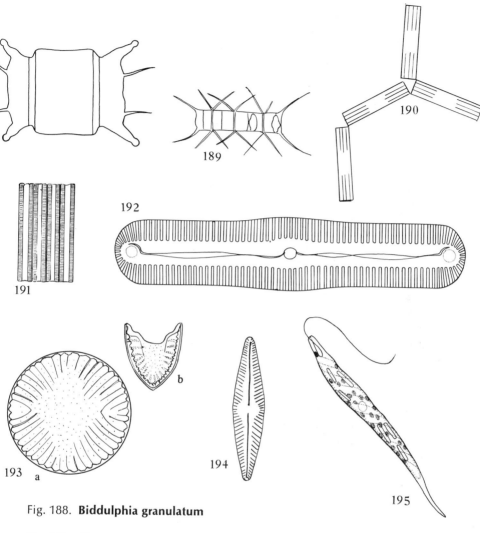

Fig. 188. **Biddulphia granulatum**

Fig. 189. **Chaetoceros** sp

Fig. 190. **Tabellaria** sp

Fig. 191. **Fragilaria** sp

Fig. 192. **Pinnularia lata**

Fig. 193. **Campylodiscus** sp: a, valve view; b, side view (redrawn from Schoenfeldt)

Fig. 194. **Navicula** sp

Fig. 195. **Euglena acus** var.

haptonema that is often seen to be coiled. There are two elongate, yellowish chloroplasts. The remarkable wall of these flagellates is composed of one or two layers of differently sized scales. The larger scales are oval-shaped and have a thickened rim and radiating, fine ridges from a central point. In some scales the face extends into a long spine with fine markings at the base. The details of these features have been determined by electron microscopy, and species differentiation depends upon this instrument. Thus far the composition of the scales is unknown (probably siliceous ?). It is considered likely that the material is elaborated by the vesicles which characterize the outer region of the cytoplasm just beneath the cell membrane.

Order Rhizochrysidales

These forms occur only as rhizopodal organisms, often faintly pigmented, but with a single plate-like, thin chloroplast. The pseudopodia of the motile forms are mostly long and needle-like. In some forms the pseudopodia of individuals are adjoined so that chains are formed. Some protoplasts have a lorica. Whereas some forms move about in the vegetative condition, others are sedentary.

Lagynion Pascher, 1912 (Plate XIII, Fig. 176), is an example of the sedentary cell. The oval protoplasts are enclosed in variously shaped (triangular or oval) vase-like loricas that have long or short necks. The pseudopodium, thin and thread-like, extends from the protoplast through the neck opening. *Lagynion* includes relatively small species which are found as sessile epiphytes on filamentous algae.

Order Chrysocapsales

FAMILY CHRYSOCAPSACEAE

In this order and family colonial, non-motile organisms are enclosed in mucilage. They are capable of returning to a motile stage directly, and thus establish new colonies. Plants also multiply by fragmentation of the colony. The order has a counterpart in the Tetrasporales of the Chlorophyta.

Chrysocapsa Pascher, 1912 (Plate XIII, Fig. 177), is the most common genus, although *Phaeosphaera perforata* Whit. has been found a number of times in the United States. *Chrysocapsa* has spherical cells embedded in a shapeless mucilage, often adhering to submerged substrates but also found commonly in the tychoplankton. The mucilage has been shown to have rod-like strands with cells borne at the apices. There are two (or three) yellowish-brown parietal chloroplasts. Like some of the Tetrasporales the non-motile cells sometimes contain a red eye-spot and a vacuolar system, indicative of a motile ancestry.

Family Hydruraceae

The family is typical of the Chrysocapsales in general basic morphology, but here the thallus consists of branched, gelatinous strands (in which the cells are embedded) and growth takes place in the apical region. The growths occur as tufted, gelatinous, and finely branched thalli, dark brown in color and rather tough in consistency.

Hydrurus Agardh, 1824 (Plate XIII, Fig. 178), is characterized by a thallus whose cells are multiseriate in arrangement in the lower part of gelatinous strands, but uniseriate in the branches. The cells are oval, with a yellow-brown chloroplast and one pyrenoid. The chloroplast is parietal within the apical wall or forward end, and all cells in the colony are oriented in the same direction. In the posterior portion of the cell is a large and conspicuous granule of food reserve.

Reproduction by cell division takes place actively. Asexual reproduction occurs when vegetative cells metamorphose to form oddly-shaped, triangular (in outline) or pyramidal, uniflagellate zoospores. A broad side of the zoospore is apical and here the flagellum is attached, the chloroplast being opposite in one of the angles. The zoospore forms a mucilaginous tube first and then divides to initiate a colony. Smooth-walled statospores develop in the apices of special branches.

Hydrurus occurs as brown, gelatinous masses attached to stones in cold streams and mountain cataracts, rarely in standing cold water. The only species recorded, *H. foetidus* (Vill.) Trev., is well named because of its disagreeable odor.

Order Chrysotrichales (Phaeothamniales)

This is a marine and fresh-water order in which the thallus is a branched or unbranched filament, comparable to the Chaetophorales of the Chlorophyta. The formation of palmelloid stages in which the cells develop eye-spots indicates a variation of or a retardation of zoospore-formation. Apparently sexual reproduction has never been observed.

Phaeothamnion Lagerheim, 1884 (Plate XIII, Fig. 179), is characterized by branched filaments which are basal-distally differentiated, attached by a broad, colorless holdfast. The cells have one or more yellow-brown chloroplasts and granules of leucosin. The plants may revert to a palmelloid colony in which spherical cells are arranged in a wide, gelatinous sheath, resembling *Palmodictyon* of the Chlorophyta. Asexual reproduction uses biflagellate zoospores as well as statospores.

These filaments, which seem to be rare in North America, usually occur as epiphytes on coarse, filamentous algae.

Nematochrysis Pascher, 1929 (Plate XIII, Fig. 180), is an unbranched, marine filament with a specialized holdfast cell. Palmelloid stages occur frequently, followed by cyst-formation. Cells of the filament may produce solitary, biflagellate zoospores. In the development of filaments by cell division the segmentation of the protoplast is curiously oblique.

Order Chrysosphaerales

In this order cells cannot revert directly to a motile state (as is possible in the Chrysocapsales). As with the Chlorococcales of the Chlorophyta, cell multiplication occurs by internal division in which daughter individuals are retained in the old mother cell for some time. The cells have the characteristics of the Chrysophyta of course. Included in the order are both marine and fresh-water forms, many of which are of uncertain taxonomic position. Some forms are cyst-like, some are with siliceous shells and spines (Chrysostomataceae **Chrysostrella**, Plate XIII, Fig. 182), or some are with wings (Pterospermaceae, a marine family). The latter and some other related forms are not well-understood. There undoubtedly are many additional marine genera as yet undescribed which eventually will be assigned to families in this order.

Family Chrysosphaeraceae

The curiously shaped cells in this family are both marine and freshwater and are enigmatic in many respects. A few forms have a siliceous lorica with spine-like processes.

Epichrysis Pascher, 1925 (Plate XIII, Fig. 181), is a genus of unicells attached to filamentous algae in fresh water. Individuals, although spherical, become closely aggregated and angular from mutual compression, and form a patch-like stratum one cell deep. The cells have a single large, yellow-brown chloroplast opposite the side of attachment. The contents include oil and leucosin. Asexual reproduction is by the formation of two uniflagellate zoospores in each cell. These are metamorphosed from the daughter protoplasts resulting from internal division. As do the motile cells of the Chlorophyta, the zoospores have contractile vacuoles and an eye-spot. This well may be a growth stage of some other alga.

Aurosphaera Schiller, 1925, is a marine genus that has a siliceous shell and bristle-bearing scales (somewhat comparable to the composition of the *Mallomonas* wall (Plate XII, Fig. 169).

Silicoflagellatae

This little-understood group of bizarre flagellates (with one flagellum in the Dictyochaceae) is thought to be related to the Chrysophyceae. Species are very abundant in marine plankton, especially in north temperate seas, and they occur in tremendous numbers in deposits dating from the Cretaceous.

The organisms have an internal, open skeleton, variously shaped (round, elliptic, triangular, isodiametric). From the rods of the skeleton extend radiating spines. The skeleton is enclosed by a close sheath of cytoplasm containing (usually) several yellowish chloroplasts. The nucleus is central. Both fat and leucosin collect as food reserve. Apparently there is no pyrenoid. According to some observers the skeleton becomes external to the protoplast when cells are mature.

A second skeleton is formed just before division of the protoplast. Some observations show that the protoplast divides and that these two segments leave the old skeleton to form new ones. *Distephanum* is the silicoflagellate which has received considerable critical study. Another family (Ehriaceae) is heterotrophic and unlike the Dictyochaceae in that all forms are apparently biflagellate.

Subphylum Bacillariophyceae

The most numerous of all the Chrysophyta, if not of all the algae, are the diatoms — ubiquitous in fresh- and salt-water, on soil, and subterranean (see p. 320). Because of geometrical expressions and the intricate sculpturings and traceries in the cell wall the diatoms are without a doubt among the most beautiful of microscopic objects. Some genera occur as filaments (but as such are not regarded as multicellular plants), as loose chains, or adjoined in mucilaginous colonies. They appear in the euplankton, in the tychoplankton, as periphyton, as brownish films on lake and stream bottoms, or as brown, gelatinous masses on stones and on the sands of beaches. Commonly they occur as epiphytes on filamentous algae and the larger

TABLE 4.1   Suggested Classification of Chrysophyceae*

SUBCLASS I. ACONTOCHRYSOPHYCIDAE

   Order 1. Rhizochrysidales
   Order 2. Phaeoplacales
   Order 3. Stichogloeales
   Order 4. Chrysosaccales

SUBCLASS II. HETEROCHRYSOPHYCIDAE

   Order 1. Chromulinales
     Suborder Chromulineae
     Suborder Thallochrysineae
     Suborder Chrysosphaerineae
   Order 2. Ochromonadales
     Suborder Ochromonadineae
     Suborder Phaeothamnionineae
     Suborder Chrysapionineae

SUBCLASS III. ISOCHRYSOPHYCIDAE

   Order 1. Isochrysidales
   Order 2. Prymnesiales

---

* Modified according to the suggestions of Bourrelly, Pascher, Christensen, and based on the work of Valakanov, Parke, and others.

thalloid algae of the sea, sometimes completely coating the host substrate. Many of their characteristics seem to relate the diatoms to the Chrysophyta, but they possess features which have led to their being placed in a separate phylum, Bacillariophyta. Because of the conjugation method of sexual reproduction used by many diatoms (the Pennatae) they were at one time grouped with the Conjugales to form the Zygophyceae.

The cell wall of diatoms (with as much as 95% silicon), characteristic of so many Chrysophyta, is in two sections. The cell or its shell is known as the *frustule*. The two pieces, one larger and fitting over the smaller as a lid does over a box, are adjoined and held in place by each having a side piece called a *girdle-band* (see Plate XIII, Fig. 183). There may be one, two, or more additional, intercalary bands besides the girdle that are inserted between the two wall sections. These may be numerous in such a genus as **Rhizosolenia** (Plate XIII, Fig. 184). In girdle (side) view these show as imbricated sections in a double row.

Each wall section has a broad surface (the top or bottom of the box) called a *valve*. In some forms the valve surface is undulate rather than flat; in others there is a flange or *keel* on the valve. The valve pieces are downward (or upward) curved (bent) into a marginal flange, often referred to as the *valve jacket* (Plate XIII, Fig. 183). This would correspond to the down-turned margins of a box lid. The connecting band (or *cingulum*) of each valve fits under these flanges and so constitutes the side pieces of the frustule. The two side pieces, which are either closed or open loops extending around the cell, usually overlap one another in the (lateral) midregion as the cell is seen from the side (girdle view).

The larger piece, or *epivalve*, and its side piece are known together as the *epitheca*; the smaller (*hypovalve*) as the *hypotheca*. When the frustule is seen from above or below it is said to be in *valve view*, whereas the view from the side (in which the girdle shows) is the *girdle view*. The same cell has quite a different appearance when seen in these two views. In valve view the frustule may be circular, triangular, or approximately isodiametric. In girdle view such cells are rectangular or cylindrical and capsule-shaped.

Cells which are isodiametric in valve view have wall ornamentation that is radially symmetrical and constitute a group of the diatoms known as the Centrales (Centricae). Another such order (or Class) is the Pennales (Pennatae) in which the valve view (highly variable) is elongate, boat-shaped, needle-shaped, lunate, sigmoid, wedge-shaped, or broadly oval. In girdle view such cells may be short or elongate-rectangular, saddle-shaped, undulated oval, and many others. The ornamentation of this group of diatoms is bilaterally symmetrical.

The differentiation between these two orders is rather clearly drawn. Some students contend, however, that one of the features used to characterize the two is not entirely constant, and accordingly they do not recognize the orders Centrales and Pennales.

The feature in question is the presence or absence of a furrow extending lengthwise through the wall of the valve. This is called a *raphe* and appears in the pennate cell but not in the Centrales (except in a few instances). The raphe or furrow, if seen in a transverse section of the wall, would show as a V-shaped groove (turned on its side) (see Plate XIII, Fig. 183). The upper arm of the "V" is called the *outer fissure*, the lower the *inner fissure*. Usually the raphe runs through the median axis of the valve wall; in others it occurs in the margin of a keel that arises from the valve, or it may be lateral to the median line. The raphe may occur in either one or both of the valves. In some of the Pennales there is no true raphe but cells may possess a *pseudoraphe*. This is a clear, longitudinal area in the median region of the valve produced by the abrupt termination of rows of puncta or other decorations extending in from the margins of the valve. At first glance this line may appear as a raphe, and may occur in one or both valves. The presence or absence and the location of the raphe and the appearance of the pseudoraphe constitute important taxonomic characters.

In the Pennales there are polar nodules and a central nodule which are internal thickenings of the valve wall. When the central nodule is laterally expanded it is called a *stauros*, especially prominent in the genus *Stauroneis*. The central nodule interrupts the raphe which extends through the wall of the valve so that the raphe appears as two lines, one on either side of the central nodule and between it and the polar nodule. At the central nodule the upper fissure extends down into the lower fissure by a *canal*; in other words, the upper and lower arms of the "V" are joined. There is also a canal that extends under the nodule and connects the inner fissure of one raphe with that of the other (see Plate XIII, Fig. 183).

The wall, especially the valve and side pieces (cingula), is composed of pectin impregnated with silicon. At least in *Navicula* the siliceous shell has been shown to be enclosed by an "organic skin." Within the silicon is a thin layer called the *silicalemma*, and this is considered to function directly in depositing silicon in the wall. A great range of new problems has been opened by the advent of electron microscopy — questions related to the origin and development of the siliceous material, and the mechanisms which control the laying down of intricate wall decorations, generation after generation, with such a great degree of precision.

The degree of silicon impregnation varies tremendously, some euplankters having scarcely any silicon in the walls. A basic material in the walls is quartz; aluminum and iron have also been shown to be incorporated in the wall. Scales of wall material are built internally and do not arise from the outer membrane of the protoplast.

There are minute canals through the wall, which is intricately patterned with groove-like etchings (*striae*), rows of *pits* (*puncta*), or *areolae*. Many of the finer markings are discernible only by electron microscopy. In some walls there appear *coastae* or ribs which in some instances may be the boundaries of chambers within the cell. *Septa* may extend inwardly from the intercalary bands, thus forming partial partitions.

The protoplast (sometimes interrupted by septa) has a central vacuole surrounded by a layer of cytoplasm. The nucleus is central. The chloroplasts are varied in shape but usually are longitudinal plates containing pyrenoids. Chloroplasts may also be oval discs or stellate masses. Pigments include diatoxanthin, diadinoxanthin, chlorophyll-a and -c, a-, B-, and e-carotene, neofucoxanthin-A and -B, in addition to fucoxanthin. Nineteen amino acids have been found in diatom composition. As much as 10.7% of dry weight of *Nitzschia linearis* is fat, of which 0.1% is sterol; 52.6% is ash and 47% is organic matter. Oil, occurring in large droplets, is the food reserve, along with chrysolaminarin and volutin.

Vegetative reproduction is accomplished by the cell first enlarging. The nucleus then divides, followed by the chloroplast dividing and the pyrenoid multiplying. The protoplast then undergoes a division in a plane parallel with the valves. The two sections of the wall become disengaged and separate. A new wall is then secreted within the hypotheca which becomes the hypotheca of one of the new cells (the former hypotheca becoming an epitheca). Similarly a hypotheca develops within the original epitheca. Thus one line of descendants in cell division remains the same size, whereas the other line becomes smaller and smaller with each division. After being reduced to a physiological minimum the smaller cells eventually form auxospores by the protoplast escaping from separated wall sections. A siliceous wall (either smooth or etched) is formed around the escaped protoplast which then assumes a dormant state. Upon germination a cell is formed of normal size. A few species are known to retain their original size following division because of the elasticity of the girdle band.

In sexual reproduction the cells undergo a conjugation (in the Pennales). Two cells become juxtaposed within a common mucilage. The nucleus of each cell then undergoes meiotic division to form four nuclei. Either three or two of the four nuclei so formed disintegrate. The wall sections separate and the contents of the two conjugants emerge. The one or two remaining nuclei from both cells then unite to form one or two zygotes (depending upon the species). These form diploid auxospores from which new vegetative cells develop. The protoplasts and their nuclei behave as gametes, of course, and are either iso- or anisogametes, with one being nonmotile and the other exhibiting amoeboid migration to it. According to studies, there are many variations in the behavior of the nuclei resulting from meiotic division.

In *Melosira*, a capsule-shaped genus of the Centrales, and in *Biddulphia* and *Isthmia* some species have been shown to have the nucleus divide by meiosis to form four daughter nuclei. Around these four uniflagellate motile male gametes are formed. These escape and unite with a protoplast of another cell in which meiosis also has occurred. Here three of the four nuclei disintegrate, leaving one to perform as a non-motile female gamete in an oogamous type of reproduction. The resulting zygote germinates to form a diploid vegetative cell. Hence all diatoms which have been investigated have no alternation of generations, but exist as diploid cells which produce gametes by meiosis.

Cells that have a true raphe may exhibit characteristic gliding movements caused by streaming cytoplasm, by circulation within the raphe, and by the extrusion of mucilage. Certain members of the Centrales also show locomotion by a process as yet undetermined. Movement of diatoms has been estimated to be from 0.2 to 25 microns per second. It occurs when cells are in contact with a substrate, or with each other. One active species is *Nitzschia paradoxa* (Gmel.) Grun. (*Bacillaria paradoxa*), the carpenter's rule diatom. Here a ribbon-like band of rectangular cells slide back and forth upon one another, drawing the ribbon out laterally to a linear series in one direction, and then back and out again in the other direction. The mechanism by which movement occurs involves the secretion of mucilage into the raphe. The mucilage, according to recent studies, comes from crystalloid bodies and from bundles of fibrils located near the raphe. After secretion, the mucilage streams along through the raphe, in a direction opposite to that in which movement of the diatom is set up. The mucilage that is extruded from the diatom leaves a track (continuous or interrupted) which can be demonstrated by staining (brilliant cresyl blue). Externally the substances occur in the form of twisted or hollow strands. It is probable that chemical and physical changes in the secreted mucilage to which the cell adheres are factors in movement. Movement can occur vertically and over rough, granular surfaces as well as horizontally. Because of the property of adherence displayed by the extruded material, the cells may remain in a vertical position even after death. Also extending from walls of some Centrales (*Cyclotella*) are fibers of chitin. These fibers also extend from *Thalassiosira*, but these are not involved in movement.

Among fossil diatoms there are 190 known genera, of which 75% are known only from that state. The majority of these are Centrales. Deposits occur as solid dunes in lands which were once sea bottom. Such deposits, as in California, Oregon, or Wyoming, for example, may be hundreds of feet thick and several miles in length (see Chap. 10). In some instances fresh-water deposits occur, and sometimes a layer of such material is found between layers of marine deposit, the plants having been carried in large numbers by streams into the sea. Studies of diatomaceous strata aid in determining climatic conditions, succession of changes, and other ecological conditions of the remote past. Likewise the history of lake basins and flowage systems, and even the past chemistry of water can be determined, especially in reference to changes from basic to acid states, or vice versa. In certain deposits there is an indication of a predominance of alkaline species, following a dominance of acid water species. Also a history of eutrophication can be ascertained. This is of course based on inferences drawn from a knowledge of the ecology of extant species.

Class Centrales (Centrobacillariophyceae)

This class, sometimes regarded as an Order, is composed of those diatoms which are mostly isodiametric in valve view, and have radially symmetrical or concentric wall markings. Commonly, cells are round in valve view (**Coscinodiscus,** Plate XIII, Fig. 185) but they may be triangular (some irregular) or quadrate. Several genera are drum-shaped or capsule-shaped as seen in side view. The valves have no raphe. Unlike the Pennales, the cells contain many small chloroplasts.

Auxospore-formation is commonly used in the Centrales. This usually is accomplished by the two wall sections separating slightly, exposing the protoplast. The protoplast swells decidedly and forms a nearly round body. This becomes enclosed by a thin silicified wall. An auxospore wall in two sections then forms within the membrane and this is ornamented in the same fashion as the vegetative cell. In filamentous species the auxospores occur in an almost continuous series, the entire filament producing auxospores simultaneously.

It is in this group that oogamous reproduction occurs (as outlined previously). In addition, genera such as *Biddulphia* form uniflagellate microspores; it is not certain whether these are zoospores or gametes.

A certain body of opinion holds that the Centrales include six families (often grouped into suborders), with 21 or more extant genera.

Melosira Agardh, 1824 (Plate XIII, Fig. 186), is a very common and widely distributed, filamentous genus, occurring in the plankton, sometimes in great abundance. The cells are round in end (valve) view, and appear cylindrical or capsule-shaped as seen in girdle view. The capsules are attached end to end, being adjoined in some species by spines at the polar margins of the valves. The valves show concentrically arranged pits and, according to species, there are prominent or obscure rows of pits on the girdle (complete or incomplete). There are many disc-like choloroplasts.

Stephanodiscus Ehrenberg, 1845 (Plate XIII, Fig. 187), has drum-shaped cells, circular in valve view, rectangular in girdle view. The valves have radiating (uniseriate and multiseriate) rows of puncta, alternating with clear, undecorated linear areas, forming a pattern like wheel spokes. Just within the margin of the valve is a circle of rather prominent spines, these located at the terminus of each of the clear sectors. The chloroplasts are either few and large, or many and small. *Stephanodiscus* is a common euplankter in mostly hard-water lakes and streams (Hudson River, e.g.).

Biddulphia Gray, 1832 (Plate XIII, Fig. 188), is a marine (rarely freshwater) genus, solitary or in chains, variable in shape but usually rectangular in outline (with processes at the corners), somewhat pillowshaped in girdle view, broadly oval and somewhat compressed in valve view. The wall is densely ornamented with aereolae. There are septa that extend in from the valves. At least one species of *Biddulphia* is oogamous.

Chaetoceros Ehrenberg, 1844 (Plate XIII, Fig. 189), has long, spinebearing, quadrangular cells in girdle view, oval in valve view. The spinelike horns appear to arise one from each corner of the four angles as seen in girdle view. The horns of one cell interlock with those of an adjoining cell so that long chains are formed. The walls are not ornamented, except possibly in the horns, which may be hollow or solid. They have practically no silicon, and are difficult to treat in diatom cleaning processes.

Class Pennales (Pennatobacillariophyceae)

In this order (with about 40 genera in 11 families) cells have one axis greatly elongated (with rare exceptions) and the ornamentation is bilaterally symmetrical. Cells are fusiform, needle-shaped, lunate, sigmoid, or slipper- and wedge-shaped. They may be symmetrical in valve view but asymmetrical in girdle view. There is either a pseudoraphe or a raphe usually in the median line of the valve. It may be in a canal in the margin of a keel, or otherwise to one side of the median line. The chloroplasts are usually two longitudinal bands, but other shapes occur.

Reproduction is by conjugation, motile gametes (microspores) being unknown. Whereas the Centrales are mostly marine, the Pennales are more common in fresh water and are both planktonic and benthic.

Tabellaria Ehrenberg, 1840 (Plate XIII, Fig. 190), is a planktonic genus in which the cells are arranged in zigzag chains, the cells adjoined at their corners. The cells are elongate with subparallel margins, but with an inflation in the mid-region, and with capitate swellings at the poles (valve view). There is a pseudoraphe bordered on each side by transverse rows of puncta extending to the margin of the valve. In girdle view the cells are rectangular. There are several intercalary bands between the girdles. In girdle view the cells are rectangular.

Within the cell are septa which extend from between the girdles and the intercalary bands toward the center of the cell. There are numerous disc-like chloroplasts. *Tabellaria* is well-known in the euplankton of hard-water lakes and plays a role in the building of slime covers which interfere with the efficient operation of sand water-filters.

Fragilaria Lyngbye, **Asterionella** Hassall (Plate XIII, Fig. 191), **Pinnularia** (Plate XIII, Fig. 192), and **Meridion** Agardh, are other genera which also are abundant in plankton. The Naviculaceae constitutes the largest family in numbers of genera and species of all the diatoms. **Navicula** Bory (Plate XIII, Fig. 194) is a very common boat-shaped or fusiform diatom with a distinct raphe. Some species have capitate poles as seen in valve view. **Cymbella** Agardh has lunate cells often found attached by gelatinous stalks to filamentous algae. **Surirella** Turpin is a boat-shaped or wedge-shaped twisted cell in which there is a keel along each lateral margin of the valve, and from this coastae extend inward toward a pseudoraphe.

Campylodiscus Ehrenberg is curiously shaped, circular in valve view but strongly bent and saddle-shaped when seen from the side (Plate XIII, Fig. 194). There is a marginal raphe and in the mid-region of each valve an indistinct pseudoraphe, the two pseudoraphes lying at right angles to each other.

Economics

Both living and as fossils (diatomaceous earth) diatoms have many important economic relationships. These are outlined in Chapter 10.

Chapter 5

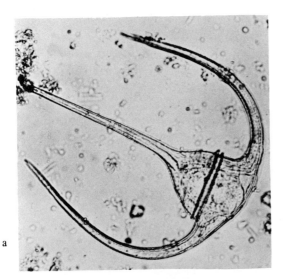

a. *Dinoflagellate Ceratium. (Walter Dawn); b. Euglena. (Robert Hoshaw)*

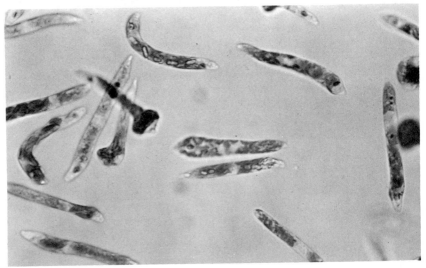

Flagellated Phyla

Algal phyla which are predominantly flagellated are the Euglenophyta, Pyrrhophyta, and Cryptophyta. These are protozoan-like organisms in many respects and include scarcely any strictly algal types. The algal forms which do occur are significant, therefore, in lending support to the concept that respective phyla have a flagellate ancestry. Except for the Cyanophyta and the Rhodophyta, in which motile cells (vegetative or reproductive) are unknown, all algal divisions show evidences of such an ancestry. It is possible, of course, that the blue-green and red algae may have had motile forms in their ancestry; if so, evidence to that effect no longer exists.

The phyla noted here can be considered as groups which have not evolved strictly algal morphologies. In the Pyrrhophyta, however, there are a few filamentous genera, and the occurrence of palmelloid conditions in the life history of many flagellates are suggestive of algal affinities. Practically all genera in the above-mentioned phyla lack sexual reproduction, cell division and cyst-formation being the predominant methods.

Phylum Euglenophyta

The euglenoids are green (rarely colorless), solitary unicells, although one order (Colaciales) includes a pseudocolonial genus Colacium. These swimming cells inhabit fresh water almost entirely, though a few are found in brackish or marine situations.

Euglenoids are cylindrical or fusiform, flattened or round in cross section. One genus especially (Phacus) has flattened, disc-like cells which, however, are sometimes somewhat triangular in cross section because of a longitudinal flange. In Trachelomonas and Strombomonas cells are enclosed by a shell or lorica which has an aperture through which the single flagellum extends. The flagella in other genera vary from one to eight.

(Usually when there is one prominent flagellum there is also a secondary vestigial or rudimentary one which in some instances seems to serve as a "rudder.") In *Euglena*, for example, the flagellum is forked near the base (or two strands join and then extend as one; cf. Plate XIII, Fig. 195). One fork is thought to represent a vestigial, second flagellum. The flagellum arises from a granule at the base of an apical reservoir, and in the genus *Peranema* (colorless) it is enclosed by pharyngeal rods (supporting bodies). The euglenoid flagellum, often acronematic, is somewhat ribbon-like and flattened and does not taper anteriorly, as shown by electron microscope studies of *Euglena*. There is a central core that extends from the granule to the tip. In *Peranema* fibrils have been described as radiating basally from the core, producing a brush effect. The pleuronematic flagella in the Euglenophyta have the usual 2 plus 9 arrangement of fibrils in the core. The sheath of the flagellum is an extension of the plasma membrane.

There is no true cell wall; instead, the outer membrane of the cytoplasm is modified to form a periplast (*pellicle*). This is either firm (rigid) or plastic, so that some forms are said to be metabolic (changing shape while in motion as in some species of *Euglena*). The periplast is often spirally striated, punctate, or granulate. In some forms the membrane, rather than being homogeneous, is a complicated series of telescopic cups or rings, one fitting within another to build the complete envelope, with the layers interconnected by thin membranes.

Pigments include chlorophyll-a and -b (the only other phylum which has the same chlorophylls as the Chlorophyta), B-carotene, antheroxanthin, astaxanthin, and neoxanthin (the latter in several genera but not all). The pigments are contained mostly in oval plates or discs (sometimes star-shaped or ribbon-like), whereas in some species the chloroplast is diffused and not definitely organized. There are pyrenoids (*Euglena*, e.g.) either in the cytoplasm or on the face of the chloroplasts. Some families are colorless but otherwise have a euglenoid cytology. Such colorless genera as *Astasia* and *Hyalophacus* contain species which are identical with certain *Euglena* and *Phacus*. As a result of metaboly food reserve collects in the form of a solid carbohydrate, paramylum. This forms grains or discs differently shaped according to genus and species; thus, there are large rods, small, bacilliform particles, or circular plates. Although starch-like, paramylum is iodine-negative.

In most genera there is a pigment-spot composed of granules. Fibrils connect this organelle with a photo-receptor, a granule near the base of the flagellum. Also a fibril extends from the flagellar granule (blepharoplast) to the centriole near the nucleus. Thus an incipient nervous system is established (cf. Text Figure 1.1).

Order Euglenales

FAMILY EUGLENACEAE

The majority of the euglenoids are included in this family. Most have chloroplasts but there are a few colorless genera; almost all genera have pigment-spots. Flagella vary in number from one to three, and can be either acronematic or pleuronematic. Whereas most are free-living some are attached, and one genus (*Euglenomorpha*) occurs in the digestive tracts of frogs. Flagella are as described for the phylum, bifurcate at the base, with a basal granule and a photoreceptor (see Text Figure 1.1).

Euglena Ehrenberg, 1838 (Plate XIII, Fig. 195), a protozoan-like genus, has numerous species. The cells are mostly fusiform but a few are strap-shaped, sometimes twisted, and many species have a pointed caudus. A few are colorless but most have disc-like or band-shaped chloroplasts (sometimes diffuse). Strains of *Euglena gracilis* have been rendered permanently colorless by exposure to streptomycin.

The pyrenoids are free in the cytoplasm or attached to the chloroplasts. Paramylum bodies are rod-shaped, and either few and large or numerous and small. The flagellum has the bifurcate base, as previously described. The pigment-spot, photo-receptor, and neuromotor apparatus are as described for the phylum. The absorption spectrum of the pigment-spot has been shown to be identical with that which induces movement as a phototactic response in organisms which do not have this organelle. It is known that movement in different species is stimulated by different light intensities. Wolken and Shin (1958) found that the greatest speed in *Euglena* movements occurred when the light intensity was at 40 foot-candles. The rhythmic movement of *Euglena* was interestingly demonstrated by a laboratory experiment with *E. deses* in England. The species, together with mud from the Thames River in which it lived, was taken into the laboratory. The cells crept into the mud and buried themselves at the time when high tide regularly occurred, and reappeared at the surface again at times of low tide.

Cells divide longitudinally after first being enclosed by a gelatinous matrix. In response to environmental changes the organisms can encyst, using a thick, lamellated wall. In this condition many species multiply and form secondary cysts. These germinate by throwing off a cap of wall material and then metamorphosing into a motile cell. At times, cells become motionless prior to dividing, and then divide repeatedly. As such, some species tend to form palmelloid growths which constitute practically the only other morphological expression of motile euglenoids.

In some habitats (the Arctic, e.g.) some *Euglena* maintain an encysted condition for indefinite periods and as yet these have not been found emerging and swimming. Sexual reproduction by conjugation has been reported, although with some question. As far as is known for certainty only vegetative multiplication occurs in the Euglenophyta (see *Phacus* below, however).

Euglena occurs as solitary cells in the tychoplankton or (with some species) as a dense growth that forms a powdery film over the surface of ponds and slowly flowing rivers. At times a pond may become blood- or brick-red when *Euglena* becomes colored with haematochrome carotenoids. This pigment seems to be formed in response to intense light. *Euglena sanguinea* is permanently blood-red but does not occur in dense growths. Many species are abundant in sewage oxidation ponds, where they play an active role. Here they survive well partly because of their ability to metabolize in anaerobic conditions. A few species are known from sandy marine beaches.

Euglena has come to be highly useful in research as an indicator in biological assays such as for vitamin B_{12}. Otherwise the genus is much used in algal culture experiments, both physiological and cytological. *Euglena* is of special interest for investigators of metabolism in darkness, wherein polysaccharides are used in the medium.

Protoeuglena Subrahmanyan, 1954 (Plate XIV, Fig. 196), is a pyriform endophyte of the marine dinoflagellate *Noctiluca*. The relatively short, broad (in the anterior end) cells are slightly flattened dorsiventrally. Although there is no euglenoid type of gullet there is an apical depression from which a long, stout flagellum arises. There is a pigment-spot that involves two rods, a lateral, plate-like chloroplast, and an ellipsoid paramylum body. The periplast is smooth. Cell division is the only reported method of reproduction. The organisms sometimes form a densely green zone at the anterior end of the host cell; at other times they swarm through the large dinoflagellate. *Noctiluca* forms a discoloration of sea-water near the west coast of India.

Phacus Dujardin, 1841 (Plate XIV, Fig. 197), is characterized by cells which are broadly oval or nearly circular in front and flattened in side view. In many there is a prominent, longitudinal flange or fold so that in end view such cells are three-lobed. Posteriorly the cells may be slightly twisted and in most species there is either a long and straight or short and curved tail piece. The periplast is rigid and longitudinally striated. Cytologically the cells are quite similar to *Euglena*, but the paramylum collects in the form of large, circular discs. Commonly there is only one disc which may occupy almost the entire diameter of the cell.

In at least one species an unusual fusion of daughter nuclei occurs within a cell, and this is followed by meiotic division to form four nuclei. Around these are organized the same amount of new cells.

Phacus occurs as solitary cells in the tychoplankton, especially in water rich in organic matter.

Trachelomonas Ehrenberg, 1833 (Plate XIV, Fig. 198), can be found scattered in the tychoplankton of ponds, lagoons, and ditches. Essentially, the hundreds of species of this genus are small, metabolic euglenoids in a shell or lorica which assumes all manner of shapes and patterns of ornamentation — puncta, granules, spines, and warts. The lorica, round, oval, or fusiform, is brown because of iron impregnation. Similarly shaped cells without iron in a thin lorica (yellowish or colorless) are placed in the genus *Strombomonas*. The flagellum opening may be surrounded by a neck, collar, or spines. Sometimes it is at the end of a long or short neck, whereas in a few species the collar extends inwardly. Posteriorly the lorica is rounded or tapered into a sharp tail piece. The cytology in general is similar to that of *Euglena*.

After division of the protoplast one of the flagellated daughter cells escapes and forms a new lorica. Occasionally akinete-like spores are produced but nothing is known of any form of sexual reproduction.

Other Families

The Astasiaceae and Peranemaceae are composed of euglenoid flagellates which are colorless and which have different flagellar morphology.

Order Colaciales

Family Colaciaceae

Colacium Ehrenberg, 1833 (Plate XIV, Fig. 199), is a small genus of uniflagellate euglenoids which become attached by a gelatinous stalk, anterior end downward, to microfauna. Following cell division (longitudinal), the daughter cell also forms a stalk. Through repetition branched colonies are eventually formed. Copepods and insect larvae are often found swimming about with plumes of *Colacium* growing from their heads and antennae. This genus should be compared with the chlorophyte *Chlorangium* which grows as an epizoophyte also.

Phylum Pyrrhophyta

These bizarre biflagellate forms abound in the oceans, where they have occurred for millions of years, although a few genera occur in fresh water. At times veritable blooms develop in the sea, such as those which produce the well known Red Tide. At least one species (*Ceratium hirundinella*) in fresh water also forms growths that color water — in this case, a grayish-brown. Almost all species are solitary motile cells, but a few form colonies (cf. the marine species *Polykrikos*). In fresh water there are drifting or sedentary cyst-like forms (e.g., **Raciborskia, Tetradinium;** Plate XIV, Figs. 208 and 209). A few, oddly, are parasitic on fish, and a palmelloid type is seen in *Urococcus*. Some genera are filamentous (*Dinothrix, Dinoclonium;* Plate XIV, Figs. 210 and 211), and are quite algal-like in habit. A rhizopodial tendency is exhibited in a few forms (*Dinamoebidium*, for example). Many marine genera (and species) show a marked distribution — tropical, arctic and antarctic, and temperate — but in general dinoflagellates are perhaps more abundant in number of species in tropical and subtropical waters.

One of the chief characteristics of the phylum is the flagella which, in almost all instances, are attached laterally in the ventral region where the longitudinal sulcus is intersected by the transverse furrow. They arise from blepharoplasts and project through pores in the wall, being regulated by a neuromotor system similar to that found in the euglenoids. The two flagella are different in morphology and in position. One is pleuronematic and band-like and lies within the transverse furrow where, by vibrations, it spins the cell on its axis. The mastigonemes are unilateral, referred to as a stichoneme flagellum. The other flagellum (acronematic?) is simple and trails, pushing the organism forward, although it is possible that the transverse flagellum assists.

In one family, Prorocentraceae, the flagella, apical and flattened, are both extended forward, for in this family there is no transverse nor longitudinal groove.

In the mid-region of the cell, near the flagellar attachment, are two (or more) sac-like vacuoles, the *pulsules*. Each is connected by a canal to the flagellar opening in the cell wall. The pulsules function as intake organelles. Chloroplasts, usually numerous, are disc-like or band-shaped and parietal, but often are radially disposed. The chloroplasts have a double membrane, at least in the genera studied electronically, which extends the entire length of the body. Each of these lamellations has three discs or thylakoids. Pyrenoids are seldom present but some genera have several in each chloroplast.

Pigments include chlorophyll-a and -c, diadinoxanthin, dinoxanthin, B-carotene, and peridinin, although the latter is not present in all genera.

In general, cells are golden-brown but some are blue, and a few marine genera are chlorophylless but have various pigments in solution. As a result, there is holophytic and holozoic nutrition and some saprophytism. Food reserves occur as both oil and starch. Some forms are parasitic.

Many genera have a very large pigment-spot (eye-spot). The nucleus (which is relatively large) is unique in having chromatin in bead-like chains during the resting stage. There may be as many as 284 chromosomes (*Ceratium*). The chromatin lacks histine protein ordinarily occurring in nuclear material. Mitrochondria are present and are known to contain DNA in some forms. Near the vacuoles Golgi bodies have been demonstrated. In many genera trichocysts occur. These have a rod with a slender extension to the cell membrane, suggesting thereby a relationship with the Cryptophyceae (Cryptophyta).

The wall contains mostly cellulose. In one class (Dinophyceae) the majority have the wall (theca) in two sections which are adjoined transversely in the mid-region. The anterior (upper) section of the wall is known as the *epitheca*, the posterior the *hypotheca*, the halves of the cell being called the *epicone* and *hypocone*, respectively.

One section of the class Dinophyceae has naked cells (*Gymnodinium*) which are covered by a smooth, outer cytoplasmic membrane. Electron microscopy may yet reveal that such forms actually have a theca. In another larger group (the thecate dinoflagellates) there is a thin or thick cellulose wall which is composed of closely fitting plates. In many there are definite sutures between the plates. The number and arrangement of the plates in the epitheca and hypotheca are of taxonomic importance. The plates (see Plate XIV, Fig. 204) are named as follows:

In the epitheca:
  apical
  intercalary (below the apicals)
  precingulars (the plates lying next to the transverse girdle)
In the hypotheca:
  postcingulars (lying just below the transverse girdle)
  intercalary
  antapical (at the posterior pole).

Reproduction is mostly by cell division longitudinally, sometimes while the organism is still swimming. Cleavage lines develop along the lines of plate junctures and follow a definite pattern. This results in very irregularly shaped daughter cells which, by constructing missing plates, form the required number to complete the adult cell. Commonly cysts are formed within the cell wall, these either taking the general shape of the parent cell or not. Cysts are especially common in dinoflagellate fossil deposits.

The coccoid and filamentous genera produce dinoflagellate-like zoospores (with two lateral flagella). These are without a wall, formed two to eight in a cell. In rare instances isogametes are formed in coccoid genera and sexual reproduction has been reported for *Ceratium* and *Gymnodinium*. It is reported that the zygote nucleus divides by meiosis but considerable uncertainty clouds information on this phase of dinoflagellate biology.

In the oceans dinoflagellates occur in astronomical numbers and along with diatoms constitute the "pasturage of the sea." Some genera, such as **Noctiluca** (Plate XIV, Fig. 200) and *Gonyaulax*, contain luminescent species, and because of their large numbers cause "phosphorescent" light when disturbed by wave or boat action. The luminescence has peaks of intensity about every 23 hours in an individual organism. The light is caused by oxidation of luciferin which involves the operation of the enzyme luciferase.

Gymnodinium brevis and other species produce sufficient toxins when they occur in bloom (Red Tide) to poison fish in large numbers. *Gonyaulax catenella*, *G. moniliata*, and *G. polyedra* or *G. Tamarensis*, when consumed by shellfish, are responsible for poisoning of human beings (see p. 364).

Dinoflagellates are tychoplanktonic or euplanktonic, an existence for which many are adjusted by having wings or horns. Marine species have been shown to exhibit diurnal migration of a phototactic nature.

Yellow snow includes a number of organisms, among them one dinoflagellate. Some species develop abundantly in the psammon and others have adopted a bizarre existence as parasites on fish and on the tentacles of coelenterates. An unnamed dinoflagellate has been found in *Cassiopeia* and the anemone *Condyleatis*, where it evidently plays an important role in the biology of the hosts. This same flagellate apparently lives in corals as well.

As fossils, dinoflagellata occur in abundance in Tertiary deposits, appearing in many parts of the world, but particularly in Australia and New Zealand findings. Some of the fossil genera are identifiable with extant forms.

The classification of the Pyrrhophyta is continually in a state of flux. Some of the complexities are due to the fact that both zoologists and botanists have constructed classification schemes, and different criteria have been used to group and to separate the numerous species and genera. Conventionally, there are two classes, Desmokontae and Dinokontae. The former lack a transverse furrow, whereas the latter have a wall in two sections (as previously described) and a transverse groove. The Desmokontae with three orders and about 13 genera have apical flagella, whereas the Dinokontae, with four orders and 46 genera (the dinoflagellates proper), have lateral flagella.

Class Desmokontae: Order Desmomonadales

FAMILY PROROCENTRACEAE

Prorocentrum Ehrenberg, 1833 (Plate XIV, Fig. 201), is characterized by cells which are flattened as seen from the side, but oval with a posterior, caudal spine as seen from the "front." The membrane is bivalved. There is a prominent tooth-like spine at the anterior end near the base of the apical flagella. The latter are of two kinds, simple and pleuronematic. The pleuronematic is directed and vibrates laterally. *Prorocentrum* is a luminescent, marine genus and one closely allied with *Exuviella*, together occurring on beach sand as well as in brackish water.

Class Dinokontae: Sub-Class Dinophyceae: Order Gymnodiniales

FAMILY GYMNODINIACEAE

Gymnodinium Stein, 1833 (Plate XIV, Fig. 203), is, as the name implies, representative of an order in which cells have no walls. The cells, which are broadly oval with the epicone somewhat narrowed anteriorly, have a transverse furrow and a short longitudinal sulcus. The flagella are both simple and pleuronematic. It is claimed that the apex of the transverse flagellum is anchored by penetrating the cell. Chloroplasts are numerous and usually golden-brown, oval discs. A few species are colorless. Many kinds occur in fresh water but most of them are marine. Several species are known to produce a lethal toxin and are the causative organism in the death of fish (Red Tide) which occurs periodically along continental shelves. It has been demonstrated that G. *splendens* (and probably others) require vitamin B_{12}. **Amphidinium** Clap. et Lach. has naked cells in which the hypocone is distinctly larger than the epicone (Plate XIV, Fig. 202).

Order Peridiniales

FAMILY PERIDINIACEAE

Peridinium Ehrenberg, 1830, emend. Stein, 1833 (Plate XIV, Fig. 204), is representative of the thecate dinoflagellates, in which the plates of the thick wall are very conspicuous and separated by sutures. The sutures usually show a fine reticulum of thickenings and areolae. These zones of plate juncture (sutures) are referred to as striated girdle bands. The plates are laid down over a thin cell membrane in which the position and shape of the plates are first marked out.

The cells are top-shaped, oval, or almost round in "front" view and only a little, if at all, compressed dorsiventrally. Sometimes there are small spines and flanges on the cells. The longitudinal sulcus extends far into the hypotheca, which has two antapical plates and five post-cingulars. The epitheca has from three to five apical plates, a varying number of intercalary plates (sometimes none), and six or seven precingular plates. There is an undetermined number of closely fitting, indistinct, small plates in the transverse girdle and the longitudinal sulcus.

Most species have a pigment-spot and yellowish chloroplasts. Reproduction is by cell division and by aplanospores that divide and form a colony of stationary cells from which the motile stages metamorphose.

Most species are marine but there are about 25 fresh-water forms, occurring in both basic and acid habitats.

Family Ceratiaceae

Ceratium Schrank, 1793 (Plate XIV, Fig. 205), contains many species which are distinct because of their prominent straight or curved horns. In the common fresh-water species, C. *hirundinella*, there is one long anterior horn composed of four apical plates, and three (or two) posterior horns, all of different lengths. There is a definite relation between horn length and the level of flotation. There are four precingular plates, whereas there are five postcingulars and two antapicals. The plates all bear a coarse reticulum of thickenings. In the longitudinal furrow there is a large, ventral plate between the post- and precingulars. Cell division takes place by a cleavage between the plates, more or less following a longitudinal plane. One daughter cell receives all of the apical plates, two precingular plates, and three of the postcingulars. The other half inherits the antapical plates, two of the postcingulars, and two of the precingulars from the epitheca. Oddly, this division can take place while the cells are swimming about.

Besides cell division *Ceratium* is known to conjugate, wherein two cells come into juxtaposition (as in the diatoms). A gelatinous tube interconnects the cells, and the protoplasts from each cell migrate into this and fuse. There is some question as to how widespread or how correctly this process has been described, as well as to what the fate is of the zygote.

PLATE XIV

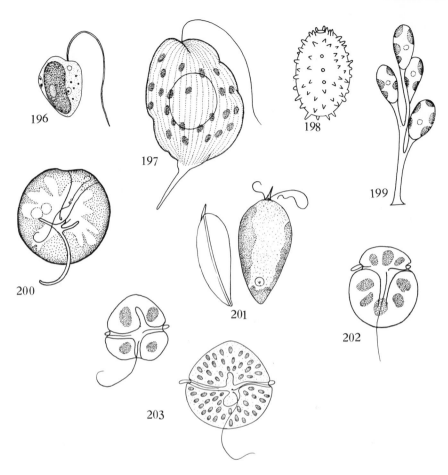

Fig. 196. **Protoeuglena noctilucae** (redrawn from Subrahmanyan)

Fig. 197. **Phacus** sp

Fig. 198. **Trachelomonas** sp

Fig. 199. **Colacium calvum,** colony on copepod antenna

Fig. 200. **Noctiluca** sp

Fig. 201. **Prorocentrum** sp "front" and side view

Fig. 202. **Amphidinium amphidinioides**

Fig. 203. **Gymnodinium** spp

PLATE.XIV

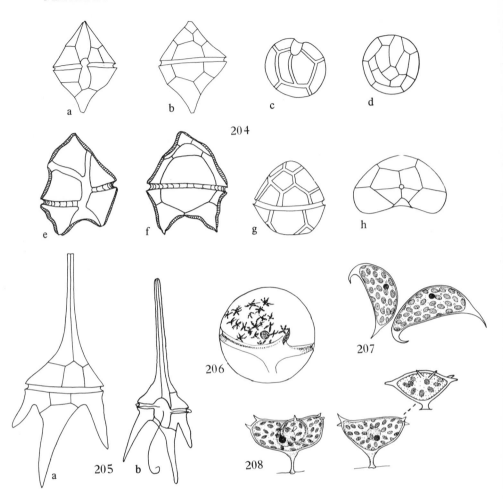

Fig. 204. **Peridinium:** a, **P. limbatum,** ventral view; b, **P. limbatum** dorsal view; c, **P. wisconsinense,** antapical view; d, apical view; e, ventral view of another species; f, dorsal view (redrawn from Lindeman); g, **P. anglicum,** dorsal view; h, apical view

Fig. 205. **Ceratium hirundinella:** a, dorsal view; b, ventral view

Fig. 206. **Hypnodinium sphaericum** (redrawn and redesigned in part from Thompson)

Fig. 207. **Cystodinium iners**

Fig. 208. **Tetradinium javanicum,** three views

PLATE XIV

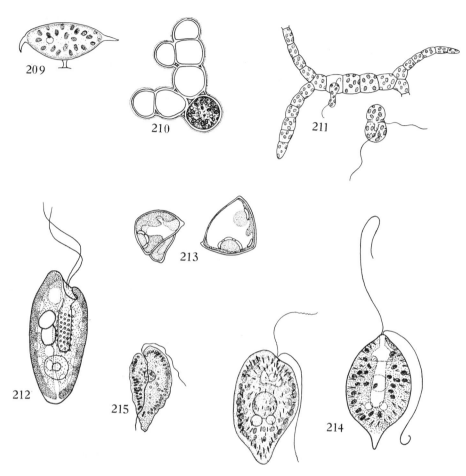

Fig. 209. **Raciborskia bicornis**

Fig. 210. **Dinothrix paradoxa** (redrawn from Pascher)

Fig. 211. **Dinoclonium Conradi,** and zoospore (redrawn from Pascher)

Fig. 212. **Cryptomonas splendida** (redrawn from Javornicky)

Fig. 213. **Tetragonidium verrucatum** (redrawn from Pascher)

Fig. 214. **Gonyostomum semen** and one other species

Fig. 215. **Hornellia marina** (redrawn from Subrahmanyan)

Order Dinococcales

These are cyst-like cells, marine or fresh-water, with thin cellulose walls, attached or free-floating. The cells are various in shape: globular, lunate, pyramidate. Attached forms have a gelatinous stalk and an adhesive disc. There are numerous brown or chocolate-brown chloroplasts. Reproduction occurs only by internal division to form dinoflagellate type of zoospores. Hence the order is comparable to the Chlorococcales of the Chlorophyta.

Hypnodinium Klebs, 1912 (Plate XIV, Fig. 206), is a large, spherical cell in which the spindle-shaped chloroplasts are arranged in numerous rosettes. The protoplast within the thin wall has a transverse and a longitudinal invagination, but no flagella occur. Reproduction takes place by the formation of two (or four?) autospores. As far as known, fusion of gametes has been observed but once.

Cystodinium Klebs, 1912 (Plate XIV, Fig. 207), is characterized by cells which are crescent-shaped and free-floating, the apices tapering to a sharp point. Species occur frequently in *Sphagnum* bogs.

Raciborskia Woloszynska, 1919 (Plate XIV, Fig. 209), are mostly transversely oval cells, round in cross section, with a sharp, curved spine at either pole. The cells are attached by a short, thick stalk to filamentous algae in fresh water.

Order Dinotrichales

This order is comparable to the Chaetophorales of the Chlorophyta. The plants (marine) are creeping filaments without basal-distal differentiation. Cells are more or less cylindrical with two-layered walls, the inner being of cellulose. There are numerous brown chloroplasts. Stored food is oil and starch. Upon division the cells form dinoflagellate-appearing protoplasts which have a pigment-spot and a transverse furrow. The new cells so formed by division can become part of the filament or escape as biflagellate zoospores.

Dinothrix Pascher, 1927 (Plate XIV, Fig. 210), has a prostrate filament with erect branches that taper slightly toward either apex. The plants occur on marine algae, reproducing by *Gymnodinium*-like zoospores formed singly in a cell.

Phylum Cryptophyta (Cryptophyceae)

This small phylum is sometimes regarded as being related to the Pyrrhophyta or is simply identified as a class of organisms of uncertain position. A place with the former seems reasonable because both groups contain chlorophyll-c and both accumulate starch as food reserve. But they vary from the dinoflagellates in the nature of carotene and xanthophyll pigments. The components of the Cryptophyta have a number of characteristics in common and together present some features which render them distinct from any other group of organisms. Hence, for consistency, a phylum status seems appropriate (at least tentatively).

Cryptophytes occur in both fresh and salt water as flagellated, palmelloid, or coccoid forms, but filamentous and strictly algal (plant-like) expressions are lacking. Whereas a few genera are colorless, in general the cells are variously pigmented: yellow, blue, or olive. The chloroplast pigments are a-carotene, c-carotene, zeaxanthin, phycocyanin-c, phycoerythrin-x, chlorophyll-a and -c, diadinoxanthin, dinoxanthin, and possibly other phycobilin red pigments. The red and blue pigments appear to be bilichromoproteins which are similar to those of the Rhodophyta and Cyanophyta. According to some observations, the chloroplasts have three or four pairs of lamellae, whereas some reports indicate that the bands have but two lamellae.

Reserve food is starch which forms a sheath around the pyrenoids. In the colorless *Chilomonas* there are trichocysts of two kinds, one long with a granular tip, and one short and needle-like with a minute grain apically. The trichocysts can be demonstrated by treatment with osmic acid.

Reproduction in the phylum is only by cell division and by multiplication in palmelloid stages.

Order Cryptomonadales

In this order are included the free-swimming, oval, or slipper-shaped cells, some of which have a cellulose membrane, whereas others are naked. There are two subapical flagella of unequal length arising from an anterior notch or depression. In the genus *Cryptomonas* at least one flagellum is pleuronematic. Chloroplasts are either several small, blue-green bodies, or one or two parietal plates. Of the three families comprising the order, the most frequently seen are members of the Cryptomonadaceae.

FAMILY CRYPTOMONADACEAE

Cryptomonas Ehrenberg, 1831 (Plate XIV, Fig. 212), is an oval cell with two pleuronematic (?) flagella which are subapical in attachment in an anterior gullet. There is a contractile vacuole near the gullet. The cells which have a gullet have been described as having trichocysts lining the cavity, these throwing off fine threads upon stimulation. The chloroplasts are yellowish, yellow-green, or reddish-brown longitudinal plates.

The only method of reproduction is by cell division after the individual has become enclosed by mucilage, or by multiplication in a palmelloid state. These organisms are found mostly in ditch- and swamp-water, especially if enriched with organic matter.

Order Cryptococcales

This order includes the non-motile members which have a cellulose wall. Reproduction is by the internal division of the protoplast to form zoospores that have unequal flagella.

FAMILY CRYPTOCOCCACEAE

Tetragonidium Pascher, 1914 (Plate XIV, Fig. 213), is a pyramidal or tetragonal cell with a folded or lobed, parietal, yellow-brown chloroplast in which there is a pyrenoid. The zoospores metamorphose to form the tetragonal vegetative cell. Associated in this phylum are the organisms referred to as Zooxanthella. These are oval or spherical yellow-green cells which live endozoically with many kinds of marine invertebrates. The cells form motile swarmers in reproduction. Studies show that there is a mutualism involved but also parasitism on the part of the animal.

Phylum Chloromonadophyta[1]

Like the Cryptophyta, this is a small order in number of genera (and of individuals) but one in which there are unique characteristics which prevent a reasonable classification of them with other recognized phyla. All members are motile, the flagella apical or subapical. It has been suggested that the group be classed with the Xanthophyceae in a major category called the Xanthophyta. Most members are fresh-water, but at least one genus (Hornellia, Plate XIV, Fig. 215) is marine.

Cells are oval to circular, and either dorsiventrally flattened or round in end view. The pellicle is thin, and there is no cellulose wall. From the anterior end there is a longitudinal furrow which in some forms (Gonyostomum) is broader toward the posterior pole. There are both colorless (Rickertia) and pigmented genera, the latter having numerous, disc-like

[1] Suggested category name, without description and diagnosis.

chloroplasts with chlorophyll predominating so that cells are shining green. Pyrenoids are wanting as far as is known at present. Further, pigments have not been completely analyzed, but it is known that they include hydroxylated lutein epoxide, lutein monoepoxide, antheraxanthin, β-carotene, and several other xanthophylls. In general the pigmentation is somewhat similar to the Xanthophyceae. Food accumulation is in the form of fatty substances or oil.

An oddity in the cytology of the chloromonads is the presence of trichocysts located just within the cell membrane, radially disposed, or in some forms occurring throughout the cell. In the rare genus *Merotrichia* the trichocysts are clustered near the anterior end. These trichocysts throw out mucilaginous stinging threads upon stimulation (physical or chemical). In the anterior end of some members is a triangular gullet (and two contractile vacuoles) and here the flagella are attached. The flagella are heterokont, the forward-directed one being pleuronematic and the backward one simple. The flagella are part of the same type of neuromotor apparatus found in the euglenoids. Reproduction is by cell division and (in some) by conjugation.

Gonyostomum Diesing, 1865 (Plate XIV, Fig. 214), is widely distributed, but rarely found, and there are but few known species. Cells are mostly flattened and pyriform, larger at the anterior end, and somewhat resembling a green hot-water bottle. The flagella are smooth, very long (although one flagellum is shorter) and are highly active. Reproduction is by cell division and through encysted stages. The most common species, *G. semen*, is found in bog water and in the tychoplankton of ponds.

Hornellia Subrahmanyan, 1954 (Plate XIV, Fig. 215), is the cause of infrequent green blooms on India's west coast, where it causes death of fish and crustacea. The cells are pyriform and very similar in shape and cytology to *Gonyostomum*. Two flagella arise from an apical gullet. The periplast is punctate (possibly related to the extrusion of threads from the trichocysts). Chloroplasts are numerous, bright green discs. Reproduction is by cell division, and by conjugation of two individuals from which a zygote is formed. Apparently germination of the zygote has not been observed.

Chapter 6

Fucus, or Rock Weed: habit of a portion of the thallus, and reproductive structures. (Walter Dawn)

Phylum Phaeophyta

Translated, the name of this phylum means swarthy plants, appropriate because the majority of the brown algae are darkly colored, chocolate- or olive-brown. Whereas some are branched filaments and are microscopic, the majority are parenchymatous thalli that are large, tough, leathery or rubbery. None are unicellular. Plants may be from a few inches to several hundred feet in length. Especially in the brown algae known as *kelps* there is a great specialization of cells (if not tissues) and these algae are more complex than any other phyla. Like the Rhodophyta, however, the architectural unit of the complex thallus is a branched filament.

The brown algae, comprised of at least 240 genera, all occur in the oceans where they obviously had their evolution, except for a few microscopic genera of questionable affinity which live in fresh water (*Pleurocladia, Heribaudiella,* and *Bodanella*). A few species are equally well-adjusted to brackish water. The Phaeophyta achieve their greatest development in the colder waters of northern latitudes, although a few genera occur in luxuriant growths around the southern tips of Africa, South America, Australia, and Tasmania.

General Characteristics

The pigments of the Phaeophyta include chlorophyll-a and -c, B- and c-carotene, flavoxanthin, fucoxanthin ($C_{40}H_{54}O_6$, which is abundant), lutein, and violaxanthin. The chloroplasts containing these pigments are either disc- or band-shaped (rarely stellate). The electron microscope has shown that there are three lamellae pairs with lipid globules between the sets of bands. True pyrenoids seem to be lacking. Ordinarily brown algal cells are uninucleate.

In addition to the leathery, rubbery texture and their pigments, other general characteristics of the Phaeophyta include a peculiar type of food storage. This is in the form of soluble carbohydrates such as the alcohol mannitol, laminarin (up to 35% of the dry weight), which appears during the later periods of plant development, and, rarely, some fats. Fucosan, possibly a waste product, also has been reported, and is included in small vesicles. There are also proteins and, more peculiarly, iodoamino acid. Sterols occur as fucosterol.

Still another peculiarity is the morphology of the zoospore, which is reniform or pyriform, with two laterally attached flagella. One flagellum is pleuronematic, the other simple and of a different length. In some forms one flagellum is rudimentary. Another characteristic of the brown algae is the abundant mucilage either contained in the thallus or extruded. This mucilage plays a number of important roles in the biology, including water adsorption so that plants remain moist during exposure at low tide.

The cell wall is in two layers — the inner of cellulose, the outer of gelatinous and pectic material — and includes phycocolloids such as algin and fucoidin. In general there is a thin outer reticular layer and an inner layer which has parallel lamellae composed of cellulose. The fibril pattern is reticulate when cells are young but becomes parallel as the cells elongate. In some forms, such as *Dictyota*, pores occur. Walls in larger brown algae are extremely tough and resistant, and when dry some of the kelp thalli become hard and "woody." Unlike many red and green seaweeds walls are not calcified except in *Padina* (Dictyotales).

The architectural range includes uniaxial branched filaments, either erect and bushy or creeping on substrates, sometimes epiphytic or endophytic.

In the majority of thalloid (macroscopic, frond-like) brown algae the general construction includes a *hold-fast*, a long or short *stipe* (which must be very flexible), and an expanded *blade* (or blades). The blade is the primary photosynthetic and spore-producing portion of the plant (although all parts of the thallus may contain chloroplasts). The blades may be a simple homogeneous plate or ribbon, or may be perforated, ruffled, or equipped with longitudinal costae (*Costaria*).

The hold-fast (often of taxonomic importance) may consist of a number of fine, root-like structures (*Dictyota*) or larger, thick and knobby *haptera*, as in *Laminaria*. Not a few brown algae have special hook-like, rhizoidal branches for a hold-fast (*Chondria, Laurencia*).

Some filamentous forms are multiaxial. Using the filament as a unit, complex thalli are constructed. These may be tubular fronds, prostrate cushions, or fronds with root-like hold-fasts, stipes, and foliose blades. Some forms exhibit heterotrichy in which there is both a prostrate and an erect portion of the thallus. There are no motile forms nor unicellular species known, but it is thought likely that the Phaeophyta have flagellated cells in their ancestry. The ancestral forms are no longer extant, however, or, on the other hand, are not recognized as such.

Growth

Growth in these thalli occurs in a number of different ways but in general it is by an apical cell(s) or an apical meristem. Many have what is called *trichothallic growth*, where meristematic cells produce and add to apical hairs forward. The cells at the base of the hairs become modified to form thallus tissue, with differentiation into an epidermal *(meristoderm)* layer, a cortical layer *(cortex)* in which mucilage canals may occur, and an internal *medulla*. The latter contains special strengthening hyphae and, in the giant kelps (*Nereocystis*, e.g.), specialized sieve tubes. Pitted walls may occur also in cortical cells. In another type of growth there is a meristematic region at the base of a blade, or at the base of a stipe. In some plants there is an epidermal cambium whereas in the complex kelps there is an internal cambium within the stalk. In a few forms the external layer of cells is meristematic and provides for lateral growth. By dichotomy in the apical region thalli of the Phaeophyta are frequently dichotomously branched or forked. Hollow floats *(pneumatocysts)* occur in many *(Fucus, Ascophyllum, Macrocystis)*. Thalli in the brown algae are either annual or perennial, with many showing remarkable powers of regeneration after much of the frond may have deteriorated. Specimens of *Pterygophora*, for example, are known to live as long as 24 years.

Fragmentation is used universally in vegetative reproduction, and zoospores (pyriform, usually with an eye-spot) are commonly employed in a sexual reproduction. Spores are formed in specialized, differentiated cells *(sporangia)*. In *Sphacelaria*, for example, special, three-pronged, anchor-like branches *(propagula)* are abscissed to serve as vegetative reproductive elements. In sexual reproduction the Phaeophyta use isogamy, anisogamy, and heterogamy (oogamy). Gametes are produced in *gametangia* showing various degrees of specialization.

Reproduction and Life Histories

Life histories are as varied as the methods of reproduction. These will be outlined below in reference to representative genera. A preliminary summary:

1. An alternation of diploid and haploid generations which are morphologically similar (isomorphic alternation); isogametes or anisogametes. (**Ectocarpales, Sphacelariales;** there is a questionable variation of this cycle in **Hapterophycus** in the Ectocarpales.)
2. An alternation of similar generations (isomorphic), but with the production of heterogametes; egg and sperm (**Dictyotales**).
3. Alternation of morphologically dissimilar (heteromorphic) generation, in which the sporophyte is small, the gametophyte dominant, producing anisogametes (**Cutleriales**).
4. Alternation of generations morphologically dissimilar in which the sporophyte is dominant, the gametophyte recessive (small), producing isogametes (**Chordariales**).

5. Alternation of a dominant sporophyte (heteromorphic) and a minute gametophyte, producing egg and sperm (**Laminariales**).

6. No true alternation, but with a diploid sporophyte, producing heterospores by meiosis; spores metamorphosing directly to act as gametes (egg and sperm) (**Fucales**).

The sporophyte generation is annual or perennial whereas the gametophyte is annual only. The type of life history is in part the basis for grouping the Phaeophyta as follows: I, Isogeneratae; II, Heterogeneratae; III, Cyclosporeae (Fucales) (see Chart 6.1, p. 231).

In habit and distribution the Phaeophyta are predominantly inhabitors of rocky reefs and shores where they are firmly attached. Many are intertidal and sublittoral to a depth of 35 meters, and many are well-adjusted to the changing environment within the intertidal zone. A very few exist free, having begun as attached plants (e.g. *Sargassum*, Gulf Weed). Also a few species (*Fucus*, e.g.) can live unattached on muddy tide flats. There are benthic forests of brown algae as deep as 100 meters in clear waters of the subtropics.

There is a relatively definite vertical zonation of many forms in reference to water depth, light, and tide action (range of water levels). The Phaeophyta are world-wide in their distribution with a concentration of many genera in the North Pacific. The largest forms grow in coastal regions which are foggy and poorly illuminated much of the time.

Class Isogeneratae: Order Ectocarpales

FAMILY ECTOCARPACEAE

In this Order and Family the thallus is a branched filament or a frond (such as *Ralfsia*) composed of adjoined filaments. The plant is mostly a bushy, arbuscular growth, from a few to ten or 15 centimeters in length. Some genera are free-living, rarely endophytic, and even endozooic. Cell division is apical or intercalary. The organs of reproduction (sporangia or gametangia) are either terminal on the branches, or intercalary. Chloroplasts are variously in the form of discs, or ribbons. Cells are always uninucleate, with one or more chloroplasts.

The life history involves an alternation of isomorphic generations: The sporphyte produces spores by meiosis in a one-celled (unilocular) sporangium; the gametophyte (in most instances) produces iso- or anisogametes in a specialized, cone-shaped series of cells, a plurilocular gametangium. The zygote resulting from gametic union germinates directly to form a diploid sporophyte.

Ectocarpus Lyngbye, 1819 (Plate XV, Fig. 216), grows as a "hank" of yellow-brown hair, usually highly branched, on rocks, on other algae, on wharf pilings, etc. The upright, somewhat tapering filaments arise from a prostrate thallus and occasionally the lower cells of the main axial filament bear rhizoidal branches which assist in anchorage.

On sporophytes terminal cells of short, lateral branches enlarge and become unilocular zoosporangia. Here, by meiosis, the nucleus divides repeatedly to form 32 or 64 nuclei around which biflagellate, reniform zoospores are produced. The zoospores escape all at one time in a utricle which then bursts to allow the zoospores to swim freely and to germinate into gametophytes.

On the latter, terminal cells enlarge slightly and then undergo repeated and successive transverse and longitudinal divisions to form rectilinear series of small, cubical cells — plurilocular gametangia. Within each cell a motile element or gamete is produced. In some species the colonial gametangial branch opens by a terminal pore through which the gametes escape, either in clusters or singly. Gametes are either iso- or aniso-, one of the fusing pair being larger or more slowly moving than the other. Gametic union forms a zygote that develops directly into a diploid plant. In some species plurilocular organs may be formed on the same plant as are the unilocular sporangia. The motile elements from the plurilocular are formed without reduction and give rise to diploid sporophytes, thus repeating and multiplying the sporophyte generation. In all, it appears that such a plant as *Ectocarpus* illustrates the incomplete dissociation of zoosporic and gametic habits, for in some instances zoospores from the unilocular sporangia have been observed to fuse.

Family Ralfsiaceae

The thallus in this marine family is an encrusting, pseudoparenchymatous growth, with both horizontal and upright, short, compact filaments and paraphyses.

Ralfsia Berk., 1831 (Plate XV, Fig. 217), is an encrusting form in which radiating filaments are adjoined laterally so that a prostrate, pseudoparenchymatous disc is produced. Plants are found in shallow water, on rocks or shells in the intertidal zone, and in tide pools. The thallus has two layers or zones with rhizoidal filaments developing from the underside. From the upper layer grow erect, photosynthetic filaments and tufts of hairs. Club-shaped sporangia develop near the base of the hairs and are interspersed among them. The gametophytes which grow from the zoospores are similar morphologically to the sporophytes but bear plurilocular gametangia on the ends of some upright filaments. There are, however, no paraphyses as on the sporophyte. The gametangia occur as one or several tiers of cells with the upper ones sterile. A biflagellate gamete is formed in each cell of the gametangium.

Order Sphacelariales

FAMILY SPHACELARIACEAE

Sphacelaria Lyngbye, 1819 (Plate XV, Fig. 218), a marine, branched, filamentous, mostly epiphytic genus, is characterized by a transverse wall-formation in the apical region (which is darkly pigmented) followed by vertical walls in the older portions. The result is a multiseriate thallus. Plants are attached by a disc or by rhizoids. Sometimes there are corticating threads which grow down along the axis. As mentioned previously, three-pronged branches (propagula) are abstricted to serve as vegetative reproductive elements. Sexual reproduction and the life history is similar to that of *Ectocarpus*. The plurilocular gametangia are subspherical or oval, borne on a short lateral stipe. Gametes are anisogamous and are borne in recognizably different gametangia. The unilocular sporangium, also on a lateral stipe, produces spores by meiosis.

Order Cutleriales

FAMILY CUTLERIACEAE

In this order and family the dichotomously branched, ribbon-like thallus grows by a trichothallic meristem. In reproduction there are both isomorphic and heteromorphic generations; hence the Order is a paradox, with some forms (*Zanardinia*) being a member of the Isogeneratae while *Cutleria* is typically a Heterogeneratae.

Cutleria Greville, 1830 (Plate XV, Fig. 219), is a subtropical genus known primarily from the Mediterranean but occurring also in the Pacific. The dominant phase is the gametophyte, a highly branched, ribbon-like (or fan-like), leathery thallus (2 dm. in length) with trichothallic growth. The cells at the base of the hairs unite and metamorphose into the usual three-zoned thallus (see p. 209). Here and there on the surface of the ribbons patches of cells dedifferentiate and divide to form a stalk cell and an outer, antheridial initial. The inner stalk cell may divide two or three times to form a three- or four-celled pedicel and may form branches.

PLATE XV

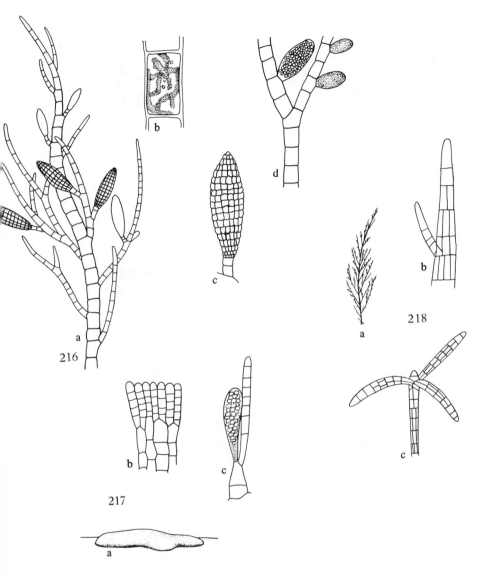

Fig. 216. **Ectocarpus** sp: a habit of portion of filament b, cell showing chloroplast (one type); c, plurilocular gametangium; d,
unilocular sporangium

Fig. 217. **Ralfsia** sp: a, habit of prostrate thallus (diagram); b, development at surface; c, sporangium and paraphyses

Fig. 218. **Sphacelaria** sp: a, habit; b, apex of branch showing multiseriate development; c, propagulum, a regenerative branch

PLATE XV

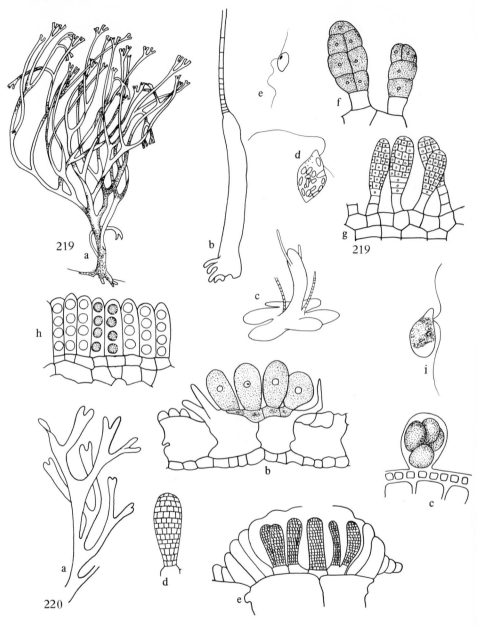

Fig. 219. **Cutleria multifida:** a, habit of gametophyte thallus; b, c, habit of sporophyte (Aglaozonia stage); d, macrogamete; e, microgamete; f, macrogametangium; g, microgametangium; h, surface sporangia; i, zoospore. (d, e, after Kuckuck)

Fig. 220. **Dictyota dichotoma:** a, portion of thallus; b, oogonia (redrawn from Smith); c, tetrasporangium; d, antheridium; e, antheridial sorus (redrawn from Smith)

PLATE XV

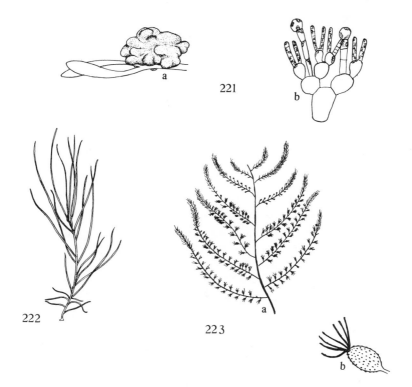

Fig. 221. **Leathesia difformis:** a, habit on **Ascophyllum;** b, marginal cells with monosporangia (redrawn from Smith)

Fig. 222. **Chordaria flagelliformis**

Fig. 223. **Sporochnus** sp: a, habit of portion of reproductive plants; b, portion of reproductive branch enclosing unilocular sporangia

Within the enlarging antheridial initial, transverse and vertical divisions produce a club-shaped cluster of rectangular cells as many as 20 cells high and with about eight cells in each transverse tier. In each cell a simple, biflagellate male gamete is produced. A pore develops in the outer (free) wall of the antheridial cell through which the gamete escapes. Similarly club-shaped tiers of much larger and fewer cells develop from the epidermis, occurring in patches or sori on either surface of the ribbons. In these cells biflagellate (but larger and more slowly swimming), pear-shaped gametes are produced.

Union of anisogametes produces a zygote that develops almost immediately to form a minute, nearly microscopic, attached sporophyte. This takes the form of a column of tissue from a horizontally developed basal portion. From the outer cells of the sporophyte, by the same process that produced gametangia, short-stalked, one-celled sporangia are produced. These too occur in sori. The nucleus of the sporangial cell undergoes meiosis, followed by a series of mitotic divisions to form up to 32 nuclei. Around these, by cleavage of the protoplast, as many zoospores are produced. These are pyriform-reniform and are biflagellate. Upon escaping through an apical pore the zoospores develop gametophytes.

The perennial sporophyte expression is so different from the annual gametophyte that it was classified for a long time as the genus *Aglaozonia*.

Order Dictyotales

FAMILY DICTYOTACEAE

In this family are flat, ribbon-like and dichotomously divided thalli which are sometimes fan-shaped. Growth occurs by an apical meristem (*Padina*), or by an apical cell (*Dictyota*). The former, however, begins its development by an apical cell only. The sporophyte and gametophyte are morphologically similar (Isogeneratae). The gametophyte (which may be either monoecious or dioecious) produces non-motile eggs and motile antherozoids. From the surface of the sporophyte, sporangia are formed in which cruciately arranged tetraspores are produced by meiosis. *Padina* is of interest because it is one of the few genera in the Phaeophyta in which lime occurs in the cell walls.

Dictyota Lamouroux, 1809 (Plate XV, Fig. 220), as described previously, is an example of the dichotomously branched, leathery and ribbon-like or membranous thallus, but one which is less branched than in *Cutleria*.

Here the alternation of generations is between isomorphic plants. The sporophyte produces unilocular sporangia from the surface in sori. By meiosis there are formed four haploid tetraspores, or at times aplanospores. The gametophyte produces on the surface either a sorus of from 25 to 50 oogonia, each with a single egg, or a series of club-shaped antheridia in each cell of which a uniflagellate pleuronematic sperm is produced. (Possibly there is also a second, rudimentary flagellum not yet observed.) In the development of sporangia and gametangia the vegetative cells in the vicinity of the sorus produce a canopy over the sorus of reproductive structures. There is a periodicity in gamete-production and discharge that is correlated with the spring tides, the gametes being released at the time of full moon.

Dictyota occurs in both the eastern and western Atlantic. Another order in the Isogeneratae is the Tilopteridales.

Class Heterogeneratae: Order Chordariales

This is a larger order of at least seven families, extremely varied in habit. In general, however, the sporophyte involves complexes of filaments that combine to form branched, tubular thalli, prostrate cushions, or globular, hollow growths of macroscopic size. Growth is trichothallic and the architecture may be monaxial or multiaxial. The gametophytes are minute, prostrate branched filaments.

Family Chordariaceae

The sporophyte in this family has branched, filiform or globular thalli in which there is a central core or axis of colorless filaments within a cortex of compact, branched filaments. The cortical cells are pigmented and photosynthetic. Growth is apical. The sporangia are formed on the outer branches of the cortical filaments.

Leathesia Gray, 1821 (Plate XV, Fig. 221), also goes by the appropriate name of Sea Potato. It is a brown, hollow, irregularly globular thallus attached to other seaweeds in the intertidal zone, especially during spring and early midsummer. The peripheral part of the thallus is composed inwardly of a gelatinous matrix in which there are dichtomously branched filaments of irregularly cylindrical cells. Exteriorly, the cells become small and form a compact palisade-like peripheral layer. Here and there the branches terminate in long, colorless hairs. Also on the tips of short branches, and just below the outer surface, occur the unilocular sporangia. Zoospores develop minute thalli of branched filaments which endure as long as one year. These bear plurilocular organs. They are suspected of being gametangia but the life history is not entirely clear. It is thought that meiosis occurs in the sporangia.

The short-lived sporophytes also bear plurilocular organs which produce *neutral spores* and these in turn develop diploid sporophytes. It is known, however, that such spores may also produce small, filamentous stages that develop sporangia again. The neutral spores appear late in the growing season after zoospores have been shed.

Chordaria C. A. Agardh, 1817 (Plate XV, Fig. 222), is a common, somewhat gelatinous genus of the North Atlantic, often growing on rocks or as an epiphyte. The thallus is a loose tuft of relatively slender, branched cylinders, the primary branches seldom rebranched. Growth is trichothallic. Unlike *Leathesia* the sporangia are borne within the thallus and at the base of the out-turned and compact filaments which constitute the photosynthetic periphery. These cortical filaments are usually but little-branched. The medulla is composed of colorless, axial filaments. Zoospores are reniform and have a long pleuronematic flagellum and a short, simple one posteriorly.

Order Sporochnales

FAMILY SPOROCHNACEAE

This order is characterized by having hair-bearing, dichotomously branched thalli in the sporophyte generation. The hairs are in tufts at the apex of each branch or lobe, with a meristematic region at the base of the hairs. The sporangia (unilocular) are borne terminally on short lateral branches. The spores form microscopic, filamentous gametophytes.

Plants are mostly known from south of the equator (a few species in north temperate waters) and are deeply benthic.

Sporochnus C. A. Agardh, 1810 (Plate XV, Fig. 223), is characterized by relatively large plants which have a pinnate, feathery type of branching, the secondary branches terminating in a tuft of hairs.

Carpomitra Kuetzing, 1842, is a common genus in the European Atlantic which grows as a flat cylinder. The small filamentous gametophyte produces egg and sperm.

Order Desmarestiales

FAMILY DESMARESTIACEAE

The plants in this order are highly branched filaments which are corticated below, or frond-like but with the branches terminating in a filament. There is a disc-like attaching organ. In *Desmarestia* the thallus usually is a flattened feathery frond with a main axis and lateral, plume-like branches in which there is a midvein. Some of the ribbon-like species may be upwards of 12 feet long. This genus is unique because of its acid-producing character. Spores from unilocular sporangia produce microscopic, dioecious gametophytes. These develop non-motile female gametes, or biflagellate sperm. The antheridia are terminal on filaments, whereas oogonia may be either terminal or intercalary.

Order Punctariales

This is a large order of some 13 families. The plants are variously shaped, thread-like, tubular, and expanded fronds. The thallus has the usual medulla of colorless cells and filaments, and a cortex that includes peripheral photosynthetic cells. There is a basal, disc-like attaching organ from which the stalk arises. Growth is intercalary. The sporangia are irregular in location, either solitary or clustered, but are plurilocular rather than unilocular in *Petalonia*. They are produced from metamorphosed superficial cells. The zoospores develop an embryonic, filamentous stage from which the mature thallus grows. According to some observations the spore may also produce microscopic filamentous gametophytes; further confirmation is needed on this point. In general the order includes plants which are diploid only, but in *Punctaria* the life cycle is better known. In some systems of classification the Punctariaceae is included in the order Dictyosiphonales.

FAMILY PUNCTARIACEAE

Punctaria Greville, 1830 (Plate XVI, Fig. 224), is characterized by broad or narrow fronds or ribbons, up to seven cells thick, from an attaching disc, but with scarcely any stipe. The thalli often bear tufts of hairs. *Punctaria* ribbons may be as long as six decimeters, and either epiphytic or attached to stones. Surface cells, either solitary or in sori, enlarge and function as unilocular sporangia. As usual, meiosis occurs in the sporangium, and the biflagellate zoospores produce microscopic, branched, filamentous gametophytes. Within certain cells of these filaments iso-gametes are produced, and from the zygote a new sporophyte is generated. Like some species of *Ectocarpus*, the diploid sporophyte also may produce plurilocular sporangia in which meiosis does not occur. Plurilocular-produced zoospores develop more sporophytes directly, either by producing simple filaments which in turn bud off growths that become mature sporophytes, or by producing more plurilocular sporangia and zoospores. An interesting variation of this life cycle occurs in *Phaeostrophion* in which there may be no gametophyte.

Order Dictyosiphonales

This order is characterized by having growth from an apical cell. The sporophyte thallus (especially in the genus **Dictyosiphon**) is a relatively multi-branched, delicate cylinder that is solid in some portions, hollow in others. Plants may be up to 10 dm. high. There is a medulla of colorless cells and a cortex of compact cells which externally are choroplast-bearing. Here and there on the surface are hairs. The enlarged, unilocular sporangial cells are produced just within the cortical layer and adjacent to the medullary region. Zoospores are formed by meiosis and germinate to produce a semimicroscopic branched filament. On such filaments uniseriate gametangial cells are formed, each cell producing an isogamete. The zygote grows into the diploid unilocular-producing plant, by first forming an embryonic, prostrate filamentous stage. When plants are mature and maximum growth has been achieved, an apical, multicellular hair is produced. *Dictyosiphon*, with its several species, occurs in northern waters of both the Atlantic and Pacific.

Order Laminariales

In this order are included the brown algae known as *kelps*, many of which are relatively huge, tough, leathery, and with a complex anatomy approaching distinct tissue differentiation. Even so, the basic unit of structure is a filament. The large thallus is the sporophyte stage in the life cycle, the gametophyte being a microscopic, creeping filament, sometimes of only one or a few cells. There is very little variation in the morphology of the gametophyte stages throughout the order, whereas the sporophyte shows considerable diversity. In general, plants in this order are well-adjusted for an existence in cold waters under overcast skies. They are particularly successful in the Pacific; only a few genera and a scant number of species occur in the Atlantic. The zone of their distribution in the Western Hemisphere is from just east of Cape Horn around Tierra del

Fuego and up the coast to the subtropical Pacific latitude; and from north temperate in the Pacific to the Arctic.

Although extremely variable, the basic morphology (as mentioned previously) involves a root-like hold-fast, a long or short stipe, and leaf-like or at least flattened expansions. Growth in length is achieved by a meristem at the base of the blade and above the stipe. The meristem increases both the blade and the stipe. In one form (*Chorda*), however, the thallus is a long, slender "shoestring." Four families are usually recognized.

Family Laminariaceae

Laminaria Lamouroux, 1813 (Plate XVI, Fig. 225), a rock-loving genus, is well-named because of the large flat blade or blades. Plants (about 20 species) occur in the sublittoral or in the lower littoral (see p. 301), sometimes growing in relatively deep water just offshore, especially along the Pacific coasts and the British Isles. There is a well-developed hapteron (or sometimes a disc), and a short stipe which broadens into a blade-like expansion (or several blades) that may be up to several meters in length (25 feet in *L. Farlowii*). The morphology of the hapteron and the form of the stipe are of taxonomic importance in differentiating species. All but one are perennial. *Laminaria* has the type of growth wherein the meristem is located at the base of the blade where it adds more to the lengthening of the stipe than to the blade. At the end of the growing season in some species the old blade is abscissed and a new one is formed. It is peculiar that growth in some species occurs more actively in the winter-spring months.

In a cross section of the stipe the usual three (or four) regions are discernible. There is an "epidermis," a wide cortex which may appear as an inner and outer zone, and a medulla. The cells in the three regions are quite distinctive in size and shape. Some of the medullar filaments extend transversely or diagonally and serve as probable strengthening devices. Here and there in the medulla certain filaments have cells which elongate but divide infrequently. These elongated cells swell and widen at the cross walls to form *trumpet hyphae*. The uppermost of the adjoined trumpet cells curiously has a distinctly larger swelling than the lower. The cross walls of the trumpet cells have pores and it is believed that these facilitate conduction as do sieve plates in the phloem of higher plants. At least in some species the trumpet cells have special thickenings and plates in the lateral walls.

Because of difference in the rate of cell division in the cortex of the stipe, concentric zones of dark and light cells are formed (the latter appearing during the time of rapid growth). These zones are referred to as "growth rings." It is in the cortex that mucilage ducts occur, these being bordered on the inner side by small, secreting cells.

On both sides of the blade, toward the end of a growing season, sori of unilocular sporangia are formed. These are club-shaped and arise perpendicular to the surface, interspersed and over-topped by paraphyses. An outer epidermal cell of the blade divides to form two — an upper which becomes a paraphysis, and a lower which develops into a sporangium. Both of these structures arise from the same initial cell.

Within the sporangial cell the nucleus divides meiotically, followed by several successive mitotic divisions so that about 64 are produced. Around the nuclei the same number of biflagellate zoospores are formed. These germinate to form dioecious, filamentous, few-celled gametophytes. The dioecious condition of the sexual plants indicates that at meiosis two kinds of spores are produced. Small cells in the male filament produce a single spermatozoid, and a large cell of the female gametophyte elongates vertically and differentiates as an oogonium, the content being a single egg. The egg escapes just prior to union with a sperm, slipping through a break in the oogonial membrane. At least in culture it appears that the male gametophyte degenerates immediately, whereas the female persists for some time. The large sporophyte immediately begins to develop from the zygote, first by putting out a rhizoid from the primary filamentous extension of the fertilized egg.

Laminaria possesses a number of economic importances (see p. 355) as food for Man and animals, and as a source of potash, iodine, alginic acid, and many other useful substances.

Postelsia Ruprecht, 1852 (Plate XVI, Fig. 226), or Sea Palms, are strikingly different from other Laminariales, but have the same fundamental internal structure and the same life history. The thallus possesses a highly developed and most efficient hapteron which virtually grows into rocky substrates. Because of this and the great resilience of the trunk-like stipe, these plants thrive on rocky reefs and headlands where, with every great comber, they are pounded by tons of water. At the summit of the stipe, which may be two or more feet high, is a crown of long, slender blades, giving the plant its characteristic palm tree appearance. These plants exist along the Pacific coast of North America in the lower temperate latitudes.

Nereocystis Postels et Ruprecht, 1840 (Plate XVI, Fig. 227), or Serpent Kelp, grows just off shore in relatively shallow water (but may occur at 90 feet), anchored by haptera from which a long, slender, hollow stipe extends. Sieve tube trumpet cells occur in the stipe of *Nereocystis* and

PLATE XVI

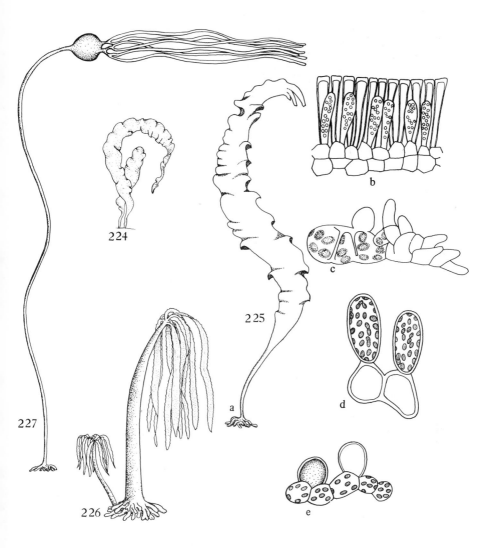

Fig. 224. **Punctaria latifolia,** habit of thallus

Fig. 225. **Laminaria Agardhii**: a, habit of sporophyte; b, section of blade showing paraphyses and sporangia; c, male gametophyte; d, e, female gametophytes. (d, redrawn from Kukuck)

Fig. 226. **Postelsia palmaeformis**

Fig. 227. **Nereocystis Luetkeana**

PLATE XVI

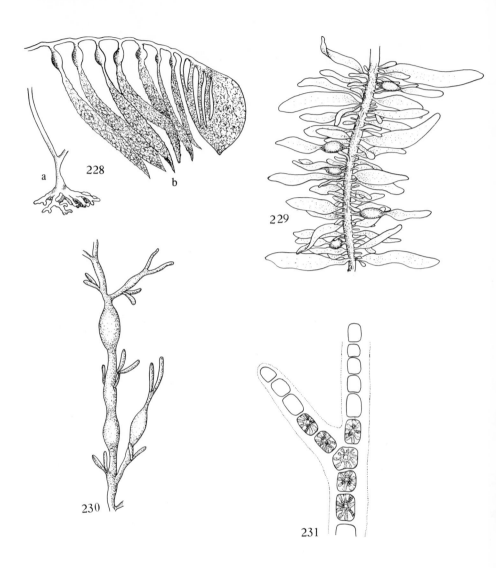

Fig. 228. **Macrocystis pyrifera**

Fig. 229. **Egregia** sp

Fig. 230. **Ascophyllum nodosum**

Fig. 231. **Goniotrichum** sp, drawn from a herbarium specimen

PLATE XVI

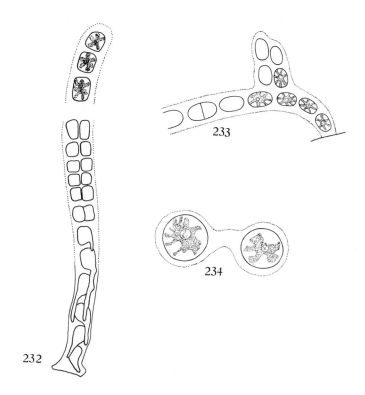

Fig. 232. **Bangia fuscopurpurea**

Fig. 233. **Asterocystis Smaragdina**

Fig. 234. **Porphyridium cruentum**

experimentally it has been shown that these have a conductive function (as in *Macrocystis*). The stipe terminates in a massive pneumatocyst or bulb-like float which may be six or more inches in diameter. From the bulb, dichotomously divided, stubby projections give rise to long, ribbon-like blades (up to five meters long). The blades are simple at first but split to form four, and by repeated dichotomies and splitting a considerable number of ribbons result. The pneumatocyst keeps the photosynthetic blades properly exposed to light at the water surface. On the blades sporangia develop on both surfaces, estimated at 6,000,000 per square inch, which explains why the water around a kelp bed becomes milky from the astronomical numbers of zoospores released. Plants may be many meters in length, and surprisingly achieve this growth in one year, so that the reproductive potentialities are very great. The zoospores produce minute male and female gametophytes.

Like *Laminaria* and other large kelps, *Nereocystis* develops well in the Pacific, and is highly important to the kelp-harvesting industry (see Chap. 10).

Macrocystis C. A. Agardh, 1820 (Plate XVI, Fig. 228), is perhaps the most spectacular of all the kelps, although *Pelagophycus*, with a length of as much as 150 feet, is also very impressive. *Macrocystis* may range from 200 to 700 feet (the measurement being questionably reported). The genus has been the subject of considerable research in respect to morphology, nutrition, and ecology.

Macrocystis has a stout hapteron which supports a long stipe, along which leaves are subtended, each with a pneumatocyst at the base. The stipe, which is at first solid, branches a few times dichotomously, and finally in a unilateral fashion. The leaf-like blades are produced by the activity of a meristematic region at the tip. Here additions are made to the stipe and to a terminal blade. The latter splits as it expands and segments form the "leaves." This is accomplished by an intermittent breakdown in the cortex of the frond thallus, which occurs at a time when the outer cortex or "epidermal" layer stops its growth. Finally the epidermis splits and a separated blade is formed. Thus there is an "evolution" of leaves at the tip of the ever-extending stipe. There are trumpet hyphae in the cortex and medulla, and these are interconnected by transverse filaments which also have sieve plates in the crosswalls. Parker (1963) found that movement of material through the stipe can take place at the rate of 60 centimeters per hour.

As in *Laminaria* and in *Nereocystis* sporangia develop on both surfaces of the blades, extensive areas being involved so that when mature, spores are shed in tremendous numbers. Characteristically the zoospores develop minute male and female gametophytes. Fertilization and subsequent development of the sporophyte is similar to the history of *Laminaria*.

Plants grow as deep as 90 feet and form veritable submarine "forests." Like other kelps they grow mostly in colder waters around Cape Horn, Tierra del Fuego, and the Cape of Good Hope, as well as along the shores of the northern Pacific. Plants seem to be confined to water of high salinity.

FAMILY LESSONIACEAE

Some students of the algae recognize the family Lessoniaceae to include *Lessonia, Postelsia, Nereocystis,* and *Macrocystis.* They also place *Alaria* (a *Laminaria*-like genus) with compound leaves, *Egregia,* and *Agarum* in the Alariaceae.

Egregia Aresch., 1876 (Plate XVI, Fig. 229), which grows along the California, Oregon, and Washington coast, is a boa-like alga. There is a flat, ribbon-like axis which gives rise laterally throughout its length to numerous, sporangia-bearing laminae, floats, and photosynthetic blades. Culture studies have demonstrated the male and female gametophytes to consist of but a few cells, sometimes of but one in the female. The life history is typical of the Laminariales, the sporophyte having 16 chromosomes, with reduction division occurring in the sporangium.

Class Cyclosporeae: Order Fucales (Cyclosporales)

FAMILY FUCACEAE

This order, with one family (or eight, depending on classification system employed), is well-circumscribed by its unique type of life history. It is a large group in respect to number of species and is world-wide in its distribution. Plants are mostly leathery but abundantly bathed in mucilage in many forms. This is especially useful to such plants as *Fucus* which is a common inhabitor of the intertidal zone. The largest member of the order is *Durvillea* in the Antarctic, which has been reported to reach nearly 40 feet in length. *Notheia* grows as a parasite mostly on its sister genus *Hormosira.*

The thallus in this order is flattened and dichotomously branched, or (uncommonly) has radial branches, as in some of the Australian *Cystoseira,* which grow as a chain of brown beads. *Sargassum* (Sea Holly, Gulf Weed) is a bushy, highly-branched thallus with many small, leaf-like blades and berry-like floats (pneumatocysts).

Rather than haptera, the fucoids have a disc-like hold-fast, an exception being *Bifurcaria*. The stipe in many forms is not so distinctly differentiated from the blades as in the Laminariales because it is often flattened and merges gradually into the expanded portion (restricted though it may be in amount of surface).

Internally the thallus shows variations of the three general regions; epidermal (meristoderm), cortex, and medulla. As in other orders the inner medulla cells do not multiply; hence as growth occurs they become much stretched and loosely arranged. From the inner cortical cells transverse filaments (hyphae) grow into the medulla region. It is noteworthy that in certain medullar filaments the cross walls have sieve plates as in the Laminariales. In several genera hair-filled cavities (cryptostomata) occur. These remain sterile or become the locations of sex organs when the plants are mature. The thallus is formed by an apical growing cell with at first three, then later four, cutting faces in addition to the basal side. The dichotomy of the apical cell leads to frequent dichotomous branching. The Notheiaceae uses many apical cells or a meristem for growth. Whereas apical cells provide for vertical growth, the lateral growth is accomplished by divisions of the external layer (meristoderm).

Vegetative reproduction by fragmentation is used by many genera (especially *Sargassum*). Zoospores do not occur in the Fucales. Sexual reproduction (here outlined for *Fucus*) is oogamous, following what is regarded by some students as an unusual type of sporogenesis.

The cryptostomata which become fertile are known as *conceptacles*, and open to the exterior by pores, *ostioles*. The swollen branch tips in which the conceptacles develop are known as *receptacles*. From the walls of the conceptacles, among the hairs (*paraphyses*), sporangia develop. The spores are of two sizes and there is a difference in the way they mature. The spores are known as *heterospores* and are cut out in respective sporangia borne either in different conceptacles on the same plant or on different plants.

The larger megaspores are produced in globular sporangia borne on a short stalk. The contents (and nucleus) act as a megaspore mother cell which by meiosis forms two spores. Subsequent division produces four spores. These then undergo a metamorphosis and divide to form eight cells which function as female gametes (eggs). In different genera a varying number of such eggs degenerate so that in some only one matures. But the total number of eggs produced by a single plant is astronomical, as in *Fucus*, for example.

Similarly, on the wall of other conceptacles, from the base of paraphyses, smaller sporangia on branched stalks are formed. Several microsporangia appear on the ends of branches of a single initial stalk. In these the primary nucleus undergoes two successive divisions. The first is meiotic, and is followed by four more mitoses, so that 64 daughter nuclei result. Around each of these a biflagellate, pyriform antherozoid is produced, and the sporangium functions, therefore, as an antheridium. The flagella are heterokont, the posterior being simple and the longer of the two, and the anterior one pleuronematic and shorter.

When mature the oogonium (modified megasporangium) wall ruptures and the eggs are liberated. The wall is in three layers: endochite, mesochite, and exochite. When the latter ruptures, the two inner layers with the contained eggs are released. The middle layer then splits, followed by the inner, which thus releases and frees the eggs. The expulsion of oogonia and the antherozoids is accompanied, if not induced, by the swelling of mucilage contained in the conceptacle. This substance contracts when the plants are exposed during low tide periods, then swells greatly with the return of sea water, thus aiding in the extrusion of the gametes. The sperm sac formed by the inner layer of the microsporangium wall gelatinizes in the water and releases the sperm. Union of gametes then occurs in open water. The eggs sometimes retain the inner layer of the oogonium wall which serves as a stalk connecting them to the persisting remains of the outer layer. The outer membrane frequently assists in anchoring the zygote.

The zygote begins to develop a diploid plant immediately (see Text Figure 6.1). There is first an elongation of the zygote, followed by three successive transverse wall formations, and the embryo becomes somewhat pear-shaped. The embryonic state shows polarity at the start, apparently determined by an auxin which begins to operate under the influence of CO_2 produced by respiration and a change in pH.

The narrow end of the embryo elongates and the basal cell cuts off the first rhizoid. Then a quadrant of cells is produced in the larger, upper (anterior) end of the embryo opposite the point of rhizoid origin. In these the three future thallus layers become differentiated through transverse and longitudinal divisions. A cell at the apex puts forth a long hair and at the base of this a meristematic cell is differentiated. Later, other hairs form here. The central, primary hair is then abscissed and the cell at its base continues to function as an apical growing cell.

Fucus Linnaeus, 1753 (Plate XVII, Fig. 235), is the familiar Rock Weed, a genus with almost worldwide distribution in the intertidal zone, and one which derives its name from the Greek word for algae, *phykos*. This is a plant which was used in Roman days as a source of a brown, facial cosmetic. The thallus has a disc-like hold-fast and a relatively short stipe

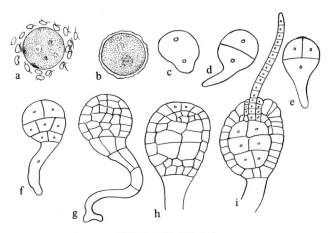

TEXT FIGURE 6.1

Fertilization and embryo-development of *Fucus*. a, egg and swarming antherozoids (in open water); b, zygote; c, early elongation of the zygote to form rhizoidal extension (polarity determined in the zygote); d, first division of the zygote, determining posterior and anterior regions; e, vertical wall in anterior part of embryo; f and g, continuing wall formations; h, meristematic region determined; i, development of first apical hair, the basal cell of this hair eventually functioning as an apical cell.

which broadens into flattened, somewhat foliose but narrow expansions. Often pneumatocysts occur along the margins of the "ribbon," and the surface may be pitted with hair-bearing cryptostomata.

Growth is by an apical cell which prevents other meristematic activity below for a short distance of a few millimeters. As in higher plants this dominance is related to a diffusion of "regulatory substances." Branching is dichotomous and when mature the apical region becomes swollen as a receptacle. The surface of these is roughened by the numerous ostioles opening into the conceptacles. The receptacles vary in shape from one species to another and there is also a variation in the level of growth in the intertidal zone. In the intertidal zone plants are exposed for half the time and must live as land plants; hence they can make good use of the water-absorbing capacities of plant mucilage. Species are perennial and some may exist for as long as four years.

Reproduction (as described) involves a life cycle in which the gametophyte has been eliminated, except for the cells produced by the meiospores that metamorphose to form gametes.

Ascophyllum Stackhouse, 1899 (Plate XVI, Fig. 230), has a thallus which is primarily a branched, flattened cylinder with numerous, lateral, leaf-like elements and receptacles on short stalks. In these there are numerous conceptacles. The receptacles may drop away after gametes have been shed. Here and there in the axis are nodose pneumatocysts. The branching is dichotomous but in the upper part of the thallus it is pinnate. In the oogonia only four eggs mature.

The plants grow in dense clusters on rocks in the same zone with *Fucus*, but often are found drifting like *Sargassum* or living in tide marshes unattached. Varieties and forms are responsive to different degrees of salinity which thus exerts a presence or absence selectivity.

Sargassum C. A. Agardh, 1821 (Plate XVII, Fig. 237), or Gulf Weed, has an elongate, much-branched axis on which lateral branchlets are borne. Plants may be up to several meters in length. The branchlets give rise laterally to numerous, small, leaf-like blades with serrate margins (hence the common name Sea Holly). Along the branchlets are separate, modified stalks on which berry-like bladders are borne. Certain branchlets (fertile) bear in place of an air bladder an elongate, finger-like receptacle. In the megasporangium (oogonium) a single egg matures. The life cycle is typically cyclosporean, as in *Fucus*.

Saragassum begins its life cycle as an attached thallus but soon becomes afloat and continues to multiply by fragmentation. This is the seaweed that has given name to the well-known Sargasso Sea in the central Atlantic. According to legend, Columbus was encouraged to continue his westward sailing by sighting *Sargassum* in the Gulf Stream. Some systems of classification place *Sargassum* in its own family.

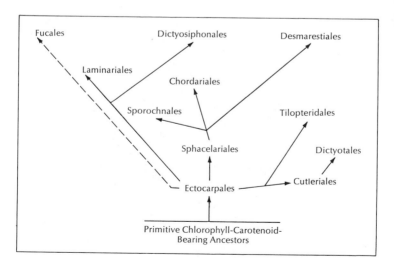

CHART 6.1   Suggested Phylogenetic Arrangement of the Phaeophyta

Chapter 7

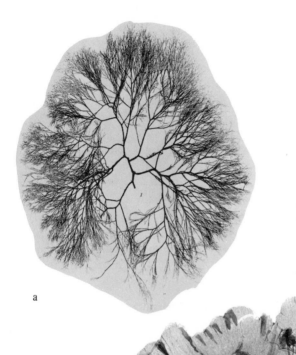

a. Polysiphonia elongella *Harv.;*
b. Nitophyllum Gmelini *Grev.*
(*Reproduced from Nature
Printed British Seaweeds,* Lon-
don, 1859)

a

b

Phylum Rhodophyta

The red algae are the most abundant in number of species and perhaps the most showy of all the seaweeds. There are approximately 200 species in fresh water, many in the tropics. They are more delicate than the brown and most of the green algae and in general are not as large. There are two groups, Bangioideae and Florideae. Plants are mostly branched, tufted filaments, or cartilaginous fronds, some forming thalloid sheets and leaf-like expansions. One-celled forms are a rarity. A pseudofilamentous type is seen in *Asterocystis*. In general there are two architectural plans. One consists of an axis with or without cortications (uniaxial); the other consists of cables or tufts of axial filaments (multiaxial), each with laterals that radiate out to the margin, outwardly forming a compact layer of small cells which are usually photosynthetic.

Whereas the Rhodophyta are widely distributed in the oceans they are perhaps more abundant in tropical and subtropical waters. A few live in the intertidal (*Corallina, Rhodochorton, Bostrychia*) but most are sublittoral. Some are able to live more deeply than any other algae, occurring in depths of 800 feet in tropical waters, where light rays penetrate more deeply. The vertical distribution is related to the ability of red pigments to use feeble light or those portions of the spectrum which penetrate to great depths. A few genera occur in fresh, mostly flowing water. Many are encrusting and calcified (sometimes with magnesium carbonate), especially the corallines, which inhabit and have aided in the construction of coral atolls. The calcified forms of the past make it possible to place the Rhodophyta in the Paleozoic. Deposits, up to 4500 feet deep, of Eocene origin are known. Remains of vegetative thalli resemble present-day Rhodophyta but taxonomic classification is uncertain. The calcareous algae are common in arctic seas today. More rarely, red algae exist in a free-floating state (cf. *Antithamnion*, along the Victoria Coast).

It is noteworthy that many genera of red algae are parasitic or epiphytic, mostly on other Rhodophyta and on closely related genera: examples include *Ceratocolax, Choreocolax, Lithothamnion,* and *Rhodochorton* on hydroids. *Colacopsis* lives entirely within the host *Vidalia* in the Rhodo-melaceae. *Choreonema* (in its own family) lives on *Jania* in the Coral-linaceae. Many are epiphytic or only partly parasitic: *Calleocolax* (Cal-lymeniaceae) is a colorless form that occurs as pin-point white growths on *Callophylis* in the same family. Many are only partly parasitic and in some instances the epiphyte is more saprophytic than parasitic.

The general characteristic of these related forms is a great reduction in vegetative growth. *Janczewskia*, for example, grows as a pink or white tubercle no more than three to eight millimeters in diameter. This sends rhizoids into the host *Laurencia*, a genus found also in the Rhodophyta.

General and Differentiating Characteristics

PIGMENTATION

The pigments of the Rhodophyta include: chlorophyll-*a*, chlorophyll-*d*, *a*-carotene, *B*-carotene, lutein, zeaxanthin, violoxanthin, flavoxanthin, *r*-phy-cocyanin, allophycocyanin, R-phycoerythrin, and B-phycoerythrin. The *b*-phycoerythrin has a maximum absorption different from other phycobi-lins in the red algae. The phycocyanin and phycoerythrin, in addition to the chlorophylls, have been shown to be effective in photosynthesis. The blue and red pigments are light-absorbing and catalyzing synthesizers. *c*-phycoerythrin, common to the blue-green algae, has been demonstrated to be present in the genus *Compsopogon*.

Species dredged from 60 meters are richer in red pigments than those which grow in shallow, more intensely illuminated waters or in the inter-tidal. *Chondrus crispus*, e.g., is purplish-green on shore, becoming reddish in deep water. Some genera are actually more brown than red.

Chloroplasts containing these pigments are parietal plates, ribbons, or axial, stellate bodies, and are reported to have single lamellae pairs rather than stacked pairs, as in the Chlorophyta and Phaeophyta. Pyrenoids occur commonly but they do not have a starch sheath, as in the Chlorophyta.

FOOD STORAGE PRODUCTS

The food storage product (see p. 30) is a peculiar solid carbohydrate, a starch known as floridean which is considered to be a glucose residue. The grains are distributed throughout the protoplast, but appear first on the surface of the chloroplast. Other carbohydrates found include floridoside, whose carbon atoms have one-third linkage; mannoglycerate; trehalose; and sucrose. In addition there are some alcohols which might be con-sidered as food reserve, as well as several fats. These are in a minority, however, in comparison with the starch and other carbohydrates.

It is likely that food reserves in various groups of Rhodophyta involve many chemically different substances as yet not investigated, and so constitute a challenge to the biochemist. Chemists have found that amylopectins comprise the starch that is found in one of the coralline algae (*Dilsea corallina*). Mannose that occurs in nearly all red algae which have been analyzed is lacking in such genera as *Porphyridium*, *Polyides*, and *Ahnfeltia*. Vacuoles lacking in the Class Bangioideae are present in the Florideae (the two Classes of the Rhodophyta). Bangioideae are uninucleate (with exceptions) whereas many of the Florideae are multinucleate (at least in age). Mitochondria occur in the cells of some genera.

CELL STRUCTURE

The cell wall involves two layers, an inner of cellulose (different from that possessed by higher plants), and an outer of pectins. The mucilages include complex and various polysaccharides, such as galactose. In many genera, especially coralline algae, the outer layer is impregnated with calcium (crystals of calcium carbonate), as previously mentioned (see p. 233). The cell wall and the composition of the red algal cell protoplast includes many polysaccharides and other carbohydrates. As much as 57% dry weight is polysaccharide (xylose, galactose, glucose). The mucilages agar-agar (15-20%) and carrageenin (50-75%) are very abundant. The fibrillar portion of the cell wall, as shown by electron microscopy, is composed of xylose, galactose, and glucose, and these are laid down in patterns of great uniformity throughout such Rhodophyta as have been studied. *Porphyra* differs from other Rhodophyta in that the wall includes polymannose fibrils. All of these carbohydrates in their relative abundance tend to characterize certain families, but not so precisely as to serve as dependable taxonomic features.

The large class Florideae is characterized in part by the possession of pores in the wall, some of which provide intercellular protoplasmic connections (plasmodesmata). In some genera the pores are open connections between cells. Pores have been found, however, in *Compsopogon* of the Bangioideae so that this differentiating feature appears to be not constant.

The original pit connection is simply formed when there is an incomplete cross wall formed at cell division. Subsequently other pit connections may be made between the same two cells or between other lateral cells. This is accomplished by division of the cell nucleus. One of the nuclei migrates to the wall where a protuberance forms and develops into a connnecting "tube." The nucleus moves into this tube, and, as the connection is made, passes through the wall and into the adjacent cell.

REPRODUCTION

Reproductive habits in the Rhodophyta are among the most intriguing of their characteristics. These habits lead to and involve life histories which are the most complex of perhaps any other class of organisms. At the least, the Rhodophyta exhibit highly refined and many times unexplainable behaviors of protoplasm, and so invite physiological and biochemical research along with morphological and genetical studies.

For a few, more primitive forms (*Porphyridium*, e.g.) cell division is the only multiplication process known. Fragmentation is employed by many but this is not relied upon to the extent found in the Phaeophyta. In simple genera cell division is accompanied by spore-formation. In the filamentous *Asterocystis*, e.g., a reproductive "spore" is formed simply by the protoplast escaping from the wide gelatinous sheath to initiate a new filament. Another simple and efficient method is that of a vegetative cell becoming divided to form four or eight elements which slip from the filaments as amoeboid regeneratives known as *neutral spores*. After a short, free-living period these contract, form a wall, and subsequently initiate a new thallus.

A somewhat more specialized asexual method uses special cells serving as sporangia. In some, a single spore is produced, surrounded by a thin wall. Such spores are called *monospores*. Spores formed in groups of four (usually with meiosis) are known as *tetraspores* (meiospores); if there are multiple divisions and several elements are produced, they are known as *polyspores*. Spores produced directly or indirectly as a result of sexual union are known as *carpospores* (the female sex organ containing the egg is known as a *carpogonium*).

All sexual reproduction is oogamous, with the male cell drifting to bring about fertilization rather than swimming. Yet it is in the variabilities of sexual reproduction and organs that the Rhodophyta show complexities. Herein, first some general features will be described, some definitions given, and types of life histories outlined. Particulars will be presented as a few representatives of the several orders are described.

Gametangia are always formed, simple though they may be, in the production of sex cells. The antheridia may be metamorphosed vegetative cells (*Porphyra*, Plate XVII, Fig. 238), or cells produced on special branches (male trichoblast in *Polysiphonia*; Plate XXI, Fig. 263). The non-motile male gamete is called a *spermatium* and the cell which produces it a *spermatangium*. Sometimes the entire spermatangium is liberated to carry the spermatium to the female organ.

The female organ is called a *carpogonium* and may be only a metamorphosed vegetative cell, or an organ produced on a special branch called

PLATE XVII

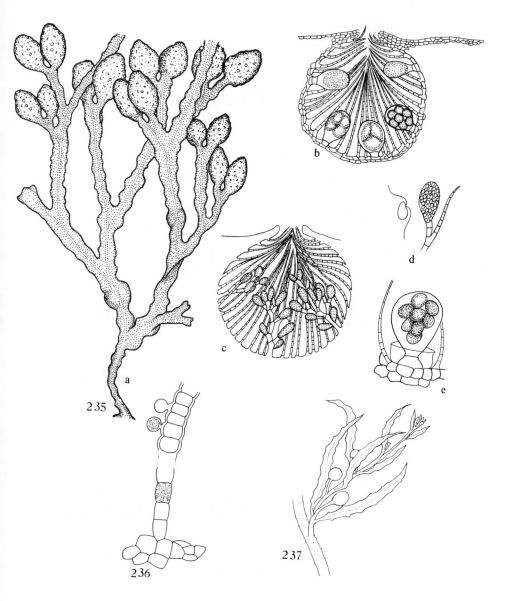

Fig. 235. **Fucus** sp: a, habit; b, female conceptacle and oogonia; c, male conceptacle; d, antheridium and paraphysis branch; e, oogonium with 8 eggs

Fig. 236. **Erythrotrichia** sp, portion of filament with monospores

Fig. 237. **Sargassum filipendula,** portion of branch with pneumato-cysts

PLATE XVII

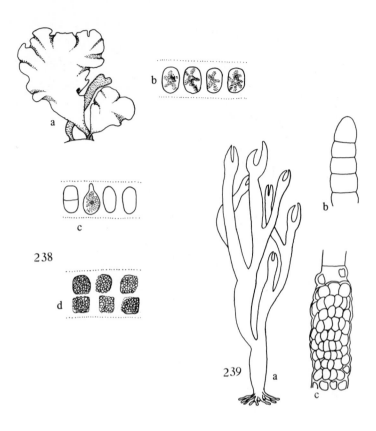

238

239

Fig. 238. **Porphyra** sp: a, habit of plant; b, section through thallus; cells with stellate chloroplasts; c, carpogonium (procarp); d, spermatia

Fig. 239. **Compsopogon coeruleus:** a, thallus; b, tip of branch with apical cell; c, formation of cortical cells

PLATE XVII

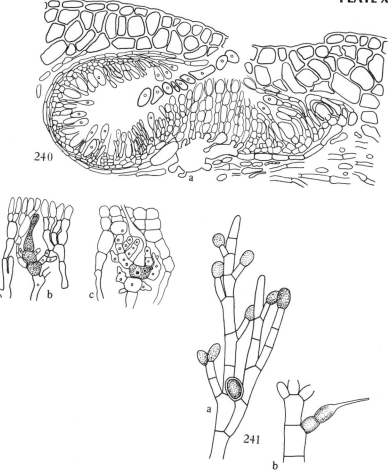

Fig. 240. **Galaxaura Diesingiana:** a, section through carposporophyte (redrawn from Svedelius); b, mature carpogonial branch; c, zygote nucleus migrating to hypogynous cell (the cell below the carpogonium on the fertile branch)

Fig. 241. **Audouinella violacea:** a, portion of thallus with monosporangia; b, carpogonium

239

a *carpogonial* branch. Or, sometimes, it may be in a special filament within the thallus. The carpogonium is some form of flask shape, the egg being the uninucleate content contained in the basal part. The narrow extended portion (long or short) is known as the *trichogyne*. When sex organs are produced in close association (respectively) they are said to form *sori*. A cavity in which several organs occur is known as a *nemathecium*. The carpogonial branch may be produced by a specialized cell cut off from a vegetative branch, the supporting *cell*. In the vicinity of the carpogonium, produced variously according to the genus, is a special differentiated cell known as an *auxiliary cell*. Either nearby or remote from the carpogonium another specialized cell or thread of cells functions in a nutritive fashion for the development of spores following fertilization. These are known as *nurse cells* or nurse filaments (tissue).

The spermatium becomes attached to the trichogyne (which may have a nucleus as well as the basal part of the carpogonium), and the walls break down so that the sperm nucleus can migrate to the egg and form the *zygote*. The subsequent fate and development of the zygote varies. At the simplest level it undergoes meiosis immediately and then divides by mitosis to form four (or more) carpospores. Sometimes from the carpogonium either haploid or diploid filaments (short or long) are produced. These are known as *gonimoblast filaments*. In some life histories cells are cut off at the tip of the gonimoblasts. These are known as *carposporangia*, and each produces a carpospore. If these are produced in a group of four they are called *carpotetraspores*. In some other genera the carpogonium fuses with an auxiliary cell and from this cell (with or without additional fusing with nearby cells) the subsequent development produces the carpospores. When a number of auxiliary cells fuse — and usually with each other as well as with the carpogonium — there is formed a large *placenta*, well-supplied with nutritive material. The direct fusion of carpogonium and auxiliary cell constitutes a combination known as the *procarp*. Sometimes an elongation or a filament grows from the carpogonium to the auxiliary cell through which nuclei pass. Such a thread is called a *connecting filament*, or is sometimes referred to as an *ooblastic filament*. The combination of carpospores, the gonimoblasts, and the fusion cells constitute what is termed a *cystocarp*, or by some, a *carposporophyte*. In some of the more advanced genera the cystocarp may become inclosed by a sheath (envelope or basket) of sterile tissue called the *pericarp*. The diploid plant produced from diploid carpospores (in most life histories) is called a *tetrasporophyte*, and produces *tetrasporangia* in which *tetraspores* (haploid) are cut out.

LIFE HISTORIES

In culture of marine red algae it has been shown that sexuality of plants and the behavior of tetraspores can vary under environmental and nutritional fluctuations. In *Pachymeniopsis* several spores in a tetrasporangium germinate in such a way as to form a single thallus, known as *syntagmatic germination*. Stages in the life cycle, gametophytic and sporophytic, vary seasonally according to genus and even species. The behavior of the zygote and the life history stages involved may be summarized:

1. The zygote undergoes meiosis and forms carpospores (haploid) contained within the carpogonium. Carpospores haploid. *Porphyra.*

2. Undifferentiated gonimoblasts develop directly from the carpogonium after the zygote has undergone meiosis and carpospores are formed at their apices. Carpospore haploid. *Batrachospermum.*

3. Carpogonium, connecting filaments or diploid zygote nucleus fuse with auxiliary cells and from these carpospores are produced. Carpospores diploid. *Scinaia.*

4. The diploid nucleus is transferred to special nutritive cells of the gametophyte. Carpospores diploid. *Gigartina.*

5. Carpospore formation is distributed widely throughout the gametophyte by wandering filaments that grow from the carpogonium and which fuse with several different nurse cells or nurse tissue so that several carpospore crops are produced in different places all from one fertilization. The cystocarp actually consists of a complex of several carposporophytes. Carpospores diploid. *Gelidium.*

The carpospores, when haploid, produce male and/or female gametophytes. If diploid they produce diploid plants (tetrasporophytes as mentioned) in which, through meiosis, the tetraspores are formed. These in turn produce gametophytes.

In referring to these types of life history it is customary to use definitive terms. A *haplont* is a gametophyte which alternates with a zygote stage only (*Batrachospermum*, e.g.). A *diplont* is a sexual diploid plant which produces only gametes (the sporophyte generation is eliminated). A *diplohaplont* refers to a plant which has an alternation of a haploid and diploid generation (*Polysiphonia*). In rare instances such as *Lomentaria rosea* the diploid plant produces only tetraspores (diploid) which in turn produce more diploid plants. Such a plant is called a *haplobiont.*

A helpful suggestion has been made in reference to classifying life cycles. One, the *monomorphous*, is a life cycle which involves one kind of individual marine plant, such as *Porphyra*, and most of the fresh-water algae. A *dimorphous* life cycle is one which involves two different types of individuals that bear different types of reproductive structures: gametangia (gametes) or sporangia (spores). There are two types of dimorphous situations. In one, the two kinds of plants are morphologically similar (*Ectocarpus* in the brown algae, *Polysiphonia* in the red algae), and are thus called *homomorphous*. In the second the two plants are different, and are thus called *heteromorphous* (*Asparigopsis* in the Bonnemaisoniaceae).

The tetraspores may produce either male or female gametophytes (dioecious or heterothallic gametophytes), or they may produce monoecious or monothallic gametophytes.

By studying the carposporophyte generation, its composition and development, phycologists have been able to construct many evolutionary trends within families of the Rhodophyta (see Table 7.1). In culture, red algae show all manner of curious variations. Female plants produce spermatangia; male plants produce tetraspores and tetraspores may produce only tetrasporophytes.

The evolutionary position of orders within the Rhodophyta is subject to more than one phylogenetic concept, but in any event the reproductive organs and the auxiliary cell are used as the basis for arrangements. Following is a common scheme, accepted by many students of the red algae, in which there is a progressive development of the procarp and the carposporophyte (if not an evolutionary trend):

I. Orders in which the procarp is lacking.
    A. Auxiliary cells lacking.[1]
        1. Plants with haplont life histories. **Nemalionales** (some)
        2. Plants with haplodiplont life histories **Gelidiales**

II. Orders which possess a procarp
    A. Auxiliary cells differentiated before fertilization
        1. Auxiliary cells unspecialized **Cryptonemiales**
        2. Auxiliary cells specialized and clearly differentiated **Gigartinales**
    B. Auxiliary cells differentiated after fertilization
        1. Auxiliary cells actually segmented previously from the cell of a branch, but do not develop and become recognizable after fertilization **Rhodymeniales**

---

[1] Also other orders of the Bangioideae as recognized by some students of the Rhodophyta (see p. 14).

2. Auxiliary cell cut off from the supporting cell of the carpogonial branch (or from another pericentral cell at the same level) after fertilization has occurred (see *Polysiphonia*) **Ceramiales**

Representative Orders and Genera

There are two major divisions (Subphyla) of the Rhodophyta. The Bangioideae, with four orders (24 genera, 90 species), are regarded as the more primitive. They may be unicellular, colonial, pseudofilamentous, and membranous plants, and microscopic or semi-microscopic to a few centimeters in length. Cells have no wall pits (although such pits are present in *Compsopogon*). The carpogonium is a metamorphosed vegetative cell, or a cell terminal on a simple branch. Spermatia are formed by cleavage of the contents of a specialized vegetative cell. Carpospores are produced by the meiotic division of the zygote within the carpogonium and these regenerate new gametophytes.

The large subphylum is the Florideae, comprised of six orders, many families, about 534 genera, and in all some 3650 species. Plants are filaments, complexes of filaments, or frond- and leaf-like. Here the cell walls have interconnecting pits. The spermatangia are budded from vegetative cells or from special cells on differentiated branches. Carpogonia are clearly specialized, flask-shaped cells, borne on special branches (the terminal cell) or on special filaments of the thallus. In addition to germinating directly within the carpogonium, the zygote may initiate a multicellular carposporophyte (see p. 236). In many families spores from the carposporophyte produce tetrasporophytes which alternate with the sexual plants.

Subphylum Bangioideae (Protofloridae): Order Porphyridiales

FAMILY PORPHYRIDIACEAE

Porphyridium Naegeli, 1849 (Plate XVI, Fig. 234), a unicellular genus, is difficult of classification and its correct position long has been held in question. A fresh-water genus, it is one of the few known, one-celled red algae. There is no evidence that this type of plant is ancestral in position. *Porphyridium* forms purplish-red to black-purple films on damp soil, especially in greenhouses. The cells are globose or subglobose, embedded in a gelatinous sheath, the individual sheaths confluent with the common matrix. The single chloroplast is stellate with one pyrenoid. The central body has been identified as anabaenin and has been observed to divide during mitosis.

TABLE 7.1

1. **Batrachospermum.** Monomorphous haplont

   gametophyte thallus ⟨ spermatangium ⟶ spermatia ⟶ zygote (2n) / carpogonium ⟶ egg ⟶

   carposporangia ⟵ gonimoblast filaments ⟵ meiosis

   carpospores ⟶ gametophytes

2. **Bonnemaisonia** (some species). Dimorphous haplont

   gametophyte thallus ⟨ spermatangia ⟶ spermatia ⟶ zygote (2n) / carpogonium ⟶ egg ⟶

   tetraspores (1n) ⟵ heteromorphic haploid ⟵ meiosis

   gametophyte

3. **Liagora.** Monomorphous diplohaplont

   gametophyte ⟨ carpogonium ⟶ egg ⟶ zygote (2n) / spermatangia ⟶ spermatia ⟶

   meiosis ⟵ tetrasporangia ⟵ gominoblast

   carpotetraspores ⟶ gametophytes

4. **Asparagopsis.** Heteromorphous haplont

   gametophyte ⟨ carpogonium ⟶ egg ⟶ zygote (2n) ⟶ meiosis / spermatangia ⟶ spermatia ⟶

   tetraspores ⟵ haploid tetrasporophyte ⟵ carpospores

   gametophytes

5. **Nemalion vermiculare Galaxaura.** Heteromorphous diplohaplont

   gametophyte ⟨ carpogonium ⟶ egg ⟶ zygote (2n) / spermatangia ⟶ spermatium ⟶

   carpospores (2n) /

   gametophytes ⟵ tetraspores (1n) ⟵ meiosis ⟵ tetrasporophyte

244

6. **Polysiphonia.** Monomorphous diplohaplont (mostly heterothallic)

gametophyte $\langle$ carpogonium $\longrightarrow$ egg $\searrow$ zygote (2n)
spermatangia $\longrightarrow$ spermatia $\nearrow$

carposporophyte (2n)

tetraspores (1n) $\longleftarrow$ meiosis $\longleftarrow$ tetrasporophyte (2n) $\longleftarrow$ carpospores (2n)

gametophytes

7. **Phyllophora Brodiaei.** Monomorphous diplohaplont

gametophyte $\langle$ carpogonium $\longrightarrow$ egg $\searrow$ zygote (2n) auxiliary cell
spermatangia $\longrightarrow$ spermatia $\nearrow$

gonimoblasts (2n)

tetraspores $\longleftarrow$ meiosis $\longleftarrow$ diploid tetraspore nemathecia

gametophytes

8. **Phyllophora membranifolia.** Dimorphous

gametophytes $\langle$ carpogonium $\longrightarrow$ egg $\longrightarrow$ zygote (2n)
spermatangia $\longrightarrow$ spermatia $\nearrow$ auxiliary cell

tetrasporic plant (2n) $\longleftarrow$ carpospores $\longleftarrow$ gonimoblast filaments

tetrasporangia $\longrightarrow$ meiosis $\longrightarrow$ tetraspores (1n)

gametophytes (male and female)

9. **Ahnfeltia.** Monomorphous haplont.

haploid plant $\longrightarrow$ monospore nemathecia $\longrightarrow$ monospores $\longrightarrow$ haploid plant

10. **Lomentaria rosea.** Monomorphous diplont.

diploid plant (2n) $\longrightarrow$ diploid tetraspores (2n) $\longrightarrow$ diploid plant (2n)

11. **Scinaia.** Monomorphous haplont (as in **Nemalion**)

gametophyte $\langle$ carpogonium $\longrightarrow$ egg $\searrow$ zygote (2n)
spermatangia $\longrightarrow$ spermatia $\nearrow$

meiosis $\longrightarrow$ gonimoblast (1n)

carpospores $\longrightarrow$ gametophytes

245

Reproduction is by cell division or by a cell forming an akinete-like resting stage which does not multiply but only perpetuates the plant. Occasionally a protoplast will escape from the wall as a neutral spore. In a related genus, *Rhodospora*, internal aplanospores are produced.

FAMILY GONIOTRICHACEAE

This is a family of uniseriate or multiseriate pseudofilaments, the cells arranged in a linear fashion within a wide, gelatinous sheath. Species are both fresh-water and marine.

Goniotrichum Kuetzing, 1843 (*Erythrotrichia* Aresch.?) (Plate XVI, Fig. 231), a marine genus, has globular or subcylindrical cells, loosely arranged in a gelatinous membrane. The filaments in tufts are attached (mostly epiphytic), and branch dichotomously. The single chloroplast is stellate. Reproduction is by monospores.

The genus is widely distributed from the Tropics to the Subarctic.

Asterocystis Gobi, 1878 (*Chroodactylon* Hansg.) (Plate XVI, Fig. 233), is the fresh-water counterpart of *Goniotrichum*. The branched filaments are usually epiphytic on other filamentous algae. The stellate chloroplasts are bright blue, making the plants very conspicuous in algal collections. This genus too reproduces by neutral spores. *Asterocystis* is widely distributed over the world but individually is rather rare, occurring as isolates.

FAMILY ERYTHROTRICHACEAE

This family includes Bangiales in which there is a true filament of adjoined cells forming slender, mostly unbranched thalli some of which are microscopic. The filaments are mostly uniseriate and reproduction is by monospores. Plants are both marine and fresh-water.

Erythrotrichia Areschoug, 1850 (Plate XVII, Fig. 236), a marine plant, consists of erect, epiphytic filaments from a hold-fast formed by rhizoidal lobes of the basal cell, or by rhizoidal branches. Chloroplasts are stellate and bright red, as are the monospores, the only known means of reproduction. (Sometimes regarded as synonymous with *Goniotrichum*.)

FAMILY BANGIACEAE

These are filamentous plants, multiseriate with basal-distal differentiation. Neutral spores are formed by the protoplast dividing into several elements. Simple organs are used in sexual reproduction, the zygote undergoing meiosis to form carpospores. The carpogonium is a metamorphosed vegetative cell which has a short lobe-like extension as a trichogyne. Spermatia are formed by divisions within a vegetative cell which metamorphoses as a spermatangium.

Bangia Lyngbye, 1819 (Plate XVI, Fig. 232), a marine (with pole to pole distribution) and fresh-water genus, begins as an unbranched, uniseriate filament but becomes multiseriate by longitudinal wall formation in the upper portions of the plant, a short distance behind the apical cell. The lower and basal cells give rise to downward-growing extensions which penetrate through the filament sheath. The chloroplasts are axial and stellate, reddish in color. As mentioned above, neutral spores are commonly used in asexual reproduction.

Plants are dioecious. A female plant has certain cells which enlarge somewhat and put forth a slight extension (comparable to a trichogyne) to the exterior. In male plants vegetative cells undergo cleavage to form several spermatia per spermatangium. The union of a drifting spermatium with the trichogyne results in fertilization. The zygote germinates immediately by meiosis, producing four or eight carpospores. These in turn produce filamentous gametophytes. Presumably, two spores have a male and two a female determiner. In germinating the spores first develop a filamentous phase resembling the genus *Conchocelis*. These stages of *Bangia* are prostrate, branched plants that penetrate and develop within shells. Of interest is the fact that *B. fuscopurpurea* spores from plants growing in northern waters grow directly into typical *Bangia* filaments, whereas plants in tropical waters (Mediterranean) produce spores which develop the *Conchocelis* stage. This phase in the *Bangia* life history is significantly similar morphologically to the comparative stage in *Porphyra* (see below). It is practically conclusive that spores produced in the *Conchocelis* stage germinate to form *Bangia* plants, but the complete life cycle invites further study.

Bangia grows attached to stones and wood in flowing water and on solid substrates along sea coasts. The fresh-water species *B. atropurpurea* appears to be more common in Europe than in North America.

Porphyra Agardh, 1824 (Plate XVII, Fig. 238), a marine genus, is a monostromatic sheet of cells which are embedded in a thick layer of gelatinous material in such a way that the protoplasts are widely separated from one another. The fronds appear as bright red, thin, "lettuce" leaves attached at the base to rocks. They occur commonly in the intertidal zone, but are often epiphytic. Plants are pale along their margins when reproductive (for some species occurring from October to

December). In favorable situations the adhesive disc may proliferate the plant by sending out lateral and upright growths. As with other members of the order, the chloroplast is stellate and axial, with a central pyrenoid. Plants are either monoecious or dioecious. Whole sections of the stroma may metamorphose at one time as spermatangia and produce as many as 128 spermatia per cell. Marginal cells become carpogonia by extending a lobe-like trichogyne.

The fertilized egg produces carpospores by meiosis within the carpogonium (in some species at least) and, as in *Bangia*, they develop embryonic *Conchocelis* stages (see p. 247). According to students of the genus, adult *Porphyra* plants develop from monospores produced on these embryonic growths. It is known that in some species carpospores develop a prostrate stroma of cells which bud off *Porphyra*-type adult plants. The Japanese who use *Porphyra* for food have capitalized on the knowledge that there are two phases in the life history, and have been able to grow this plant in extensive seaside cultures.

Order Compsopogonales

FAMILY COMPSOPOGONACEAE

Compsopogon Montagne, 1850 (Plate XVII, Fig. 239), is sometimes placed in the Erythrotrichaceae. This fresh-water, branched, filamentous genus grows in flowing water, and is usually epiphytic. Plants are attached by rhizoidal, prostrate growths at first, but become free-floating and sometimes troublesome in irrigation ditches, especially in the southwest United States. The plants produce monospores which germinate to develop a prostrate, branching system as a juvenile stage. This gives rise to the erect, eventually corticated filaments. This genus shows a heterotrichous habit similar to that of *Lemanea* and *Batrachospermum*. The filament is basically uniseriate, growing from an apical cell. But behind the apex the cells divide repeatedly by both longitudinal and transverse walls so that a compact cortex is produced. The cells may have many small, disc-like chloroplasts.

Subphylum Florideae

In comparison with the Bangiaceae this group is characterized by having much more complex thalli (mostly macroscopic), more complex sex organs and reproductive processes, and in having cells with interconnecting wall pits. Architecture includes both monaxial and multiaxial filaments. In the former there is one main filament developing by an apical cell. Derivatives of this cut off lateral branches, or lateral (pericentral) cells (as in *Polysiphonia*, e.g.). In the multiaxial thallus there are several filaments involved, each with its apical cell. From apical cell derivatives lateral branches develop, either forming a compact, parenchymatous thallus, or repeatedly branched, sometimes fleshy, fronds.

Order Nemalionales

In this order the carpogonial branch is simple, arising from a vegetative cell. The auxiliary cell is lacking. The thallus may become complex when secondary or adventitious meristematic cells or regions develop (often at the base of branches). Plants may be haplobiontic, with meiosis occurring in the carpogonium, but in some *Nemalion* and in **Galaxaura** (Plate XVII, Fig. 240) there is a diplobiont alternation of generations.

Family Chantransiaceae (Acrochaetiaceae)

This family represents the simple type of thallus among the Florideae. Plants may be sparsely or abundantly branched filaments, and most are semi-microscopic. Reproduction is by monospores and also sexually by spermatia and eggs. Several genera are incompletely known and are only tentatively assigned to this family. Research on them might be fruitful in determining evolutionary relationships.

Audouinella Bory, 1823, emend. Papenfuss, 1945 (Plate XVII, Fig. 241), is an attached, sparsely but repeatedly branched filament of cylindrical cells, with little or no tapering at the anterior end. Plants are gray- to violet-green in color, with plate-like or ribbon-like, usually twisted chloroplasts (one per cell). Species occur in flowing water such as rapids, dams, and waterfalls.

Early in the development of the filament, monosporangia (with a monospore each) are formed at the ends of short branches. The monospores form new plants and this reproductive method is repeated.

Plants may be either monoecious or dioecious. The carpogonia, with a relatively long, narrow trichogyne, occur at the ends of short, special carpogonial branches. Spermatangia are budded off in rather dense sori at the ends of vegetative branches. The zygote possibly divides by meiosis to initiate gonimoblast filaments (one or two cells long) on which are borne one or a series of carpospores. But it is likely that carpospores produce tetrasporic plants because such plants have been found. This would indicate an alternation of a haploid, sexual generation with a diploid, sporophyte generation, with meiosis occurring with the formation of tetraspores.

Acrochaetium Naegeli, 1861 (Plate XVIII, Fig. 242), is a genus of many species, growing as epiphytes on various larger algae. Plants are essentially microscopic, but form visible, bright pink tufts, consisting of uniseriate filaments, sparsely or abundantly branched. There are erect filaments from prostrate growths (or sometimes from a single, large basal cell). Some branches end in hairs. The chloroplasts vary from one to several parietal plates (often lobed).

In some species sporangia tend to be borne unilaterally along the ultimate branches. These may bear one or two to several spores. Spermatangia usually occur in small aggregates along the branchlets. The carpogonia are simple and one-celled, terminal on a one-celled stalk, or intercalary. The gonimoblasts develop from the carpogonium. Reduction division occurs with the formation of spores.

Rhodochorton Naegeli, 1861 (Plate XVIII, Fig. 243), a marine genus, appears much like *Audouinella*, but the erect filaments arise from a prostrate plate. Plants grow on rocks or as epiphytes, or as epizoophytes on bryozoans. The upright filaments have cylindrical cells with many fusiform or disc-like chloroplasts. Sporangia producing four spores each are borne at the ends of short branches, especially near the apex of the thallus. The carpogonium is simple, and may be sessile or terminal on a short branch. The life history appears to be very simple but subsequent studies may elaborate it.

FAMILY BATRACHOSPERMACEAE

This family has five fresh-water genera which are monaxial but have different degrees of complexity in the amount of involvement with secondary vegetative elements and branchings. In some there is a juvenile stage which reproduces by monospores repeatedly. This phase eventually gives rise to the adult stage. As far as known, plants are monomorphous haplonts.

Batrachospermum Roth, 1797 (Plate XVIII, Fig. 244), is a highly branched, fresh-water genus (one species reported from brackish water) which grows in length by an apical cell. Behind the apical cell, its derivatives in the filament after elongating cut off four small cells in a whorl at the apical end. These initiate lateral branches of elliptical or pear-shaped cells which are much smaller than those of the main axis (which for the most part are cylindrical). Thus the thallus appears as an axial filament with whorls of dense branches, all encased in a

PLATE XVIII

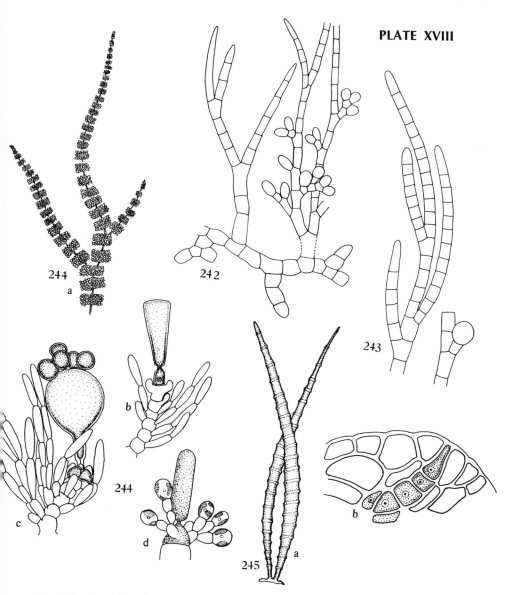

Fig. 242. **Acrochaetium** sp, portion of thallus with monosporangia

Fig. 243. **Rhodochorton** sp

Fig. 244. **Batrachospermum:** a, habit of thallus; b, **B. sinense,** carpogonial branch showing prominent trichogyne (redrawn from
Jao); c, carpogonium and spermatia of **B. sinense;** d, gonimoblasts

Fig. 245. **Lemanea** sp: a, habit; b, **L. fluviatile,** carpogonial branch (redrawn from Kylin)

PLATE XVIII

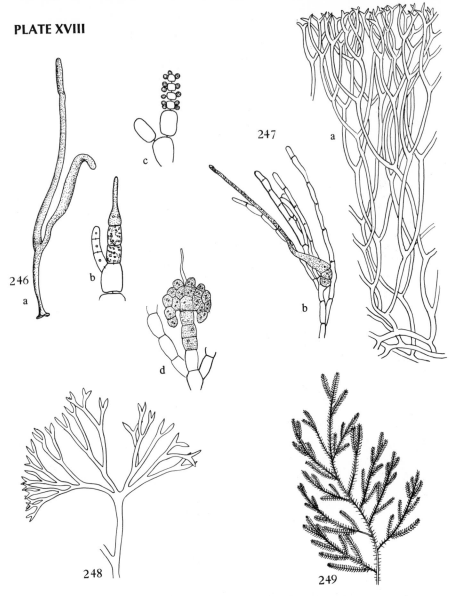

Fig. 246. **Nemalion multifidum**: a, habit; b, carpogonial branch; c, spermatial branch; d, carpospore-formation, developing gonimoblasts (redrawn from Smith)

Fig. 247. **Liagora erecta:** a, habit; b, carpogonial branch (redrawn from Balakrishnan)

Fig. 248. **Scinaia** sp, (drawn from herbarium specimen)

Fig. 249. **Bonnemaisonia** sp

soft, amorphous mucilage. Many of the terminal cells bear setae. From the same nodes that give rise to the whorls, branches of unlimited growth may develop also; these repeat the branchings of the main filament. Further, from the nodes, lateral filaments are put forth that creep down along the main axial cells to form a loose cortex. These in turn may give rise to short, out-turned branches.

The thallus of *Batrachospermum* may be up to 15 centimeters in length, and is usually gray-green or violet-green to tan-colored (according to species). The chloroplast is diffuse (or there may be several parietal discs), with one pyrenoid.

Species are either monoecious or dioecious. The spermatangia appear as budded, grape-like cells at the apices of certain branches of the whorls. Near the base of a vegetative branch a special three- to five-celled branch develops. The terminal cell is a carpogonium, with a prominent, inflated trichogyne which is either cylindrical or spatula-shaped, according to species. The lower cells of the carpogonial branch give rise to short, erect filaments that grow up and eventually partly enclose the carpogonium.

The zygote divides by meiosis and then by mitosis. The four resulting nuclei then continue to divide and to pass out into short gonimoblast filaments that develop from the base of the carpogonium. The carposporangia are cut off at the tip of these short proliferations and the dense clusters form "cabbage heads" throughout the whorls of sexually mature plants. The carpospores (haploid) germinate to form juvenile plants with the habit and appearance of *Audouinella*. These reproduce by monospores repeatedly (as described previously). Eventually a juvenile plant will give rise to a branch with a growth plan characteristic of the adult *Batrachospermum*. The life cycle, although there are two expressions in the haploid phase, is one in which the gametophyte generation alternates with a one-celled diploid (zygote) stage.

Batrachospermum occurs as arbuscular tufts, or streaming bush-like growths on sticks and stones in flowing water. Some species occur in pools, especially acid *Sphagnum* bogs where they develop well on the vertical sides of clear, cold pools in the mat.

Sirodotia Kylin, 1912, is a genus very similar to *Batrachospermum* in vegetative morphology. But it differs in that the gonimoblast filaments are long and wandering. Carposporangia are formed in scattered clusters, borne laterally from the gonimoblast here and there throughout the thallus. Thus, there is an advantageous multiplication of carpospores from one fertilization. Plants are found in fresh water (usually flowing); although one specie has been found in brackish situations.

FAMILY LEMANEACEAE

In this family the thalli are cartilaginous or firmly gelatinous, solid or hollow, branched or unbranched, and macroscopic in size. The plants grow in fresh or in mildly brackish water. The thallus is a complex of filaments, but essentially there is a main axial filament with an apical growing cell. The carposporangia develop from all cells of the gonimoblasts, not cut off only at the tips as in *Batrachospermum*. The gonimoblasts themselves are several cells in length.

Lemanea Bory, 1808, emend. Agardh, 1828 (Plate XVIII, Fig. 245), grows as cartilaginous, finger-like spurs with swollen nodes, and internodes. The thalli are tan-colored or olive-brown to blackish, and occur in swiftly flowing water at the brink of dams and waterfalls, often forming dense patches. Some species occur on boulders in cold, mountain or woodland streams; *Lemanea* rarely grows in brackish water.

When examined internally and microscopically the thallus is seen to be a complex of filaments. Essentially there is an axial filament and its lateral threads that form a cable through the center of the spur. From cells of the axial filament a whorl of four branches radiate outward and at their tips cell division gives rise to a compact cortical zone and "epidermal" layer. Hence the thallus appears more or less hollow, consisting of a central cable and a somewhat removed cortex. The architecture arises essentially from a primary filament that grows by an apical cell. This cell adds to the length of the filament by transverse wall formation only. A millimeter or so below the apical cell its derivatives in the main filament undergo longitudinal (periclinal) division which results in a central cell surrounded by four lateral or *pericentral* cells. Then the axial cells undergo a remarkable elongation but do not divide. This results in open spaces, with a long cell surrounded near its apical end by four pericentral cells. The central axis becomes intertwined by smaller *hyphal* filaments so that a sort of cable is produced. The pericentral cells elongate radially and by continued cell division at their tips form a rather complex cortex (composed of longitudinal filaments). Each axial cell therefore has four radiating ray *cells* or tie cells that support the outer "shell" or cortex. The outer cells are chloroplast-bearing.

When plants are mature and sex organs begin to develop, prominent pore-like openings appear at the nodes of the "fingers." In the node region spermatangia form on the surface. In the same plant, carpogonial filaments develop on special branches within the nodal tissue or between the nodes. The zygote undergoes meiosis and the usual gonimoblast filaments develop from the carpogonium. Many carpospores are formed from each zygote because each cell of the gonimoblast becomes a carposporangium. Carpospores are liberated through the nodal pores. The haploid spores form an embryonic or prothallial filamentous stage (comparable to the juvenile stage of *Batrachospermum*) and from them *Audouinella*-like (*Chantransia*) plants develop. Later from these the adult *Lemanea* thallus appears as a special branch. According to Magne reduction division may occur in the prothallial filament so that the gametophyte actually grows as a branch on a diploid generation.

FAMILY HELMINTHOCLADIACEAE

This is a relatively small family with eight genera and some 88 species. The thallus is complex, with axial cells and out-turned branches which are compact externally, as in *Lemanea*. These branches form a dense cortex and are enclosed by mucilage. Plants are mostly elongate, linear, and sparsely branched cylinders.

Nemalion Targioni-Tozzetti, 1818 (Plate XVIII, Fig. 246), grows as a slender, reddish, and sometimes branched "worm" on rocks in the intertidal zone, especially where there is very active water. The thallus is constructed of many axial filaments, each with an apical growing cell. The intertwined axial filaments give rise to lateral branches which have fascicles of secondary branches at the outer perimeter. The plants are softly cartilaginous because of the rather firm mucilage in which the filaments are encased. The tips of out-turned branches bear a colorless hair.

At the tips of certain branches a vegetative cell may divide rapidly to form a series of about five colorless cells that constitute a *spermatangial branch*. From each cell of the branch a radially arranged quartet of spermatangia are cut off, the contents of which are pigmented spermatia.

On a basal (inner) cell of a lateral branch from the main axis, a cell known as the *carpogonial branch initial* is cut off. The cell, by two or as many as four successive divisions, forms a branch of from three to five cells, constituting the carpogonial filament. The terminal cell of this branch is a carpogonium. When mature it has a very long, slender trichogyne that reaches toward the exterior of the thallus.

Curiously, the nucleus of the spermatium divides after it comes in contact with the trichogyne. After the walls have dissolved where the spermatium adjoins the trichogyne both sperm nuclei move into the carpogonium, one of them migrating down to the egg nucleus. The zygote nucleus soon divides with meiosis and a wall forms to create an outer (upper) and an inner (lower) cell. The nucleus in the latter dissolves, but this cell becomes useful later. The outer cell nucleus divides by mitosis and develops a protuberance from the carpogonial wall. The bulge becomes separated by a transverse wall and this becomes the primary (initial) cell for the development of a gonimoblast filament. Successive divisions of the outer cell nucleus form additional initials so that a dense head of gonimoblasts develops around the base of the carpogonium. Meanwhile the upper cell of the carpogonial branch fuses with the lowermost of the two cells formed when the zygote divided. This fusion constitutes a placental cell which contributes food to the development of the gonimoblasts.

The terminal cells cut off at the tip of the gonimoblasts become carposporangia and each produces a carpospore. The old carpogonium and its surrounding cluster of carposporangia together with the placental cell constitute a carposporophyte. The carpospores produce an embryonic, filamentous stage that endures throughout the winter and later gives rise to the adult thallus. This is accomplished by the spore forming a parenchymatous mass of cells. From these a number of erect filaments develop which intertwine to produce a single Nemalion thallus. The plants develop as annuals. In at least one species of Nemalion (N. vermiculare) the carpospores are diploid and form small filamentous tetrasporophytes which produce tetraspores by meiosis, showing a heteromorphic alternation of generations.

Liagora Lamouroux, 1812 (Plate XVIII, Fig. 247), a genus which inhabits the sublittoral, illustrates an unusual type of life history (see p. 244). Liagora is a relative of Nemalion, but is light-colored because of an external deposit of lime. Plants are highly branched tufts, rather soft and flexible in some species or somewhat rigid in others. The branches may be at right angles to one another, giving a test-tube brush effect. The branching is repeatedly dichotomous, and tends to be fasciculate in the outer parts of the thallus. The genus is confined mostly to warm water, such as the Red Sea and the Mediterranean. The internal structure varies from Nemalion also in that the central axis contains large cells, intertwined with slender filaments. According to some observations, the life history differs in that carpospores at the carpogonium divide (in a sense germinating in situ) to form four tetraspores. It is thought that these are produced by meiosis, the tetraspores producing haploid plants. Other and more convincing studies show that in L. farinosa, at least, the carpospores, after liberation, grow into a prostrate filamentous stage with some erect branches. This is known as the Acrochaetium-stage. On these plants tetraspores, as well as monospores, are formed by meiosis, and these in turn produce prostrate filaments that later bud off branches which become adult gametophytes. Monospores from the sporophyte regenerate other tetrasporic plants. Hence this life cycle is heteromorphic, with the sporophyte as the recessive phase.

FAMILY CHAETANGIACEAE

A pericarp develops around the carposporophyte in this family. Plants are erect, usually bushy, and somewhat cartilaginous. Rarely are there external lime deposits. Internally the axial filaments form laterals very similar to the organization of the Helminthocladiaceae (q.v., p. 255).

Scinaia Bivona, 1882 (Plate XVIII, Fig. 248), is a dichotomously branched and gelatinous-textured, cylindrical thallus, mostly of deep water. Plants are attached by a disc-like hold-fast. There is an axial core which gives rise to out-turned, dichotomous branches. Growth is apical and gives rise to filaments in the core. The cells of the out-turned branches are of two sizes and are pigmented, whereas the terminal cells that form a compact epidermis are colorless. Some of the epidermal cells, the smaller of two sizes, metamorphose as monosporangia. Other small cells may produce hairs.

Spermatangia develop from the inner branches but eventually are exposed at the surface. The carpogonial branch likewise develops as a lateral from the out-turned dichotomous filaments, and consists of but three cells, with the terminal cell the carpogonium. The intermediate one of the three cuts off four *nurse* cells and the lower cell develops sterile filaments which eventually extend up and around the gonimoblasts and their terminal carposporangia. After fertilization the diploid nucleus then undergoes meiosis and, at least in *S. furcellata*, all but one of the four nuclei so formed disintegrate. The remaining nucleus becomes the primary gonimoblast nucleus. As the gonimoblast develops it branches to form a number of carposporangia. Each cell produces a single carpospore which escapes after a pore-like opening appears in the outer layers of the thallus. Carpospores develop haploid sexual plants.

FAMILY BONNEMAISONIACEAE

This family includes slender, gelatinous, branched plants with a pericarp that develops from tissues in the vicinity of the carpogonium. Typical of the order, there is an axial series of cells from apical growth and this axis is enclosed by a rather thick cortex; short branches form a compact external surface.

Bonnemaisonia Agardh, 1822 (Plate XVIII, Fig. 249), is a feathery, branched thallus in which fine laterals arise from a much more robust axis in a pinnate fashion. The genus grows attached (on rocks or as epiphytes) along European and North American west coasts. The sex organs are similar to those of the Nemalionales. Reproduction varies somewhat, and the life cycle is uncertain in that the gonimoblasts may produce either haploid or (possibly) diploid carpospores. A pericarp of branched filaments develops around the gonimoblasts and their terminal carpospores. The carpospores, if haploid, produce minute filaments on which tetraspores are formed (without meiosis). The tetraspores in turn produce the larger gametophytic plants. The tetrasporophytes have been identified in the past as species of *Hymenoclonium*, *Falkenbergia* and *Trailiella*. Feldmann has shown that in *B. asparigoides* the minute filamentous stage can give rise to gametophytic branches without producing tetraspores.

Asparagopsis Montagne, 1940 (Plate XIX, Fig. 250), is a repeatedly and bushily branched thallus, firmly gelatinous and attached in the sublittoral zone. The general aspect is that of a feathery frond, the branchlets being mostly alternate. Some branches form prominent hooks. In the development of the thallus a space forms between the axis and the peripheral cortex. The pericarp forms from the tissues immediately adjacent to the carpogonial branch. Carpospores are formed by meiosis and these germinate to form filamentous plants which have been described previously as a separate taxon, *Falkenbergia rufanilosa*, or as species of *Trailiella*. This phase is tetrasporic and is, of course, haploid. Tetraspores form the adult plant.

Order Gelidiales

The genera of this order are narrow, branched, gelatinous thalli in which a complex carposporophyte (not merely carpospores) originates directly from the carpogonium (plants diplobiontic). The construction is multiaxial with apical growth — large central axial filaments and a cortex of compact, smaller cells. Ordinarily auxiliary cells are not formed. The entire thallus is firmly gelatinous.

Gelidium Lamouroux, 1813 (Plate XIX, Fig. 251), consists of plants which are somewhat pinnately branched, gelatinous, flattened cylinders, erect and relatively cartilaginous. Thalli grow in dense, sometimes extensive, patches on rocks and are often exposed at low tide. The plants have persisting basal extensions which produce new shoots an-

PLATE XIX

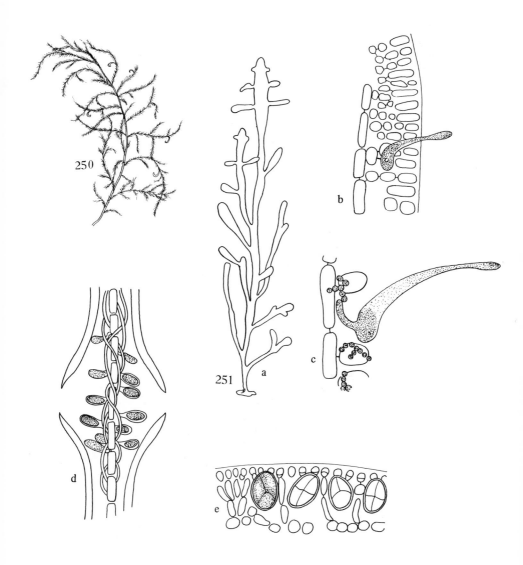

Fig. 250. **Asparagopsis**

Fig. 251. **Gelidium:** a, habit; b, carpogonium; c, fusion of carpogonium with nurse cells; d, carpospore-formation; e, tetrasporangium

PLATE XIX

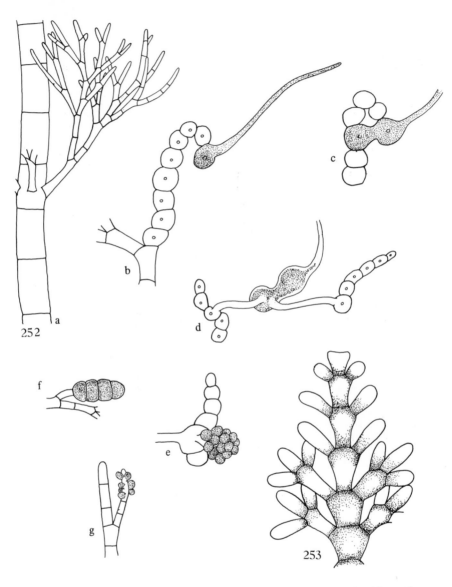

Fig. 252. **Dudresnya:** a, portion of axis with one whorl of branches, b, carpogonial branch; c, fusion of carpogonium with fourth cell of carpogonial branch; d, ooblasts fusing with nurse cells (auxiliary); e, gonimoblasts developing from nurse cells; f, tetrasporangium; g, spermatangia

Fig. 253. **Corallina**

PLATE XIX

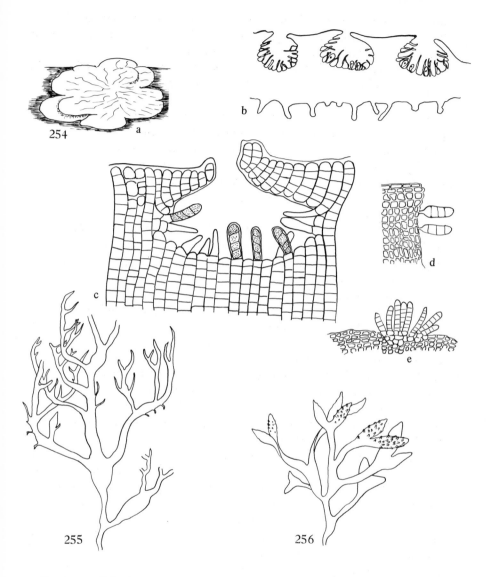

Fig. 254. **Hildenbrandtia:** a, habit of crustose growth; b, diagram of cross section, location of tetrasporangia in conceptacle; c, section of conceptacle wall and tetrasporangia; d, development of erect filaments from surface of thallus

Fig. 255. **Gracilaria**

Fig. 256. **Gigartina**

nually. Plants vary from 1 cm. to 1 m. in length. Each shoot and branch has a single, actively dividing apical cell. This is the most important of the genera from which agar-agar is obtained.

In development, older axial cells cut off four radiately arranged laterals, or pericentral cells. Each one of these produces a lateral branch which at the tips is repeatedly branched and adds to the outer, compact cortex.

Plants are dioecious. The spermatangia develop in extensive, elliptical patches on both surfaces of the somewhat flattened branches of the thallus, and sometimes on specialized branches. Female plants bear carpogonia on special vegetative branches of the frond which have a prominent invagination at the tip. A short distance back from the apical cell a basal cell of an out-turned vegetative branch within the thallus cuts off a cell which becomes a carpogonium, the trichogyne of which is a long neck-like extension that reaches out beyond the surface of the thallus. Meanwhile, from some of the four pericentral cells that were segmented from each axial cell, chains of small cells are developed. These are dense with food material and eventually come to have a nutritive function (nurse cells).

After fertilization a long, wandering, many-celled gonimoblast filament grows out of the carpogonium, with the nucleus being diploid. This filament grows along the axial row of cells in the thallus and among the nurse filaments. Here and there gonimoblasts develop, producing clusters of vertically extending, one-celled carposporangial branches. Each branch produces a carpospore. These escape by the cooperation of the vegetative thallus which forms pores in the cortex in the region of the carpospore sorus. The sorus well might be a composite of spores produced by gonimoblasts from several different carpogonia.

Carpospores produce tetrasporophytes which are morphologically similar to the sexual plants. Near the surface of flattened branches certain cells enlarge and function as tetrasporangia. In these the diploid nucleus divides meiotically to form four, cruciately arranged tetraspores, which in turn produce sexual plants. The spores do not develop walls until they have been liberated. As in many of the other Rhodophyta, the spore first forms a prostrate pad of cells. From this primary growth more than one apical cell may be differentiated, each one of which initiates a new filament.

Order Cryptonemiales

This is a very large order of highly diversified morphologies and with several variable types of gonimoblast development. There are usually nine (or 12) families recognized, and some 85 genera. A chief characteristic of many is the possession of sunken pits or conceptacles, on the walls of which reproductive structures are borne (hence the crypt portion of the order name). Reproductively, one characteristic is the possession of auxiliary cells that are produced on special branches in the thallus. The auxiliary filaments may be cut off from the same initial cell that produces the carpogonial filament, or they may be borne elsewhere in the thallus.

Plants may be uniaxial or multiaxial. A large group in this order are lime-encrusted, calcareous corallines; others are soft and membranous thalli.

Family Dumontiaceae

In this family there is an illustration of the ability of the carposporophyte to increase greatly the reproductive capacity. As in most other families, the carpogonial branch develops from near the base of lateral, out-turned elements in the cortex. It consists of as many as nine cells and this filament may have one or two branches as well as some short, sterile filaments borne on the basal or initial cell of the carpogonial branch. As usual, the terminal cell functions as the carpogonium, and two of the lower cells become differentiated as nurse cells. On nearby special branches certain cells are specialized as auxiliary cells. After the spermatial nucleus has united with the carpogonial nucleus, a lobe extends from the carpogonium toward the nurse cells, and the diploid nucleus passes into it and two cells are cut off at its tip. These cells then fuse with the nurse cells, the diploid nucleus multiplies, and from this reservoir cell long threads develop, each carrying a 2n nucleus. The threads extend to and fuse with auxiliary cells. The diploid nucleus divides and is cut off by a membrane. From this cell so delimited gonimoblast filaments grow out and fuse with other auxiliary cells and from these many carpogonia are produced. There is therefore a multiplication of the number of spore-producing gonimoblasts. **Dudresnya** (Plate XIX, Fig. 252) and *Dumontia* are examples of this family.

Family Corallinaceae

Corallines are mostly plants of rocky shores, intertidal or sublittoral. Their vertical distribution (to a depth of 225 feet or more) is related to turbidity, temperature, and light. Without a doubt light and salinity are largely responsible for geographical or latitudinal distribution.

This is a calcereous family, the thalli being either prostrate (Melobesioideae) or erect (Corallinoideae) and, as the name suggests, coral-like in superficial appearance. In many the growth is entirely prostate, with a floor of lime-encrusted cells. Others have upright systems of branches which are multiaxial and which form jointed segments. As mentioned for the order, there are conceptacles (pits) lined with an epidermal-like layer, the *peri-thecium*. Spermatangia are borne on short branches, clustered to form a sorus in the male conceptacles. Three-celled carpogonial branches are borne at the basal periphery of the female (cystocarpic) conceptacles. Likewise, on tetrasporic plants, tetrasporangia are produced on the wall of conceptacles. Paraphyses are also borne on the walls of these pits.

In this family there is a fusion of the carpogonial cell with the lower-most one of the carpogonial branch into which the zygote nucleus passes. From this fused cell ooblastic filaments grow out and fuse with specialized auxiliary cells, these having been cut off previously from the base of vegetative branches. This is followed by the fusion of many cells to form a large reservoir. From the periphery of this reservoir carposporangia are put forth, with one carpospore each. Tetrasporic plants are formed from diploid carpospores and the tetraspores (formed by meiosis) grow into sexual plants.

Corallina Linnaeus, 1758 (Plate XIX, Fig. 253), assumes many forms, in general being erect, jointed, branched cylinders or flattened "horns." As mentioned, the upright portions arise from prostrate, calcified sections of the thallus. The erect portions have opposite, pinnate branching. *Corallina* is found in both warm, tropical waters and in frigid seas.

Internally, the jointed fronds show a multiaxial construction with many dichotomously branched filaments forming a central cable. These are composed of long cells that have lateral connections. In at least some species the ends of cortical filaments are terminated by hairs. Out-turned branches at certain levels form "nodes" and the ultimate cells of these branches form a cortex. The outer layers of cells become calcified except at the joints (constrictions of the thallus) so that flexibility is provided. Just what controls the deposition of lime so that this zone is non-calcified is not known. In growth and the construction of new joints of the thallus, the axial cells become much elongated but do not divide immediately. The tips of these cells become congested with cytoplasm and a wall forms at the base of the swelling. From these cells, the new joint is formed, while the lower segment continues to elongate and to thicken its walls as a joint connection is constructed.

Reproduction occurs as outlined in the family characteristics. Thalli are either monoecious or dioecious. Two-celled carpogonial branches arise from the terminal cells of the filaments which line the conceptacle, the carpogonium, as usual, at the end. The initial, so-called mother cell may form several "trial" carpogonial filaments, one of which matures. The antheridial branches from the wall of the conceptacle bear much elongated spermatangial cells. In these the spermatia round up and are liberated, but remain attached to the wall of the spermatangium for some time by a hair-like stalk. The tetrasporic plant has conceptacles in which much-enlarged cells on one-celled stalks undergo meiotic division to form tetraspores in a tier.

FAMILY HILDENBRANDTIACEAE

Hildenbrandtia Nardo, 1834 (Plate XIX, Fig. 254), is sometimes referred to the Squamariaceae. The thallus is a relatively thin, horizontal, encrusting growth on rocks, both on marine shores and in fresh-water streams. The lower layer of the stratum is composed of horizontally growing filaments. From these arise relatively short, vertical rows of cells, compactly arranged. As far as known plants are all tetrasporic but this suggests undiscovered gametophyte generations. Tetrasporangia are produced on walls of conceptacles, with the tetraspores being cruciately arranged.

Order Gigartinales

This is a large and entirely marine order with some 20 families and over 80 genera. These are widely distributed in both tropical and frigid waters. Their morphology and habit are varied: membranous, leaf-like, encrusting, or gelatinous filiform. But they are grouped by the fact that the auxiliary is an enlarged cell in a nearby or remote vegetative branch and a cell which has been specialized or determined prior to fertilization. Sometimes the auxiliary cell is the vegetative cell which cuts off the carpogonial filament. Usually in the other orders the auxiliary cell is cut off and/or determined after fertilization.

Internally, the structure may be either multiaxial or uniaxial and there is a corticated zone. Spermatangia are developed on the apices of the external ("epidermal") cells, whereas carpogonial branches occur in the cortex within. The diploid nucleus is carried from the carpogonium to an auxiliary cell by ooblastic filaments and from this the gonimoblasts are formed. Tetrasporic plants produce tetrasporangia either in sori just below the external layer, or from the surface and scattered.

FAMILY GRACILARIACEAE

Thalli in this marine family are mostly strand-like or filiform-branched and firmly gelatinous. The cylinders are usually compressed but may be round in cross section. The internal architecture includes a rather wide medulla of large, globular-compressed cells and a narrow cortex of smaller, chlorophyll-bearing cells. The axial filament becomes lost in the development of the medulla.

The spermatangia are borne on surface cells or on the walls of sunken pits, located here and there over the thallus. Carpogonial branches, which are two cells in length, are borne from cortical cells, subsurface. Gonimoblasts develop from the carpogonium after the latter has fused with an auxiliary cell.

Gracilaria Greville, 1830 (Plate XIX, Fig. 255), has a highly and irregularly branched filiform thallus which arises from a prostrate plate of tissue. The strands are somewhat flattened, and cartilaginous. Spermatangia and carpogonial branches are borne as previously described. The two- (or three-) celled carpogonial branch is located near the surface of the thallus. After fertilization the carpogonium fuses with the supporting cell of the carpogonial branch and with others. From this enlarged reservoir gonimoblasts are put out and carposporangia are cut off at the tips. A layer of tissue develops at the base of the developing cystocarp and this is interconnected with the surrounding pericarp (see p. 240) filaments. A shell of compactly arranged vegetative cells develops around the carpospores, forming a several-layered pericarp embedded within the thallus and all together forming a poriferous protrusion from the thallus. The pore provides an exit for the carpospores which form tetrasporic plants morphologically similar to the gametophytes. The tetrasporangia develop in the outer cortical layer; the spores are tetrapartite, formed by a transverse and a longitudinal wall, rather than cruciate. Because of the large quantities of gelatinous material in Gracilaria it is one of the several genera providing agar-agar.

FAMILY GIGARTINACEAE

This is another family in which the supporting cell of the carpogonial filament serves as an auxiliary cell. In this order the plant may be filiform or strand-like, or leaf- or frond-like. The outer cortical cells are radiate and in recognizable filamentous series. The carpogonial filament is three-celled and the supporting cell may cut off secondary carpogonial filaments. The procarp develops in a cavity (nemathecium) which is borne on a special stalk or protrusion on the surface of the thallus. In each nemathecium a single cystocarp matures. Likewise in the tetrasporangial plants the sporangia develop as sori within the thallus or in specialized lateral branches of it.

Gigartina Stackhouse, 1809 (Plate XIX, Fig. 256), contains either cylindrical or foliar thalli which are twisted and have infolded margins. When mature they are papillate or spotted with sori of sporangia or of cystocarps. The fronds grow from perennial, prostrate expansions which regenerate erect branches each year, with most active growth occurring in spring and early summer. Plants occur on rocks in the intertidal and in tide pools

Internally, the thallus has an indistinct multiaxial structure. Back of the growing points a medulla of many colorless filaments is formed. The cortex external to the medulla has longitudinal filaments that are composed of smaller cells which at the periphery form an outer pseudoparenchymatous layer.

The spermatangial sori are irregular in shape and are borne on the surface of separate plants from the carpogonia. The carpogonial filaments, as mentioned, are borne at the base of a cortical branch within a papillate nemathecium. The branch is three-celled and is so strongly curved that the carpogonium lies but a short distance from the supporting cell. In some the supporting cell gives rise to a secondary carpogonial branch.

After fertilization the carpogonium is fused with the supporting cell which thus acts as an auxiliary cell. The zygote nucleus migrates into the auxiliary cell and then divides. For each nucleus a gonimoblast (diploid) grows inwardly. When mature, the carposporophyte consists of many branched gonimoblast filaments and each cell becomes a carposporangium. Meanwhile a layer of vegetative cells forms a nutritive layer about the mass of carpospores and this is brought into contact with the carposporophyte by long, thread-like (haustorial) elements. At the same time the surrounding cortex tissues increase and expand to form a nemathecium with a pore to the exterior. Carpospores are produced throughout the summer. The liberated carpospores produce tetrasporic plants in which tetrasporangia occur in sori in nemathecia within the cortex, produced throughout the winter. Reduction division occurs with tetraspore-formation. This is a gel-producing plant, the gel being especially abundant during fall and early winter.

Chondrus Stackhouse, 1797 (Plate XX, Fig. 257), or Irish Moss, is also representative of the Gigartinaceae in which the supporting cell is the auxiliary cell. The plants are highly lobed, crinkled, foliar, and rather crisp fronds. They grow in tufts from a hold-fast and form extensive beds over rocks in the intertidal and sublittoral zones. The carposporophytes develop well within the thallus, not in special papillate outgrowths. The tetrasporic plants are recognizable by having a pebbled surface caused by the tetrasporangial sori. Like *Gigartina* carpospores are liberated during summer months, and the tetraspores in winter.

In Ireland this genus (*C. crispus*) is known as Carrageen. It is gathered by hand and by dredging and because of its mucilage has many uses both domestically and commercially (see p. 354). It is harvested from many Atlantic coastal areas, especially during summer months, the period of greatest production, and the time when, fortuitously, regeneration is most active.

FAMILY FURCELLARIACEAE

This marine family includes highly branched filiform or membranous thalli in which the auxiliary cells are remote from the carpogonial branch. The plants are cartilaginous or fleshy and, especially in the thread-like forms, with the branches round in cross section, although the main axis may be flattened. Internally, like the Gigartinaceae, the cortical layers are composed of radially arranged cells. The medulla is filamentous but a primary axial filament has been lost.

The spermatangia are produced superficially (externally). The supporting cell of the carpogonial filament is on an inner cortical cell and the auxiliary cells are cut off from other inner cortex cells. The life history is as outlined in the characterization of the order.

Furcellaria Lamouroux, 1813 (Plate XX, Fig. 258), is characterized by plants which are erect and rather bushy or sometimes sparingly and dichotomously branched. They are usually brightly colored and inhabit the sublittoral. There is a stout, prostrate, rhizoidal growth from which the erect portion of the thallus arises.

The spermatangia are borne terminally on outer cells of special small, swollen branches of the thallus. The primary male cells cut off a pair of mother cells and each of these produces two spermatangia; these may undergo a second division. The supporting cell of the carpogonial filament produced one to several four-celled carpogonial elements. The gonimoblast filament eventually fuses with the auxiliary cell from which carposporangia are produced. There is no pericarp produced around the cystocarps. The tetrasporophyte produces tetrasporangia in which the spores are cut out by three transverse walls.

Order Rhodymeniales

Plants vary from filiform to membranaceous, arising from a hold-fast. They grow in both intertidal and in sublittoral zones, often occurring in

PLATE XX

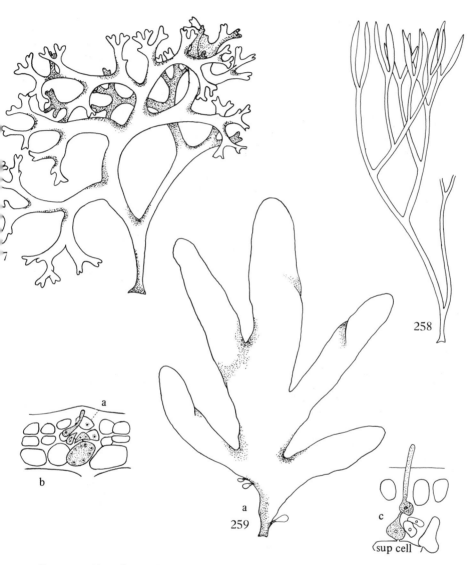

Fig. 257. **Chondrus crispus**

Fig. 258. **Furcellaria** sp

Fig. 259. **Rhodymenia:** a, **R. palmata** (drawn from herbarium specimen); b, **R. pseudopinnata,** carpogonium (redrawn from
Sparling); c, carpogonium fusing with basal cell of carpogonial branch

269

PLATE XX

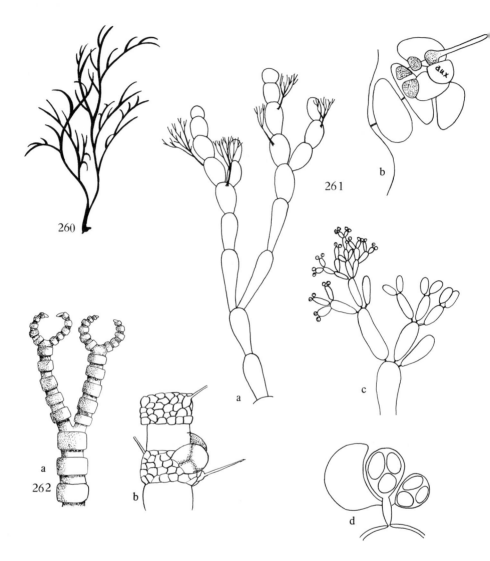

Fig. 260. **Lomentaria Baileyanum**

Fig. 261. **Griffithsia:** a, **G. globulifera,** portion of plant showing location of branched hairs; b, **G. pacifica,** carpogonial branch (redrawn from Kylin); c, spermatangia; d, tetrasporangia (redrawn from Kylin)

Fig. 262. **Ceramium:** a, **C. diaphanum,** habit of apex of branch; b. **C. fastigiatum,** node with cortical cells and tetrasporangia

tide pools. Internally, the plan is multiaxial. In a few forms the central region is hollow. There is a three- or four-celled carpogonial branch and there are one or two auxiliary cells for each procarp. The auxiliaries are borne as one or two cells on the end of a short branch that is produced from the same supporting cell that bears the carpogonial branch. The filament that bears the auxiliary cell is developed before the egg is fertilized but the auxiliaries themselves do not become completely differentiated until afterward. The cystocarps in this order become enclosed by a pericarp.

FAMILY RHODYMENIACEAE

This family includes cylindrical (sometimes hollow), stalked thalli or membranous and dichotomously lobed fronds. Cylindrical forms may be radially branched. Internally, the medulla is composed of large cells and show no longitudinal filamentous arrangement. The cortex is relatively narrow and is composed of small, photosynthetic cells in radiate series. The spermatangia occur in usual fashion from surface cells. The carpogenic branches and auxiliary cells are as described for the order. Gonimoblasts become highly branched and their proliferation produces a large number of carpospores. The carposporophyte (cystocarp) becomes enclosed by a pericarp which swells to form a pustule on the plant. On the tetrasporophyte the tetrasporangia may be in sori or scattered.

Rhodymenia Greville, 1850 (Plate XX, Fig. 259), has strap-shaped, leathery, leaf-like fronds which may have either dichotomous or pinnate divisions. These are among the largest of the red algae and may be up to five decimeters in length, ten or more centimeters wide. There is a short stipe-like extension from a disc-like hold-fast. The spermatangia occur in sori on the surface of the frond, formed by mother cells that are produced by transverse divisions of the outer cortical cells. Each produces a pair of primary initials and these divide to form two spermatangia each.

The three-celled carpogonial branch arises from a large, multi-nucleate cell which also cuts off a two-celled branch, and from this an auxiliary cell is delimited. This comes to lie next to the carpogonium with which it fuses after fertilization. Also the cells of the carpogonial branch fuse, producing a multi-nucleate cell which becomes involved in the enlarging auxiliary cell. The cell which originally cuts off the auxiliary cell then develops connections with the surrounding cells in a nutritive fashion. There is a great multiplication of outlying cells to form a wall about the developing cystocarp. The gonimoblasts meanwhile proliferate and become thread-like, each cell becoming a carposporangium. There is often a considerable space between the carpospore mass and the cystocarp wall.

Tetrasporangia are in sori scattered over the surface. The spores are formed by a longitudinal and transverse division during which meiosis occurs. For the common North American species, *R. palmata*, only tetrasporic plants are known.

Rhodymenia grows in northern waters from the intertidal to sublittoral zones. The plant is harvested, partially dried, and used as a salty confection, known as Dulse, particularly in such maritime countries as Norway, Scotland, Nova Scotia, and New England. It is also used as a food and as a medicine (see p. 349, sq.).

FAMILY LOMENTARIACEAE (CHAMPIACEAE)

In this family the thallus is mostly cylindrical, branched, and filiform; in a few instances the thallus is membranous. Growth is by an apical meristematic region and from it is formed a cortex of large cells surrounding a hollow with a loose weft of transversing filaments. These filaments bear secreting cells laterally. The outer cortical cells are small and somewhat radially arranged.

Plants are dioecious and the spermatangia are formed from patches of surface cells functioning as initials. The carpogonial branches (usually three-celled) are borne on supporting cells from the inner cortex. Like the former family, the supporting cell also cuts off auxiliary cells.

Lomentaria Lyngbye, 1819 (Plate XX, Fig. 260), is a cartilaginous, sparingly branched thallus, the branches round in cross section, gracefully curved and tapering. The branching tends to be unilateral in many instances. The development of the carposporophyte is similar to that in the Rhodymeniaceae, although there is not so much fusion prior to the formation of carpospores. The carposporophyte becomes enclosed in a protruding pericarp which has a pore. The wall cells surrounding the gonimoblasts elongate and form a loose tissue to enclose the carpospores.

Order Ceramiales

This is a large order in respect to number of genera and species, and the range of form is correspondingly extensive. Because of the refinements in the sexual reproductive process and in the life history, and because of the disappearance of the heterotrich thallus (the entire plant being upright), this order is regarded as the most advanced in the Rhodophyta. Among other "advanced" features is the direct fusion of the carpogonium and an auxiliary cell.

The most common form of growth perhaps is the filiform, branched, and bushy type (*Ceramium*, **Griffithsia** [Plate XX, fig. 261], *Polysiphonia*). Some are membranous and foliose (*Grinnellia*) or cartilaginous, whereas a few (*Martensia*, *Claudia*, e.g.) are net-like. In all, the plan of growth is by a primary filament with an apical cell. In the development of the thallus the axial filament may become corticated and hence polysiphonous (*Polysiphonia*). In the family Ceramiaceae the corticating cells are known as pericentrals. Sometimes the cortication consists of rhizoidal filaments which completely or incompletely invest the central axis.

A fundamental characteristic in common, although seemingly minor, is the development, after fertilization, of an auxiliary cell directly from the supporting cell of the carpogonial branch. The stimulus provided by the fusion of the carpogonium with the auxiliary cell leads to the production of gonimoblasts from the procarp.

Family Ceramiaceae

Plants in this family are filamentous, with arbuscular branching. The architectural unit is an axial filament with an apical growing cell but with cortications developing at nodes. The result is that the thallus has a beaded appearance. The cortications vary in extent and in pattern according to genus. The cells which are cut off laterally from the central axial cells appear first as a ring. Sometimes the lateral cells develop filaments that grow up or down along the central axis. Among the characters commonly present are slender, colorless (one-celled) hairs, or cellular prolongations at the tips of many branches.

Plants are dioecious. The spermatangia occur on differentiated, short branches or from patches on cortical cells. Carpogonial branches consist of four cells from a supporting cell which is a specialized member of a series of pericentral cells cut off a short distance behind the apical region. The supporting cell also produces some sterile vegetative cells and finally one or two auxiliary cells which lie near the carpogonium. The carposporophyte may or may not be enclosed by a pericarp. Tetrasporophytes have tetrasporangia which occur just beneath the thallus surface and are borne in a variety of ways. There may be one tetrasporangium at a node and it may have a stalk cell. Several tetrasporangia may occur in a whorl and in some instances each is enclosed by an involucre of cells that arise from proliferating cortical elements. In some species tetrasporangia occur on special branches. Variations in carposporophyte and tetrasporangial developments are numerous and only a few examples can be considered.

Ceramium Roth, 1797 (Plate XX, Fig. 262), is characterized by arbuscular thalli with abundant alternate or dichotomous branching which, because of the zonations or corticating cells, present a beaded appearance. Plants grow both in tropical and northern waters, epiphytic largely, both in the intertidal and the sublittoral zones. As mentioned, there is a principal axis that bears whorls of smaller, corticating cells. These may or may not develop so as to enclose completely the axis between the nodes (specific variations). Most species show a pair of hooked, dichotomous forkings at the tips of the branches.

Spermatangia occur as dense sori on the surface of corticating cells on some of the upper branches. The supporting cell may produce a colorless hair cell and either one or two carpogonial branches. Later it cuts off an auxiliary cell. As described, the carpogonium and an auxiliary cell from the supporting cell fuse to initiate carpospore formation. By the time the carpospores are mature a few short vegetative branches from the immediately surrounding thallus develop in an involucral fashion over and around the cystocarp.

Family Rhodomelaceae

Like the former family, these plants are attached, arbuscular, and usually profusely branched. The branches are long and brush-like, or fasciculate and bushy. Growth is by an apical cell of a primary filament. A short distance back of the apical cell the derivatives divide by vertical walls so that each cell becomes surrounded by a specific number of cortical or pericentral cells. There may be as many as 24 laterals (siphons), depending upon the species. The cells all have pit connections and the thallus becomes polysiphonous. In some forms the cortex becomes complicated by secondary cells or by rhizoidal elongations of the pericentral cells. A cell cut off by a diagonal wall from an axial cell forms a uniseriate, short, and eventually forked branch called a *trichoblast*. The cells of such a branch are colorless.

Spermatangia are produced on such a hair-bearing trichoblast, occurring in grape-like clusters, or in some genera as plates of cells. The carpogonial branch develops from a supporting cell that is located on a so-called *fertile trichoblast*. This supporting cell also cuts off sterile cells and later, following fertilization, the auxiliary cell. The cystocarp resulting from fertilization becomes enclosed in a prominent pericarp. Tetrasporic plants from the carpospores produce tetrasporangia that are cut off from the inner side of pericentral cells. Reduction division occurs with the formation of cruciately arranged tetraspores.

Polysiphonia Greville, 1824 (Plate XXI, Fig. 263), is a large, polysiphonous genus with some 150 species. Plants occur in the sublittoral as well as in tidal marshes, brackish estuaries, and tide pools. They are arbuscular and, depending on species, have either open or fasciculate branching.

Filaments and corticating cells have been described. Corticating cells may be present in lower parts of the filament only, with the upper region being monosiphonous and uniseriate. Colorless, uniseriate trichoblasts may develop from any axial cell that is removed by two or three cells from the apex. From the same axial cell a specific number of pericentral cells are cut off. Primary branches of the thallus are produced by initials cut off from the axial cells, usually before the corticating pericentrals are formed. In some species primary branches are produced in place of trichoblasts.

Plants are dioecious. In male plants certain trichoblasts are specialized to become fertile, spermatangial branches. Such a trichoblast divides dichotomously in its development. One or both divisions may be spermatangial. The lowermost of cells of the branch remains sterile, whereas the upper ones cut off several pericentral cells. These in turn cut off spermatangial mother cells on their outer faces. These in turn divide to produce a varying number of spermatangia, the result being a compact, cone-shaped cluster of spermatangia. Efficiently, other spermatangia can develop repeatedly as old ones are cast away.

Similarly on a female plant a fertile trichoblast is formed. The cell that gives rise to the trichoblast is one of several cells cut off pericentrally and is referred to as a fertile pericentral cell. The initial produces a short trichoblast of from five to seven cells. The two lower cells of this branch cut off pericentral cells. On the uppermost of these two series of pericentrals, the one that lies adaxially (on the side toward the primary axis of the thallus) becomes the *supporting cell*. This then forms a four-celled carpogonial branch, the terminal one being the carpogonium with a relatively long trichogyne. Meanwhile the supporting cell divides, first *basally* to form a *sterile filament initial*, and then laterally to form a second such initial (*lateral sterile filament*). Subsequent divisions of the basal initial is delayed, but the lateral one divides immediately to form a two-celled and later a four- to ten-celled filament. This occurs as fertilization takes place, after which the basal sterile filament initial divides to form a two-celled filament. Meanwhile the supporting cell again divides, this time cutting off an auxiliary cell which lies in close approximation to the carpogonium. With fertilization, fusion of the carpogonium and the auxiliary cell occurs so that the diploid nucleus can pass into the auxiliary. As the gonimoblasts begin to develop there is a general fusion of the supporting cell, the already fused auxiliary-

PLATE XXI

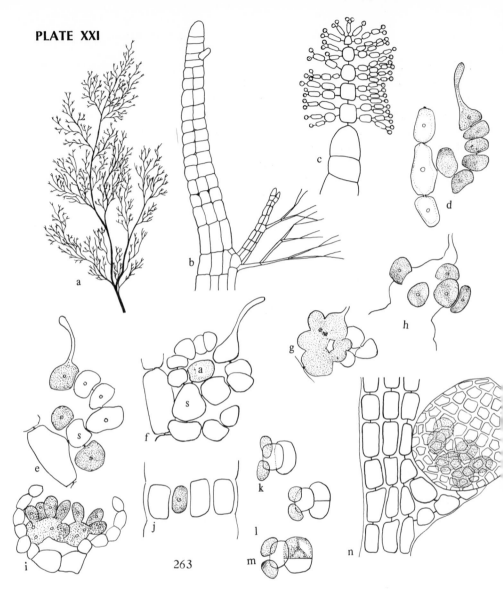

263

Fig. 263. **Polysiphonia:** a, habit of much-branched species (drawn from herbarium specimen); b, **P. denudata,** branch showing multiseriate development and a trichoblast; c, spermatangia; d, carpogonial branch from supporting cell; e, sterile filament initials cut off from supporting cell; development of sterile filaments; f, auxiliary cell (a) cut off from supporting cell(s); development of sterile filaments; g, fusion of carpogonium, auxiliary cell and sterile cells; h, development of gonimoblasts; i, gonimoblasts from placental cell; j, fertile pericentral cell of tetrasporophyte axis; k, daughter cell and 2 cover cells cut off from fertile cell; l, transverse division of fertile cell; m, division of upper cell to form tetrasporangium; n, **P. Harveyi,** mature pericarp containing carpospores

carpogonium, and the cells of the sterile filaments, so that a large placental element is formed. The numerous gonimoblasts each bear a carposporangium within which is a diploid carpospore.

Around the carposporophyte a large, urn-shaped *pericarp* develops from some of the trichoblast cells near the supporting cell. This is widely open outwardly permitting the escape of the carpospores.

The tetrasporophyte is similar morphologically to the gametophyte. In the branches, which become swollen and twisted, any one pericentral cell from a whorl around the central axial cell may function as a *tetrasporangium initial*. This differentiated cell behaves in a complicated but highly interesting manner, and with variations according to species. It first forms a *daughter cell* outwardly. This cell divides to form, from its upper surface, two so-called *cover cells* and a lateral *peripheral cell*. The fertile pericentral element undergoes transverse division, resulting in an upper *tetrasporangium* and a lower *stalk cell*. Meiosis, followed by mitosis, occurs in the former, resulting in four cruciately arranged tetraspores. These escape by a splitting of the "sporangial wall," accompanied by a lifting away of the cover cells. Two of these spores produce male gametophytes, and two produce female gametophytes.

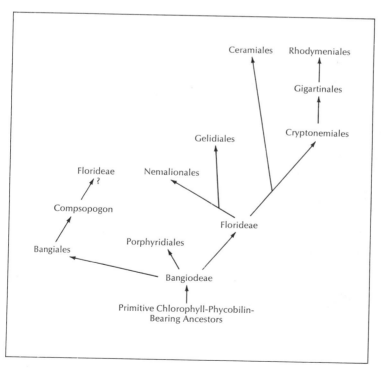

CHART 7.1   A Suggested Phylogenetic Arrangement of the Rhodophyta

The Intertidal Zone requires highly specialized adjustments from plants and animals that
inhabit the shoreline. (G. W. Prescott)

Ecology

Ecology, the interrelationships of organisms and their environment, is a limitless facet of biology. In fact, to make an ecological study or to analyze algal relationships descriptively, one must be either simultaneously or intermittently a phycologist, a morphologist, a biochemist, a physicist, a geologist, a meteorologist, a geneticist, and a taxonomist. A few of the more important aspects of algal ecology will be outlined below, but actually it is not possible to select "important" ecological factors. This is because all factors are important, and because the factor which may be highly critical for one organism or group of organisms is relatively less so for others. Importance is determined, of course, by the kind or degree of response that an organism is able to make and by the physiological demands of this or that species.

The conditions of the environment to which organisms must make adjustment, or which determine the successful life of an organism, or indeed its very presence, are referred to as "factors," a much overworked term. In a sense the various factors are the same the world over; these differ, however, in amount or degree, with the result that various types of recognized habitats and different classes of "conditions" must be taken into account.

The ecological factors which act as selective agents (directly or indirectly) for all forms of life include:

1. Water.
2. Chemical elements dissolved in water (including such substances as nutrients; vitamins; salts and minerals; antibiotics and toxins).
3. Gases (oxygen; carbon dioxide); atmospheric or in solution.
4. Temperature: variations; range: rate of change.
5. Light: intensity; duration; periodicity (especially for photosynthetic organisms).
6. Current: mechanical disturbances in air or water; duration; intensity.

7. Physiographic: shape of basin; shore-line configurations; etc.
8. Substrate: chemistry and physics.
9. Biological Factors: predators; parasites; competitors; antagonisms.

Adjustment to some of the above-mentioned factors presents problems for aquatic plants which are relatively unimportant for terrestrial plants, and vice versa. Such problems are solved in different ways. Obtaining gases, for example, is not as much of a problem for terrestrial plants as it is for aquatic. Light, important for land plants, is just as important for aquatic plants, but essential amounts are less readily obtained for the latter. Currents in water are much different in their potentialities and effects than wind.

Organisms differ, of course, from one another, in respect to the kind and/or amount of these factors which they require, or to which they can make adjustment. One result is that we find species both widely or narrowly distributed in Nature; we find different combinations of organisms in various habitats; we find varying quantities of organisms; and we find a vertical distribution of aquatic organisms.

Theoretically, there could be a more universal and equitable distribution of animal and plant species (especially aquatic); the difficulty arises from individual requirements which lead to what is often referred to as "selectivity of habitats." In other words, overly simplified, the chief reason why a particular lake, stream, or ocean shore does not have representatives of all (or of at least more) species of algae is that the conditions are not suitable for all. The element of chance — the unmeasurable factor — must be considered, but judging from observations there has been sufficient geological time for this factor to have been rendered inoperative. For example, we know of some species of fresh-water algae which have a wide, disjunct distribution. *Staurastrum polonicum*, e.g., has a type locality in Polish mountains, but has been found otherwise only in the mountains of western North America. Time and chance which made possible such a disjunct distribution should have placed this species in many other suitable habitats within this range. Subsequent collections may locate it elsewhere but at present we can infer that this species is highly selective of its habitat conditions. Similar instances are known for north-south distribution of species — a further reminder that even with barriers there has been time and opportunity for a wide and a more equitable distribution of individual species. Distribution in all directions, but especially north-south, is accomplished by air currents, migrating birds, and by aquatic animals. Studies by Schlichting (1961) have shown the ability of birds to carry many species on feet, beak, and feathers.

When compared with terrestrial organisms, aquatic organisms have in general a greater species distribution over the face of the earth, though some are confined to very narrow and sometimes isolated regions as endemics. All too often, however, species which are regarded as endemic subsequently appear in other, sometimes distant habitats. The genus *Draparnaldiopsis*, with but few species, shows a tendency toward endemism, with one species found in California, one in Montana, another in India. There are many species of desmids which appear to be endemic in the Indonesia-Malay sector. Marine algal species have opportunities to become more widely distributed than do fresh-water, partly because there are fewer physical barriers, and partly because sea water, in general, provides more nearly uniform factors of chemistry and temperature than terrestrial environments. Even so, some species or some genera are much limited in their distribution, occurring only along certain sectors of coasts or at certain depth ranges. Rhodophyta seem to have more members of restricted distribution than others, but *Durvillea* (Fucales) is confined to subantarctic waters around the Falkland Islands and southern New Zealand. A number of Rhodophyta are known only from Australia. Further, there are associations which occupy only certain broad regions of the seas; cf. the arctic and antarctic floras, which are circumpolar (*Scytothamnus australis, Iridaea cordata*). Okamura reports the genus *Coccophora*, known only from the Sea of Japan.

For practical purposes, the ecology of fresh-water and of marine algae will be considered separately, although many aspects are similar.

Ecology of Fresh-Water Algae

Variations in ecological conditions are reflected in both distribution and in periodicity, which are more noticeable in some habitats (or locations) than in others. Periodic variations are related of course to degrees of change in the environment and also to the specific response that plants are able to make according to their metabolic idiosyncrasies (e.g., their normal life cycle). It has been pointed out that habitat characteristics are correlated with many similarities in morphology among quite diverse groups of algae occupying the habitat.

Fresh-Water Ecology: Light

Light is a highly critical factor, of course, because of its role in photosynthesis. It has secondary importances, such as influencing germination of reproductive elements (spores); determining polarity and plane of wall formation in cell division; influencing the rate of cell division in some forms

(Cyanophyta according to some studies); movement in Cyanophyta and diatoms, etc. Furthermore, temperature is influenced by light. Some germlings are phototropic in one part, and negatively so in the rhizoid region. Because of light's fundamental role, it is to be expected that both vertical and horizontal distribution are regulated in part by light intensity, duration, and periodicity. Continuous light in the Arctic was found to have an inhibitory effect on the phytoplankton uptake of C^{14} at least at the surface.

Vertical distribution is determined by the capacity of different genera (or even species) with different pigments and varying metabolic mechanisms to make use of the light which penetrates the water. Obviously, algae which grow in feeble light at abysmal depths have the necessary light-absorbing pigments. Penetration presents the critical problem. In the first place, much of the potentially available light is lost at the surface by reflection; thus, even when the surface is smooth, between 20 and 25% of light is reflected. But water seldom has a flat surface and as much as 70% of incident light may be lost by reflection from wave-roughened water.

Second, depth of penetration may be regulated by latitude. The more nearly vertical are the rays of light, the deeper the penetration. Latitudinal distribution therefore is related to both vertical and horizontal distribution factors and helps to explain the exclusion of low latitude species from the high. Submersed habitats at high latitudes receive much less light than in the equatorial zone because of the angle of incidence and the correspondingly greater amount of water through which the light must pass to reach submarine plants. It has been estimated that in the median latitudes (40's) a photosynthetic day at 20 meters is 11 hours long, whereas at 40 meters the day is about 15 minutes long. In the Sargasso Sea red light penetrates to 60 meters, green light to about 139 meters, blue light to 170 meters, and violet rays to 180 meters. By contrast, off the Massachusetts coast it was found that red rays penetrated to 16+ meters, blue to 24 meters, green to 29 meters, and violet to 27 meters. The water of the Sargasso Sea is from two to four times more transparent than that of the Gulf of Maine. Hence, plants which live at different depths are those which are physiologically adjusted to varying qualities of light. Blue-green algae are known to be richer in phycoerythrin when they occur at great depths. But this is a specific matter because other plants with the same pigmentation occur in the ordinary photosynthetic zone. Dutton and Juday (1944) found no change in pigmentation of phytoplankton from surface to ten meters.

Of light which is not reflected as much as 60% is lost in the first two to five meters by scattering and by absorption. Unfortunately for the algae, the light waves which are absorbed first are those which are mostly used in photosynthesis (the red, yellow, orange waves with 6500-8000 A). Other waves with shorter vibrations (violet, blue) penetrate further.

Other factors which govern the amount of light and which therefore have an ecological effect are color of water, amount of suspended matter, and elements in solution. In hard water lakes (high calcium and magnesium), for example, absorption is much more rapid than in soft water. The natural color of water varies greatly; those with higher indices absorb light more quickly than those with low color indices. It is difficult to make generalizations relative to the relationships between these conditions and species distribution because of the impossibility of isolating factors, many of which are interacting. For example, the genus *Nitella* contains several species which are adjusted for existence in darkly colored waters at depths up to ten meters, where most other algae are excluded. But it is more than likely that other factors aside from reduced light operate in such a selection.

Because a large percentage of photosynthetic rays are disseminated rapidly below five meters, the upper 15 feet of fresh water constitute the "photosynthetic zone." The zone deepens or narrows in relation to latitude, water color, amount of suspended matter, etc. It is in this zone that the majority of fresh-water algae occur, especially plankters (both euplankton and tychoplankton). Rarely are benthic algae found deeper than 15 meters in fresh water, but occasionally *Dichotomosiphon tuberosus*, *Cladophora profunda*, *Oscillatoria* spp, and a number of diatom species are dredged from 90 feet. *Hildenbrandtia rivularis* and *Bodanella Lauterbornii* have been reported from 15 to 35 meters.

Whereas insufficient light is a problem and a selector for some species, intense light at or near the surface may require adjustment and adaptation for others. One adjustment to strong light which conceivably interferes with optimum photosynthesis, is made when ordinarily green algae become red or orange because of carotenoid pigments, such as haematochrome. *Euglena* on pond surfaces, *Chlamydomonas* in snow, *Haematococcus* in rock pools, and red or rust-colored subaerial *Trentepohlia*. The carotenoids are considered to afford fortuitous protection by serving as a light screen. *Melosira italica* is known to be inhibited by intense light, and the inability of most algae to adjust to strong light may well explain the paucity of species in highly illuminated habitats. But of course temperature and water chemistry play a role also. Not a few algae which are subaerial, especially Cyanophyta (some Chlorophyta also), seem to be protected against intense light by having darkly colored, mucilaginous sheaths (*Scytonema* spp, *Stigonema* spp, *Gloeocapsa rupestris*, *Gloeocystis* spp).

Naturally, penetration of light into bodies of water is related to seasonal changes, at least in the median and high latitudes. In tropical zones vertical rays penetrate more deeply over longer periods of time. Thus the development of many algal species in lower levels (especially when below the photosynthetic zone) is determined by the seasonal recurrence of suitable light. Other factors being optimum, light alone can account for the periodic appearance of algae in vertical distribution.

Plankton species buoyed in the upper water levels often become concentrated at or near the surface because of their pseudovacuoles (bluegreen algae). It is thought that the same vacuoles, because of their refractibility, serve protectively against strong light. *Microcystis aeruginosa*, *Anabaena flos-aquae*, *Aphanizomenon flos-aquae*, *Oscillatoria rubescens*, and *Gloeotrichia echinulata* are examples of surface-loving plankters which contain pseudovacuoles.

Some lakes of sufficient depth stratify in respect to temperature, forming an *epilimnion* and a *hypolimnion* (the zone between establishing a break known as the *thermocline*). The upper epilimnion zone is one which in summer is about the same temperature throughout all depths and in which water is circulating. The thermocline is one in which the temperature drops with every meter of depth, and below this the hypolimnion in which there is a uniformity of low temperature to the bottom. Organisms are about evenly distributed in the epilimnion because of water circulation. In the hypolimnion any organisms are subjected to conditions of stagnation where they do not have the benefit of being carried by currents into a favorable photosynthetic position, and where death and falling-out exceeds multiplication. At the time of hypolimnion-epilimnion over-turn (which occurs twice a year) the complete circulation of the water redistributes plankters throughout the full depth of the lake and they pass much less time in the photosynthetic zone. This acts as a limiting or at least selective factor in respect to both quantity and quality of the flora. The over-turn distribution is coupled with the fact that at the time of year in which it occurs (winter or summer depending on the hemisphere) light is less in any event (at high latitudes especially). Over-turn is often accompanied by or subsequently followed by plankton pulses, especially diatoms.

East-west horizontal distribution cannot be determined by light, and within a wide range of latitudes light has little influence on south-north distribution. But beyond the Arctic and Antarctic Circles, and perhaps even below these latitudes, the extreme variabilities in light-dark periodicity, in addition to the low angle of incidence, constitute a critical factor.

Quantitative and qualitative investigations of algal species in the Arctic show clearly that light is much more important than temperature in selecting species and in determining numbers of individuals. Although species are few in number, dense growths of plankters develop in arctic lakes during the periods of 24 hours of daylight even though water is ice-covered and the temperature is 0–5°C.

Fresh-Water Ecology: Temperature

There are both direct and indirect effects of temperature which are critical in algal ecology and distribution. Obviously for each species there is an optimum temperature or temperature range at which metabolism (including photosynthesis) occurs. In fresh water the optimum temperature for the great majority of algae lies between (10) − 15 and (20) − 25°C. But it is known that for the same species there is an optimum temperature for photosynthesis, one for general metabolism, and one for sexual reproduction. Extremes of temperature therefore exert a selectivity of species and determine which ones can or cannot exist in a particular habitat or area. As with light, it may be the range (favorable or unfavorable), the rapidity of temperature change, or the duration of favorable or unfavorable degrees which operate as ecological factors. In warm water, plankton species have an overall smaller size than do those in cold water, but large plants appear to have greater success in reproduction. Also it has been observed that desmids in cold water have an increase in number of arms (radiations of semicells).

Temperature is indirectly responsible for conditions of ecological importance. For example, ice resulting from low temperatures plays an important role in producing mechanical injury, decreasing light penetration, causing concentrations of dissolved elements, etc., and is thus able to exert a great selectivity of species. Similarly, high temperatures (especially in hot springs) determine the kind and quality of gases in solution and the chemistry of the water.

Temperature changes induce lake stratification (see p. 284) and so influence water currents. These in turn are reflected in vertical distribution at different times of the year, and conceivably may have a selective influence on the actual presence or absence of species.

Air temperatures may be as low in algal habitats of medium latitudes as are those in the Arctic, and of course such water as is not frozen remains at slightly above 0°C. But the duration of water at suboptimum temperatures for long periods of time in the Arctic and Antarctic, and the rate of temperature change constitute selector factors. Likewise the near zero temperature of snow and ice is a factor that selects species and determines the paucity of the flora in alpine habitats.

Water temperatures change more gradually in median latitudes than in the Arctic and Antarctic. The annual range of temperature is greater in many environments of median latitudes (0.5–12.5°C. in the Arctic; 0.5°–32°C. in Iowa, e.g.). Unfavorable temperatures are more important in ecology when accompanied by unfavorable light conditions. As mentioned in connection with light (p. 284), the latter is more important than temperature (alone) in determining the presence or absence of species. It is obvious that species which occur under arduous, frigid conditions are clearly those which have the ability to adjust; others are excluded. As has been stated so often, the Arctic or a geyser basin (temperature up to 85°C.) is characterized by the species which are not present as much as or more so than by the species which are. This is true because, in general, species which occupy habitats with extreme conditions are mostly the same species which are found under more ordinary circumstances along with countless other species that, apparently, cannot make the adjustment to radical environments. Field and laboratory studies in fresh-water algae in the Arctic have shown that after being frozen and encased in ice for over a month, algae and protozoa can be revived within a few hours when cultured at room temperatures. It is also obvious that many organisms ignore frigid conditions in arctic habitats. Arctic lakes and tundra pools are frozen solid from September 15 to June 15 or later; yet, within three or four days after the appearance of open water, pools are teeming with microbiota. We know from observation that many of these have not passed through nine months of freezing in a cyst or zygospore state, but are in a vegetative condition of suspended animation. At the same time, one adjustment that many species make to a frigid environment is to maintain themselves in a permanent encysted condition during which time some metabolic activities continue. This is especially true for motile forms. Whichever other forms may also exist in this manner will not be known until culture studies of them have been made.

Winter plankton in frozen lakes of north temperate regions exist below ice successfully, the composition and amount being related to amount of light which in turn is determined by duration of snow cover. Chrysophyta are dominant in such situations (diatoms especially), along with *Cryptomonas pusilla*, e.g. The level which receives from 0.5 to 20% of incident light supports 95% of the plankton.

Multitudinous investigations purport to draw a positive, causal relationship between temperature and biota quantity (and quality). These correlations well may be incidental in most instances. In opposition, experimental studies have shown that a species of diatom, for example, increased its division rate as temperature increased through the summer, while there was an overall decrease in the number of daylight hours. Even so, factors other than temperature may have operated. Outside the range of optimum temperature for metabolism, or in the upper and lower limits of the range, most species are not responsive to temperature change. The analysis of temperature influences in nature is highly complicated unless individual species are considered. For while some species are decreasing and dropping out of a flora as temperatures drop, others (especially some planktonic diatoms) are reaching a peak of development.

The relationships of algae to high water temperatures are discussed in connection with hot springs on pages 17 and 328 and with low temperatures on page 326.

Fresh-Water Ecology: Chemical Factors

If any of the ecological factors can be regarded as more important than others, it would be water chemistry (elements and substances in solution). Other factors being equal (or approximately so) two bodies of water in close proximity may have drastically different biotic composition. Not only may the quality of the biota be different, but two such bodies of water may also vary in their productivity. The only explanation that can be offered is that the medium is different chemically.

The British limnologist Pearsall (1922) stated the relationship between aquatic biota and water chemistry very clearly:

> It should be quite clear that in no case can we affirm that the mass of plankton (or any other form of life) is proportional to the total concentration of substances dissolved in the nutrient medium. It is and must be some function of the limiting ion (or ions, i.e., the substance present in the smallest quantity proportionate to the amounts required by the plant. One cannot, for instance, regard the sea (with 3.5% of dissolved solids) as an almost limitless nutrient medium for plant growth, when it contains only the smallest traces of phosphate and nitrates.

In reference to phosphates and nitrates, it might appear odd that after three billions of years the seas have not accumulated greater concentrations of nitrates and phosphates. The explanation lies partly in the fact that such substances are in an unsoluble or bound form in the abysmal depths, and partly in the fact that these elements are taken up and incorporated in the biota of the sea. As more and more nutrients enter the sea, the greater is the development of living matter, thus taking dissolved substances from the water.

Chemical characteristics include: (a) Elements dissolved from the soil in the immediate vicinity, or from drainage. These elements include the basic, essential elements required for plant metabolism: hydrogen, oxygen, carbon, nitrogen, phosphorus, calcium, magnesium, iron, sodium, plus trace elements such as zinc, copper, manganese, silicon, and others. (b) Organic substances, derived from bacterial and fungal decomposition (in solution or as suspended colloids, including both household and industrial wastes). (c) Organic compounds released as metabolites from algae themselves (extracellular or intracellular), including antibiotics and toxins. (d) Gases dissolved from the atmosphere or from soil. (e) Vitamins derived from bacterial action, or from organic matter contributed from other plants and animals (B_1, B_{12}, thiamin). Any or all of these various types of substances may act (by their presence or absence or quantity) in a critical way to determine the kind and quality of algal species.

It is impossible to make any generalizations in respect to which one or more of the chemical factors might be more important because of specific requirements. An element that is essential for one species is of minor importance for another. An extrametabolite may be inhibitory to one species (or to an entire group) but innocuous to another. There are, of course, basic elements essential for all plant life that must be available. The relationship of chemicals to species selectivity is complicated and altered by the interactions of elements and substances in the medium. Numerous and endless culture studies of algae have demonstrated the specific requirements for the essentials, and also the effect of highly complex chemicals and trace elements in algal growth, productivity, and reproduction.

Examples of Chemical Factor Relationships

It is well-known that adding fertilizers to waters (both lake and stream) increases productivity of plankters as well as of larger filamentous algae. Nitrogen, phosphate, and potassium in the ratio of 12-24-12 (N–P–K) causes a marked increase, particularly in diatoms and flagellates, within three weeks. Such artificial stimulation often leads to over-abundance, followed by upset biological conditions (cutting off of light to benthic organisms, decay and subsequent oxygen depletion, etc.). Phosphorus is known to be important in a number of ways, one being that it facilitates the uptake of nitrogen. Fertilizers added may induce a harmful blanket of filamentous algae and there may be a winter-kill of fish as a result of super-abundant developments of plankton and filamentous algae.

For every 1000 kg. of nitrogen, 20,000 kg. of plankton substance is possible. Experimentally it has been shown that phosphorus in the amount of 10% of available nitrogen is necessary in order to use the nitrogen.

Because of chemical composition, fresh-water bodies can be classified as hard (basic, alkaline, the Baltic type, pH above 7.0), or soft (acid, Caledonian type, pH below 7.0), or brackish (saline with salts, pH above 7.0). Brackish-water organisms usually show a wide range of tolerance to salinity but the optimum is usually less than that of ocean water. Platymonas in culture, however, shows a preference for salinity greater than that of sea water. If some waters are rich in certain elements (sulphur, iron, etc.) they often are so identified. In spite of variabilities and numerous exceptions, it is possible to characterize such bodies of water by the nature of the biota they support (see Table 8.1). Thus it is well-known that hard-water lakes are predominantly populated by Cyanophyta-diatoms (*Microcystis, Aphanothece, Asterionella*). Soft-water lakes (and, more rarely, streams) support Chlorophyta (*Bulbochaete, Desmids, Nitella*). But there is a group of Cyanophyta which are characteristically present in acid situations (*Stigonema, Hapalosiphon* spp). Brackish water, high in sodium chloride and other salts, supports halophytic blue-green algae such as *Microcoleus*, Chlorophyta such as *Enteromorpha*, and Rhodophyta such as *Bostrychia*. Highly brackish brine lakes usually have species of *Microcoleus, Dunaliella, Stephanosphaera*, and *Platymonas*. It is noteworthy that Great Salt Lake diatomaceous deposits are of fresh-water species and that algae in brine lakes are more nearly similar to fresh-water genera than to marine. Great Salt Lake has a salinity greater than that of the sea. Obviously, the concentration of salts inhibits the appearance of most fresh-water species.

Because some algae demand certain elements much in excess of what others require, the presence or absence of optimum amounts limits species distribution. Diatoms, for example, require silicon for wall construction. Often a combination of elements constitutes a determining factor. For example, many blue-greens demand more nitrogen and more phosphorus than do many other algae. Some forms are able to take up generous quantities of nitrogen (used in protein synthesis) when the phosphorus content is relatively high (above 0.3 ppm.). Lakes which are advantageously supplied with bicarbonates (for a source of CO_2) and which are enriched with nitrates and phosphates become "garden spots" for such Cyanophyta as *Microcystis, Anabaena*, and *Aphanizomenon*. When these elements are present, along with a source of Vitamin B_{12}, super-abundant growths of blue-green plankters appear. Vitamins and possibly trace elements are important determiners here, for a body of water may be suitably supplied with nitrogen and phosphorus and not develop algal blooms. Most profuse growths of plankton occur during periods of increasing temperature; in northern latitudes such growths have been associated with "dog days," when water temperatures rise from 20°C. to 27 or 32°C. But *Aphanizomenon flos-aquae*, a common late summer bloom-producer, may also form dense growths beneath winter ice, late in the spring after the snow cover has disappeared and when light penetration is increased. This is an example of the ecological importance of water chemistry and light in contrast to temperature.

It has been demonstrated in many ways, especially under culture conditions, that algae pass extrametabolites into the water, or may release substances upon the breakdown of cells. These substances may be inhibitory or toxic to other algae, and even to the species themselves; whereas it is also possible that the extrametabolites may serve as stimulators to other plants (and animals). Thus, biologically produced chemicals may act as selectors of species and so determine distribution. For example, seldom if ever are *Microcystis aeruginosa* and *Aphanizomenon flos-aquae* found in the same body of water at the same time, although the habitat may be highly suitable for both of these common plankters. Whichever species becomes established first dominates the habitat. In contrast, when extrametabolites are stimulants or at least non-toxic, interdependent associations of species are usually established. For example, in hard-water lakes adequately supplied with nutrients there is almost invariably an association of *Lyngbya Birgei, L. major* (or *L. aestuarii*), *Coelosphaerium Kuetzingianum, Microcystis aeruginosa, Asterionella formosa* and *Stephanodiscus Niagarae, Pediastrum Boryanum, Scenedesmus quadricauda,* and *Ceratium hirundinella.* This and other similar associations make it possible for a microscopist to "type" a body of water by examining its biota.

When some essential elements such as iron and sulphur occur in unusual concentrations in a habitat they may be toxic and drastically inhibitory. High sulphur content (as sulphates) produces essentially mineral water with attendant chemical characteristics (e.g. formation of hydrogen sulphide gas). One role of sulphur as a determiner of diatom distribution is the apparent involvement of sulphur compounds in the uptake of silicon, essential for wall construction. Iron, besides its role in metabolism, is used by many species (desmids, e.g.) in their walls.

The general chemical nature of a fresh-water body reflects its "type" in reference to its productivity and limnology. Lakes which are low in electrolytes are soft-water bodies. They are frequently "young" lakes with a low pH, and lie over basaltic or igneous rock. Such lakes are said to be *oligotrophic* (poor feeders, i.e., poor producers). They are frequently deep lakes (a mean depth greater than 20 meters) with a V-shaped basin, and have a relatively small amount of water volume in contact with the bottom. They have no shoals, only a narrow shore (beach) line, and are nearly devoid of aquatic vegetation. Such lakes further are low in productivity of algal bulk, although they may have an interesting variety of species (especially Chlorophyta, including desmids and *Nitella*). An oligotrophic lake may have 10-40 kg. dry wt. plankton per hectare. The dissolved matter is usually less than 100 ppm.

Conversely, lakes which have aged or which from the start are shallow, saucer-shaped basins are called *eutrophic* (true feeders with, for example, 177 kg. dry wt. plankton per hectare). Commonly they overlie calcareous rock or receive drainage from limestone. These lakes, characteristically with a mean depth of less than 20 meters, are well-supplied in electrolytes, and in aging have become enriched with nutrients, including an abundance of carbonates or bicarbonates (calcium or magnesium). In general, lakes

TABLE 8.1* Characteristics and Classification of Lakes †

	OLIGOTROPHIC	PAN-OLIGO-TROPHIC	SIDERO-TROPHIC	EUTROPHIC
SHAPE OF BASIN; HYDROGRAPHY	V-shaped; often glacial	V-shaped; usually high alpine glacial	In general, with characteristics of true oligotrophic	U-shaped basin; flat
AGE	Young	Young		Old
AMOUNT OF VOLUME IN CONTACT WITH BOTTOM	Little	Little		Great
DEPTH	Up to hundreds of feet	Deep		Shallow (15-150 ft.)
TEMPERATURE	Cold to 15°C.	Cold		Warm to 32°C.
BOTTOM	Rocky; little sediment; igneous	Rocky		Silted; *Gyttja*
BACTERIAL ACTION	Little	Little		Active
MARGIN	Little beach; no shoals			Wide beach; shoals
SUSPENDED MATTER	Little; low color index			Large amounts; high color index
ELECTROLYTES	Low in calcium; magnesium half-bound carbonates			High in calcium; magnesium half-bound carbonates
ALKALINITY	Less than 40 ppm			90-250 ppm
SULPHATES	Less than 5 ppm			50-125 ppm
OXYGEN	70-60% saturated at bottom	90% saturated at bottom		40-0% saturated at bottom
IRON	Low		High	High
pH	Below 7.4		Below 7.0	7.4-9.2
PHYTOPLANK-TON	Low; Chlorophyta, desmids, selected diatoms	Mostly lacking	Restricted	High; diatom-cyanophyta; blooms common

* See Thiemann and Naumann; also Pearsall, *Jour. Ecol.* 9:241. 1922.
† This is very general. Every lake has its own combination of features.

high in calcium are also rich in nitrates. Calcium is capable of forming salts of fatty acids derived from sugar of photosynthesis, and in other ways enters into the metabolism of algae. The bottom of the eutrophic lake is heavily sedimentized in most instances and there is a profuse development of aquatic plants. The algal flora, especially Cyanophyta and diatoms, are rich also; hence the eutrophic lake is often referred to as a "blue-green-diatom type." Partly because of relatively high temperatures and because of excessive bacterial action, especially in the hypolimnion, a eutrophic lake becomes oxygen-poor.

The chemical qualities of these two types of waters, with the other associated factors, determine not only the presence or absence of algal species, but also productivity. In all, the eutrophic and mesotrophic (see below) lakes include a rich mixture of algae representing many groups. Because of their nutrient resources these lakes are subject to blooms of blue-green plankters such as *Aphanizomenon*, *Microcystis*, and *Anabaena*.

A lake which is aging rapidly may have some oligotrophic shoreline, depth, and bottom characteristics, although its chemistry and productivity are eutrophic. Such a lake is said to be *mesotrophic* (see Table 8.1, p. 291). It is usually highly productive and has a blue-green-green-diatom combination of species, with possibly 100 kg. dry wt. plankton per hectare. There is often an inverse ratio between the amount of plankton and depth.

A body of water which has "aged" and is passing through eutrophy finally becomes *dystrophic* and subsequently disappears after becoming first a marsh and then a *Carex* meadow. As a marsh it becomes unsuitable for strictly aquatic algae and is populated by *Nostoc pruniforme*, *Microcoleus paludosus*, *Vaucheria sessilis*, and sometimes *Aphanothece stagnina*, the latter forming profuse growths in the seeps or on wet soil.

Whereas the advanced age of a lake and its limnological properties are strikingly reflected in the changes of the flora toward a cyanophyte dominance, other types of algal floras also undergo modification. For example, there is an increase in the number of planktonic diatom genera as a lake becomes more and more eutrophic. The benthic diatom genera (*Cymbella*, *Gomphonema*, *Epithemia*) are superseded by such plankters as *Asterionella*, *Fragilaria*, *Tabellaria*, and *Meridion*. It must be noted, however, that some species of these genera are common to both soft- and hard-water lakes. The chlorophyte genera such as *Oocystis*, *Treubaria*, *Golenkinia*, *Tetrallantos*, and *Eremosphaera*, which are often characteristic of an oligotrophic lake, disappear. Replacing them in a eutrophic habitat are *Pediastrum* spp, *Botryococcus Braunii*, *Coelastrum microporum*, and many species of *Scenedesmus*.

At the same time, eutrophic lakes show a predominance of *Dinobryon* spp, *Synura uvella*, *Mallomonas* (some species), and as a lake passes into dystrophy, the euglenoids are characteristically abundant.

In Wisconsin, Waubesa Lake (eutrophic) produced 216 pounds of plankton per acre as compared with Crystal Lake (a soft-water and semi-oligotrophic lake), which produced 41 pounds per acre. Productivity in five oligotrophic lakes in Denmark was compared by Nygaard (1949). He found that quantitative production (as determined by chlorophyll readings) closely paralleled a quantitative index. This index was obtained by relating the total number of Cyanophyta-Chlorophyta-Centrales Diatoms-Euglenophyta with total number of desmid species. Oligotrophic lakes have an index below 1.0; those which are decidedly eutrophic have an index above 1.0.

The ratio of K-Na to Ca-Mg in Lake Erie was found to be 0.17. When this ratio is more than 1.5, desmids are the predominating flora. Comparing this number to the Great Lakes' average of 0.16 gives an index as to the type of flora which in general characterizes these bodies of water. By way of another comparison the Na-K/Ca-Mg ratio in alkaline water is 2.6; in surface water the average is 0.19; in the sea, 1.4.

It is noteworthy that lakes poor in calcium support predominantly carbohydrate-producing species of plankton, whereas calcium-rich lakes have mostly fat-producing species. Peridiniaceae (belonging to a group of algae which can produce both oil and starch) when occurring in calcium-poor water are decidedly starch-producers. But the genus *Ceratium*, which is less selective of its chemical environment and is more cosmopolitan, produces starch and oil. This relationship is borne out by *Staurastrum paradoxum*, also highly cosmopolitan, a desmid that stores both starch and oil. Significantly, fat-producing organisms contain calcium soaps in the wall as well as calcium pectates, illustrating the importance of calcium and its relation to species selection.

pH in itself is probably of little direct importance in determining algal distribution, though it can be used as a "flag" to reflect chemical conditions which are critical. A few algal species, for example, can endure acid situations where the pH is as low as 3.2, and are thus found only at low levels (pH 3.2–4.8). Most desmids, many Chlorococcalean Chlorophyta, some euglenoids, many diatoms, Cyanophyta such as *Chroococcus turgidus* and *Stigonema ocellatum*, and a few dinoflagellates are selective of a pH between 7.0 and 5.0. At the same time, some desmid species are more nearly ubiquitous and are found in water with a pH on both sides of neutrality. Planktonic blue-greens and diatoms are abundant in water with a high pH (7.4–9.0) and are adapted to live in water which becomes increasingly more basic during the period of high photosynthetic activity through the summer (when the pH may rise from 7.8 to 9.4 or higher).

Culture studies of fresh-water algae have disclosed many of their physiological demands, including the role of chemical elements and substances. Experimentation has included the subjection of various species to many inorganic and organic media, involving trace elements and highly refined substances. Whereas these studies have applicable values for physiological research and laboratory studies on reproduction, we are not able to apply many of the results of culture work toward an explanation of algal distribution and occurrence or reproduction in nature.

Fresh-Water Ecology: Currents

It is clear that convection currents in lakes and stream currents in flowing water constitute ecological factors that determine at least local distribution of aquatic organisms. Convection currents and those arising from seasonal over-turn of stratified lakes account in part for diurnal and periodic variation, as well as succession in plankton populations. Such currents can be of ecological importance in a number of ways. For example, plants are carried into the photosynthetic zone. This can be especially advantageous if the water carries a heavy load of suspended matter, for beyond the first foot of water there would be a low penetration of light. Such currents also provide circulation of nutrient elements from the bottom into the photic zone, at least during the time when there is no thermocline. But the ever-changing conditions of temperature, nutrient level, and flotation (light factor) are not conducive for many species of algae.

Whereas water movements in a lake are of but little direct importance in reference to selectivity of species, the more forceful and continuous currents in streams are highly so. Two of the relationships involved here are critical: one of nutrition, and one of mechanics. Thus, if any algae are to exist in streams they must make certain morphological and physiological adjustments, including (1) an ability to develop proper anchorage structures; (2) construction of a flexible and resilient thallus; (3) the ability to assimilate in a medium of rapidly changing chemical composition (including gases); and (4) adaptation of reproductive habits and structure to stream conditions.

The algae in streams include both planktonic and attached species, and whether one type is more abundant than the other depends upon so many variables that no generalizations are possible. In respect to attached forms, they can be (1) epiphytic; (2) epipelic (attached on mud and sand); or (3) epilithic (on rocks or other firm substrates). In habit of growth, attached algae take two expressions, prostrate and incrusting (film-forming), or erect and streaming.

In streams which permit the growth of larger aquatic plants, epiphytic algae are abundant. Many species of *Oedogonium*, *Blubochaete*, *Gongrosira*, and *Stigeoclonium*, for example, occur (other ecological conditions being suitable). On mud and sand dense growths of diatoms form a brown film, often appearing as a layer of sludge and overlooked by the collector. In such habitats can also be found mat-forming, filamentous blue-greens such as *Phormidium*. *Vaucheria* and *Dichotomosiphon* felts grow on sand and mud, the former in shallow water especially. On rocks and submerged wood (depending on temperature and other factors) there are many forms sensitive to high oxygen-content, such as *Lemanea, Batrachospermum, Cladophora*, and *Enteromorpha*. *Lemanea*, which is well-adjusted to rushing water, forms dense turfs on rocks at the brink of waterfalls and dams. Here also are many film-forming and colonial diatoms such as *Cymbella* and *Gomphonema*. *Rhizoclonium* and *Vaucheria* species too form streaming masses from rocks in flowing water, along with *Tetraspora*. *Nostoc parmeloides*, *Hildenbrandtia* (Rhodophyta), and *Monostroma* (Chlorophyta) occur in cold and sometimes torrential streams at high altitudes. It is thought that aeration is critical for the above-mentioned plants, whereas, obviously, they are capable of developing anchorage systems that many other species cannot. This involves an as yet unexplained tendency to anchor on the down-stream side of boulders, as illustrated by *Cladophora glomerata*, *Nostoc parmeloides*, and the saccate *Boldia* (Rhodophyta).

From the standpoint of nutrition, it might be supposed that the problem of taking elements from flowing water might be greater for plants in sweeping current than in quiet water. But laboratory experiments (with constant temperature and light) and field observations (Whitford, 1960) have shown repeatedly that algae in currents grow better and take up elements in greater amounts (using P^{32}, e.g.). The uptake of P^{32} was 5.1 times greater in current than in still water (Whitford and Schumacher, 1964). Currents remove solutes and suspended matter from the surface of algal cells and so increase the diffusion gradient and hence the rate of osmosis. It was noted that the current must be at least 15 cm./sec. to provide the benefits and the increases. Of 14 plants used in such experiments, most of them showed facilitated growth, as opposed to little or no growth of the same species in quiet water (representatives of Cyanophyta, Chlorophyta, Chrysophyta, and Rhodophyta tested).

In respect to water chemistry, the nature of the substrate (rock or wood) seems to have a causal bearing on selectivity. It is frequently noted that attached (lithophilic) algae in streams occur only on certain types of rock, some selecting calcareous, some granitic, some sandstone. The geological and geographic background of the stream determines, in part at least, the chemical composition of the water. The amount of P, N, Ca, Mg, C, and the other elements vary in streams, of course, and are, therefore, determiners of biota. Most streams are hard water with a pH above 7.0 but soft-water streams do occur and these have a characteristic flora (certain diatoms, desmids, *Batrachospermum* spp and *Draparnaldia*; also some species of *Lemanea*).

Plankton (potamoplankton) of streams varies according to: (1) chemistry of the water (including gases and nutrients); (2) temperature; (3) amount of suspended matter, all of which are related to (4) elevation (nearness to headwater, or to mouth). Accordingly, the plankton from headwater to outlet varies tremendously (in quantity and quality) and the plankton of one stream at one level (of elevation) varies with that of others. Streams which have similar critical factors, however, often show similarities in the composition of the flora.

Because the medium is constantly moving it is difficult to obtain a clear analysis of stream plankton. Samplings from stations throughout the entire length must be coupled with repeated samplings from selected stations throughout a year. In general, streams carry fewer numbers of plankters than do lakes, but over a year's time, the potamoplankton equals that of lakes.

Plankton in rapidly flowing, spring-fed streams, especially near the head waters, is practically non-existent. Such forms as occur are usually derived from pools or marshes at the headwaters, or there are benthic forms which have been torn loose. Temperatures are often low near the head (especially if the stream is from melting snow or glaciers), and nutrients are low. Hardwater springs, although high in oxygen, are frequently high in sulphates and carbonates and low in necessary nitrates and phosphates.

At higher elevations, the ill-smelling chrysophyte *Hydrurus foetidus* and a few genera of diatoms may be the only algae present, and these are ordinarily attached. Downstream, where currents slacken, temperatures and nutrients increase and a stream (having had contributions from many tributaries) takes on a few lacustrine characters. Here the quantity and quality of the microbiota likewise increase. The water has had time to be exposed to light and to gases. It is judged that water must be several weeks "old" before it reaches maximum productivity.

Slowly flowing streams in lower reaches sometimes develop *Euglena*, *Microcystis*, and *Aphanizomenon* blooms of short duration — indicators of high nutrient-content and a source of vitamin B_{12}. Plankters which are tolerant of pollution are volvocoids, especially *Chlamydomonas* spp, *Euglena viridis*, *Scenedesmus*, *Oscillatoria*, and many diatoms. Below sources of pollution (human wastes) at a distance which permits organic matter to be oxidized, the algal flora may become abruptly abundant. *Stigeoclonium*, a useful index of pollution (certain species especially), becomes conspicuous, forming tufts on all submersed objects, often choking a small stream. Many stream surveys have shown degrees of pollution-tolerance by algal species. Palmer (1963, e.g.) pointed out that *Euglena viridis*, *Nitzschia palea*, *Stigeoclonium tenue*, *Oscillatoria tenuis*, and *O. limosa* show a distinct tolerance of pollution. It is appropriate to use such species as reliable index organisms when pollution is suspected. Counts made in

Texas streams have shown plankton counts to be as high as 1,000,000 per ml. (diatoms) in polluted waters. Unpolluted streams support such filamentous chlorophytes as *Cladophora* and such diatoms as *Nitzschia linearis*. Hence the presence of these forms is a helpful indication that a stream is not polluted. As pollution increases in a stream, either in distance or in time, fewer and fewer species become more and more abundant.

The flora which appears in lower reaches of a stream represent: (1) species which have originated in lakes, swamps, and marshes in the headwaters and which are transient, having been carried into the outlet by currents and do not (or may not) complete their life history; (2) forms which are commonly found in and which are adjusted to stream conditions and which continue to multiply and to complete their life history (referred to as *autopotamic*); and (3) lacustrine species which have been forced to enter a stream, can adjust to rheo-conditions, and are able to multiply in transit (*eupotamic*). The latter includes diatoms especially. Species which occur in lateral lagoons and marginal swamps are more clearly lacustrine and are so regarded (*tychoplanktonic*).

The effect of lake plankton entering a stream is illustrated by the observations of Chandler (1939). Some of these are summarized in Table 8.2.

TABLE 8.2   Percentage of Algal Species in Lake and Lake Outlet

	% OF SPECIES IN LAKE	% OF SPECIES IN OUTLET
CYANOPHYTA	19.10	16.06
BACILLARIOPHYCEAE	62.08	62.66
CHLOROPHYTA	2.33	2.40

Table 8.2 indicates that the composition of the flora is about the same in the outlet as that within the lake, but this changes markedly in lower levels. In a heavily vegetated zone of a stream the potamoplankton decreased by 70% within a distance of 20 m.

Affecting the flora in lower reaches, often causing a reduction in what otherwise might be a rich flora, is the amount of suspended matter. This increases decidedly of course in the lower reaches of streams and rivers as they approach their mouths. As is well-known, there is a heavy load in such rivers as the Hudson, Mississippi, Columbia and Potomac. The lower sections of such rivers are poor producers, containing in their plankton mostly transient species. To be sure, such downstream populations are influenced by other factors such as pollution by toxic metals, oil, and various industrial wastes. Floras in lower river reaches are usually abundant in late summer when there may be blooms of *Euglena*, *Microcystis*, and *Aphanizomenon* occurring in those sections which have received enrichment of nutrients. Incidental pulses of potamoplankton are thought to be due (at times) to diurnal admission of benthic organisms.

Whitford and Schumacher (1963) made a floristic examination of streams throughout their courses and their observations are summarized in Table 8.3. Of all algae, the diatoms only are distributed throughout the entire stream course. Generalizations are difficult or meaningless in attempting stream characterization because no two streams are quite alike and no two sectors of a stream are similar.

TABLE 8.3	Number of Algal Species at Three Stream Altitudes (After Whitford and Schumacher, 1963)		
	MOUNTAIN	PIEDMONT	PLAIN
SEEPS AND SPRINGS	2	7	4
BROOKS	13	22	23
CREEKS	24	40	56
RIVERS	23	79	89
DITCHES	33	60	59
pH	6.0-6.5	6.5-7.0	5.2-6.5

Ecology of Marine Algae

With 139,000,000 square miles or about 71% of the earth's surface occupied by oceans (to a depth of five miles or more), it is seemingly paradoxical that marine vegetation (aside from plankton) should occupy only the narrowest fringes of the continents (about 2% of the marine surface). Because of their biology (and because of what evolution has dictated) marine plants must be attached, and obviously only in water levels which receive proper illumination. Accordingly, marine algae are, with rare exceptions, concentrated on shorelines and in the zone of relatively shallow water, leaving the great expanses of the sea to the plankton.

Marine phytoplankton is composed almost entirely of dinoflagellates, diatoms, and silicoflagellates. This aspect of the marine flora is especially abundant of course in the photosynthetic zone, and occurs in "patches" or meadows that are carried along on surface currents. These constitute the "pasturage of the sea" on which the animal life of the oceans depends. Furthermore many animals on land and numberless millions of birds also depend indirectly on phytoplankton.

The ecological factors that regulate marine algal distribution and the composition of floras are the same as those related to fresh-water algae. These factors may be classified as: (1) chemical (nutrients, salts, dissolved substances, pH); (2) physical (including dynamics or physiographic factors) as well as tides and water movement; and (3) biological (competition, epiphytism, predation).

In response to seasonal variations, especially in respect to light and temperature, there are corresponding changes in the number and kinds of algal species, both planktonic and littoral. Because of the prevalence and persistence of perennial dominants in some zones along shore lines (the Fucaceae and Ulvaceae, e.g.), variations in floral composition are not always clearly evident. A few relationships of ecological factors will be outlined below.

Marine Ecology: Currents and Water Movement

Of the above factors, one to which marine algae are subjected that freshwater algae are spared is tidal movement. Tides vary tremendously in different parts of the world, in both amplitude and number per lunar day. Amplitudes may vary from a few inches to as much as 70 feet (Bay of Fundy).

Usually there are two high (semidiurnal) and two low tides, though certain areas are characterized by as few as one and others by as many as four. The neap tide is lower than the spring tide in which water level rises more and reduces less. Tides, in addition to the fact that currents (wave action) are infinitely more severe in the sea, create an environment that requires highly refined adjustments.

Tides and wave action produce both direct and indirect effects. They determine the type of hold-fast, as well as the rapidity of spore and zygote germination, all of which are related to the degree of shelter or of exposure. Tides and wave action determine the height (width) of vegetational zones, especially the intertidal and the zone above high tide levels. The height and width of the zones are also related to the pitch of the shoreline. The effects of tidal currents, strong or weak, not only regulate the flora composition, but also determine the amount and rate of erosion. The latter in turn determines to a large extent the amount of silt and suspended matter. All of these affect the length of exposure of plants to the air during low tides, and many other aspects of algal ecology.

Because of the severity of currents and tides, plants must be pliable and resilient, yet tough and leathery if they attain macroscopic size. They develop exceedingly strong hold-fasts (*haptera* or *adhesive discs*) which in many instances actually grow into rocks. *Postelsia palmaeformis*, for example, grows in the most turbulent waters, but develops poorly in protected situations. Furthermore, the habitat is such that, at least in the tidal zone, all plants in this particular zone are submersed about half of the time and exposed to the air and desiccation half of the time. And when low tide occurs during daylight, plants are exposed to strong sunlight. This calls for a dual existence on the part of seaweeds: they must be both terrestrial and aquatic.

Exposed plants make use of abundant mucilage and have especially thick walls. When exposed, plants must be able to adjust to great variation in osmotic pressure, especially in those regions that are subject to frequent and heavy rains. Furthermore, in northern habitats, shore algae are subjected to severe treatment from ice, and thus require great powers of regeneration.

Whereas many aspects of the shore habitat are rigorous, some of the ecological factors that are exceptionally critical in fresh-water algal distribution are not so demanding or difficult to meet in the oceans. For example, temperatures are more nearly uniform (vertically) because of wave action and turbulence, and seasonal maximum-minimum ranges are less. Nutrients (always important) are possibly more uniformly provided because the sea is the recipient of all elements leached from all the lands; over the aeons of time substances in solution have become relatively evenly distributed. Light, critically important, is one factor, as previously mentioned, that is responsible for the over-crowding of marine vegetation in a zone which is at the same time subject to severe wave action and water-level vacillation. Thus the requirements for adequate light induce some indirect ecological conditions which vary somewhat from those affecting fresh-water algae. There is, for instance, excessive crowding, widespread epiphytism, and intense competition for photosynthetic light waves, gases and nutrients. Further, the requirement for light and for a foothold forces plants into a zone that is in a continuous state of flux, turbulence, and violent assault by tons of water that every few seconds come crashing down on them.

The adjustments that plants make to a marine environment have led to decided vertical, horizontal, as well as geographical distribution. Vertical distribution and zonation will be considered first.

Marine Ecology: Zones

Three zones are recognized in respect to vertical distribution, taking into account, nevertheless, certain variations (in kinds and numbers of plants) due to specific shoreline configurations such as flat, sandy beaches, tidal flats, marshes, mangrove swamps, and estuaries. Although there is slight uniformity in distribution of genera (both horizontally and vertically) in floras along coastal sectors, there is vertical variation that is induced by latitude, edaphic factors, etc. The height or extent of these zones is of course related to the height of waves and tides, which vary locally. Further, the slope of the shore has a marked effect on zonations, determining such features as tide pools.

LITTORAL ZONE

This is the zone intermittently covered and uncovered by tidal and wave action and, depending upon the shoreline configuration, may be divisible into Upper Midlittoral and Lower Midlittoral Zones. In mid-North America, along the Pacific Coast for example, the Littoral Zone is characterized especially by such Phaeophyta as *Ascophyllum, Egregia, Fucus,* and *Laminaria*, particularly when the shore is rocky. The upper fringe of this zone often has *Pelvetia canaliculata* and *Catenella opuntia* as conspicuous forms. Besides occurring on rock masses *Ascophyllum* grows commonly on rock-fragmented beaches. It is possible to refer to the Midlittoral as the fucoid zone because of the prevalence of *Fucus* and *Asophyllum* (and sometimes *Laminaria*). Although seasonal changes do occur among the components of the fucoid zone, the association appears to be persistent throughout the year, partly because most of the species are perennial. In Australia *Hormosira* replaces *Fucus* and *Laminaria* of the northern hemisphere. Also in the Littoral Zone are *Chondrus* and *Corallina* (Rhodophyta) and *Ulva* and *Enteromorpha* (Chlorophyta).

When this zone includes flats occupied by mangrove and other halophilic Angiosperms which are affected by tides, there are brackish water red algae such as *Bostrychia* and *Caloglossa; Catenella* (in subtropical areas); and *Caulerpa, Penicillus,* and *Acetabularia*.

If the topography includes tide pools (protected microhabitats) there will be many delicate, filamentous Rhodophyta such as *Polysiphonia, Callithamnion,* and *Corallina; Monostroma* in the Chlorophyta; and the brown alga *Cystoseira*. Many species growing in the Sublittoral occur in such protected sites of the Littoral and this accounts for some of the variations noted when one sector of coast is compared with another.

When there are sandy beaches in the Littoral, brown patches of diatoms occur, along with blue-green algae and dinoflagellates. On tidal flats out of reach of strong currents, but still within the Littoral Zone, several genera of green algae are to be found. These include *Ulothrix* and *Enteromorpha; Vaucheria* in the Chrysophyta; and cyanophytes such as *Oscillatoria, Phormidium, Lyngbya,* and *Rivularia*.

In subtropical regions the midsection of the Littoral is occupied by such genera as *Caulerpa, Hypnea, Laurencia,* and the delicate *Bryopsis*. The lower part of the Littoral is characterized by *Caloglossa, Lomentaria, Ceramium, Gelidium,* and *Polysiphonia* (Rhodophyta); *Boodlea* (Chlorophyta); *Sargassum, Dictyota,* and *Alaria* (Phaeophyta), forms which commonly belong to the Infralittoral but extend their range into the Littoral. In the Arctic and Antarctic this zone is barren of algae, except for diatoms and occasional cyanophytes, because of the scouring action of shore ice.

SUPRALITTORAL ZONE

This is the fringe adjoining and just above the Littoral. The upper levels are sometimes referred to as the Black Zone, and are almost invariably occupied by dark marine lichens such as *Verrucaria* and by black cyanophytes. Below the upper fringe is the splash zone, wetted when winds or tides are strong, or by tsunamis. It is kept moist most of the time but is subject to intense light and in some parts of the world to seasonal drying. This zone varies tremendously in respect to geological features, humidity, rainfall, etc., and these affect the amount and kind of organisms that occur. Here, rather consistently, are found, besides barnacles, several species of cyanophytes such as *Pleurocapsa fuliginosa*, *Calothrix contorenii*, *C. scopulorum*, *Rivularia atra*, *Phormidium corium*, and *Lyngbya majuscula* (which may be dominant), as well as *Bangia* (Rhodophyta). In the Arctic *Prasiola crispa* and *Ulothrix australis* occupy the zone.

Depending on the configuration of the shore, the Supralittoral may contain tide pools that are alternately salt, brackish, or fresh. Here can be found *Prasiola*, many microscopic genera such as *Dunaliella*, and dinoflagellates.

Occasionally orange-colored *Trentepohlia* forms conspicuous patches just above the splash zone, whereas just below, in more moist situations, the felt-forming *Vaucheria* grows. The species composition of the Supralittoral changes as one compares different sectors of the coast, but the morphological types are, in general, much the same.

INFRALITTORAL (SUBLITTORAL) ZONE

This zone extends downward from that lowest fringe of the Littoral which is regularly exposed to air during spring tide to the lowest low water that is rarely if ever exposed to the air. In some ecological classifications, the Infralittoral extends from the low water level of the spring tide to a depth of two to four feet. Actually, the Infralittoral can include the entire coastal zone of vegetation which is continuously submersed. By underwater surveys (Scuba diving) such zones of vegetation can be determined.

In the Infralittoral, with its very active waters, *Sargassum* spp are common and almost universal inhabitants. Here (in temperate latitudes) are found many members of the Phaeophyta: *Alaria, Postelsia, Agarum, Laminaria, Lessonia, Desmarestia*. In some sections offshore zones include dense beds of *Macrocystis, Pelagophycus,* and *Pterygophora*. Rhodophyta such as *Gigartina, Chondrus, Gastroclonium,* and *Delesseria* are found here (as examples of the very common and representative genera). In subtropical waters *Codium* and *Batophora* (Chlorophyta) are found, along with *Champia, Gracilaria, Grateloupia,* and the widely distributed *Chondrus*.

In Antarctica, *Monostroma, Phyllophora, Iridaea,* and *Hildenbrandtia* are found in the upper Sublittoral (down to a depth of 30 feet). Amazingly, 23 species or 6.6% of the total benthic flora of the Ross Sea were dredged from below 37 meters, whereas ten species came from an almost unbelievable depth of 668 meters. The biology involved is unknown, but speculation is invited as to whether plants recovered at this depth had been carried there accidentally, although specimens were attached to a substrate. *Ballia callitriche* grows only below 37 meters and represents an elittoral species.

Around Cape Horn and Tierra del Fuego two species of *Macrocystis* dominate the Sublittoral. These forms occur about all the islands of the Subantarctic and also are found around the tip of Africa and around the Australian islands. In the Arctic Chukchi Sea, beds of Phaeophyta have been found at about 39 feet, including *Phyllaria, Dermotodea, Laminaria saccharina,* and *Desmarestia viridis,* along with seven Rhodophyta. Here the spotted zonation seems to be related to rocky substrates.

Algae in the Sublittoral die very quickly when or if they become exposed, for they are less adaptable than Littoral species. Many of the upper Sublittoral algae are the ones which extend down into deep water (15 meters or more); cf. such genera as *Nereocystis, Laminaria, Pelagophycus* in the Pacific.

In the non-rocky zones of the Sublittoral there are mostly only films of diatoms and skein-forming Cyanophyta. Sometimes young plants of the Ulvales can be found attached to coarser sand.

The composition of the floras in these several zones may change according to seasons, of course, but that of the Infra- or Sublittoral changes the least, partly because it is the least affected by temperature and water changes. Diatoms too show a periodic fluctuation, with an abundance in tide pools beginning in the autumn. Tide pools may be dominated by *Enteromorpha* and *Monostroma* in summer, but these forms are found attached in the Midlittoral Zone in winter. On the other hand, certain red algae such as *Dumontia* and *Delesseria* or *Scytosiphon* in the Phaeophyta appear in higher zones in winter and occur in lower zones during summer. The migration up and down is regulated by both light and temperature, as well as by ability of plants to regenerate from fragments (vegetative reproduction).

Marine Ecology: Horizontal Belts

Horizontally, zones of algae constitute recognizable "girdles" of generic associations which are more or less obvious along some coasts, less so in other sectors. Belts are regarded as being composed of habitat niches in which water-level variations (and other factors) are the same or similar (as outlined above). In the boreal and Subantarctic the girdles show considerable consistency, although there is a diminution in both the number and the height of belts in the North Atlantic (for example, in the Faeroe Islands).

The girdles of eastern North America are similar to those of Europe (in general composition of species). Tropical shores have similarities with the Mediterranean belts, where sand and gravel shores have *Udotea, Halimeda, Caulerpa,* and *Sargassum.* Calcareous forms often predominate. Also in the tropics, where water temperatures may be as high as 25°C., coral reefs and atolls support *Lithothamnion, Corallina,* and *Lithophyllum* on the seaward side. Zooxanthellae and dinoflagellates are also found in corals and tunicates. On the leeward side are *Halimeda, Caulerpa,* and *Dictyosphaeria.*

In habitats which include sheltered mangrove swamps there is a belt characterized by *Bostrychia, Catenella, Caloglossa, Caulerpa,* and many film- or mat-forming Cyanophyta.

In making analyses of floras comprising the above-mentioned zones, and in studying the distribution of species, the periodicity of wetting, the levels of neap and spring tides, and the length of exposure time become important. As is well-known, there is in each 24 hours (usually) a higher water spring tide and a lower water neap tide, alternating with a higher low ebb tide and a lower low ebb tide. The different levels attained by tides, fluctuating as they do throughout the year, are referred to as:

HHW	Highest high water level
LHW	Lowest high water level
HLW	Highest low water level

Such designations are extended to include and/or to differentiate neap and spring tides. Thus:

HHHWN	Highest high of the high water of neap tides
HHHWS	Highest high of the high water of spring tides
LLHWN	Lowest lower high water of neap tides

HHHHWS   Highest higher high water of spring tides
LHHW   Lowest higher high water
HLHW   Highest lower high water

In north and south temperate latitudes the winter months, as might be expected, display the most marked reduction in both quantity and quality of the floras in these zones. In most sectors the winter depletion is followed by a sudden revival that coincides with increased insolation of spring.

Marine Ecology: Distribution

World-wide distribution of marine algae presents many intriguing problems for which there are correlations but no good explanations. Temperatures seem to play a deciding role in north-south distribution patterns, whereas east-west distributions are apparently related to a number of factors: water currents, ancient inter-ocean connections (now gone), dispersal by birds, etc. Many species, such as *Codium mamillosum*, for example, possess disjunct distribution. This species is reported from the tropical mid-Pacific and from the southwest coast of Australia (with no intermediary stations). *Neomeris annulata* is more widely distributed, but in widely separated sites: the Caribbean, the Southeast Asia zone, Madagascar, the Red Sea, and the south Pacific (according to Svedelius). With such a wide range of localities one may well query why the numerous habitats between are not represented. It has been noted that the floral composition in the Caribbean and the Indian Ocean is very similar, and that some species are found only in the Indian Ocean and in the western Atlantic. It is significant that in many instances two or more species of a genus have practically similar distribution patterns.

Such distribution, then, is subject to speculation, one thought being that disjunct localities are the remains of former, more continuous distribution patterns for a species or genus. It is risky to regard species as endemic because such a designation is subject to frequent correction as surveys and collections are made; yet there are many taxa which, to date, seem to be confined to particular regions. Most of the species found in the Subantarctic occur only there, especially some larger brown algae, and it is claimed that endemism exists more in the Southern Hemisphere than in the Northern, especially in the vicinity of Australia.

When viewed geographically, the marine algal flora of the world (particularly benthic algae) has its greatest concentration in five regions: (1) western north Pacific, temperate (2) eastern north Pacific (Japan); (3) Australian sector; (4) southwest Africa; (5) Mediterranean Sea. These regions are in contrast to almost "desertous" sections such as the far western Caribbean and the east coast of Central America. Here rocky reefs, ordinarily ideal for littoral algae, are completely destitute of plants.

It is reported that as many as 400 species occur in the region of Monterey Peninsula alone, and Scagel has reported 478 species in 189 genera from the north Pacific, and has indicated that there are probably at least 500 species. The Gulf of Mexico, poor in littoral flora, has a relatively rich sublittoral flora.

Marine Ecology: Persistence

Many algae, like terrestrial vegetation, grow as either annuals or as perennials, and it is interesting that some of the largest of the seaweeds attain their growth as annuals. Feldmann (1937) developed a useful classification of algae according to duration and habit of growth (see p. 35):

I. Annuals.
   A. Ephemerophyceae: Plants which develop from a zygote or spore by immediate germination. Examples: **Cladophora** spp, **Monostroma, Polysiphonia.**
   B. Eclipsiophyceae
      1. Plants found during one part of the year, and obvious; the other part of the year existing as microscopic growths. Examples: **Sporochnus, Nereia, Asperococcus.**
      2. Plants found as obvious growth forms during one part of the year; existing as cysts or resting stages at other times. This type may be referred to as the Hypnophyceae. Examples: **Ulothrix, Oedogonium, Vaucheria, Porphyra** (protonemal stage).

II. Perennial.
   A. Phanerophyceae. Plants in which the entire frond is perennial; growing erect. Examples: **Codium, Fucus, Phyllophora.**
   B. Chamaeophyceae. Plants in which the entire frond is perennial but growing as a horizontal encrustment. Examples: **Lithophyllum, Hildenbrandtia.**
   C. Hemiphanerophyceae. Plants in which only part of the erect frond is perennial. Examples: **Chondrus, Cystoseira, Sargassum, Laminaria.**
   D. Hemicryptophyceae. Plants in which only the basal part persists throughout the year when other parts are gone, as a disc or as a creeping filament. Examples: **Cladostephus, Griffithsia, Acetabularia, Gymnogongrus, Lemanea.**

Marine Ecology: Water Chemistry

The seas may be thought of as a gargantuan culture vessel, nurturing a teeming and proliferating ferment of protoplasm. The culture medium is a rich amalgamation of salts, minerals, and elements in solution, some nutritious and necessary for life, others antagonistic. The sea has been both the cradle and the graveyard of countless thousands of kinds of organisms since the beginning of time. As waters of seas became more and more enriched, and more salty, the inhabitants, through phsyiological adaptations, adjusted to the chemistry of their environment. The degree of success of their evolution is reflected in the multitudinous marine species which have been eliminated. As has often been said, life is the exception and not the rule.

As a culture medium the substances in solution are not uniformly concentrated, because of the great depths and breadth. Areas near the mouths of great rivers that inject a continuous stream of suspended matter and elements in solution will have greater concentrations. Many elements and substances are in greater supply in the waters near shore and over the coastal sections of the continental shelf, where plant life brings about a concentration of organic matter and where the decomposition by bacteria and fungi recirculate elements.

Of the 44 known elements and substances in the sea, analyses show the following general breakdown: 1.0% is calcium; 1.0% potassium; 4% magnesium; 31% sodium; 54% chlorine; 0.2% bromine; 8% sulphates; and 0.2% carbonates. In addition there is present iodine, nitrogen, oxygen, and carbon dioxide in trace amounts. Whereas the salt concentration is approximately 3.5% (or 35 gs./1000 gs. water) depending upon depth and location, the percentages vary from nearly 0.0 to 40% (Red Sea, e.g.). Even in the same general area of the sea (within a strait or fjord) concentrations may vary from 28% to 34% (34 gs./1000); and in great depths the salinity varies from 1.0 to 3.0%.

Organisms therefore must maintain high osmotic pressures but they must also be able to adjust to changing concentrations of the medium. Variation in salinity produces a more pronounced or at least observable effect on plankton than on the benthic flora. It is to be expected that marine organisms vary tremendously in their ability to adjust to ranges in salinity, and this in itself is a determining factor of selectivity and distribution. Some species are sensitive to a very narrow range of salinity percentages, whereas others can adjust to a range of from 0.0% to 3.5%. This is shown by the successful growth of some species (especially Ulvaceae) on the hulls of ships which pass from salt into freshwater channels.

Alaria, Costaria, Laminaria, and Odonthalia are a few examples of genera which can adapt to a wide range of salinity, whereas Postelsia,

Lessoniopsis, Iridaea, and *Dilsea* are confined to high levels of salinity. Algae that live in upper range tide pools must be able to withstand drastic variations in salinity. By evaporation during times between replenishment of water from the sea, the concentrations may become two or more times that of salt water in the ocean. Also, at other times, rain water may dilute the tide pool to a near fresh-water condition.

It has been found by culture experimentation that deep-water algae have an osmotic pressure that is resistant to salinity 1.4 times that of sea water, whereas plants of the upper Sublittoral and tide pools can adjust to concentrations 2.2 times that of sea water. Further, Sublittoral algae are much more sensitive to increases in salinity than are Littoral. Littoral algae (those which are adapted to exposure at low tide) are resistant to salt concentrations three times that of sea water. Such adjustments seem to be related to small cells and dense cell contents possessed by most Littoral algae such as *Porphyra,* for example. Another adjustment that some intertidal algae possess is that of being able to survive even after cells have become plasmolyzed (e.g., some of the filamentous Rhodophyta like *Polysiphonia*). It is known that algae of the Littoral have a little-understood mechanism for concentrating salts in opposition to diffusion gradients.

Phosphates and nitrates (0.2 ppm. max.) are relatively scant as compared with many fresh-water habitats, yet just as important in nutrition of marine plants. Accordingly, productivity and species distribution are regulated. The effect of higher concentration is noted in coastal areas which are influenced by inflow of rivers bearing leachings and wastes from the soil. It is well-known, however, that organic pollution from urban areas have an inhibiting effect. The relationship of nitrates and phosphates to distribution and selectivity is seen more clearly in the phytoplankton. A good example is the blooms of dinoflagellates when nitrate content increases periodically in offshore waters. In fact, the uptake and exhaustion of nitrates and phosphates by the more advantageously located plankters probably has a direct bearing on the sudden reduction of attached seaweeds along some shores. Periodically, substantial masses of seaweeds are cast onto the shore where they may remain long enough to undergo decay. This subsequently releases concentrations of phosphorus, nitrates, and other substances which act as growth stimulators of sublittoral plants.

The sea is alkaline, with a pH ranging generally from 7.5 to 8.4, though it may get as low as 7.3. Plants long since have adjusted to this facet of their chemical environment. Changes in pH through photosynthesis may create a situation unsuitable for many algae and hence act as a selector, or determine the domination of some species over others. Most algae studied, however, are able to survive pH ranges from neutrality (or slightly below) to pH 9.6.

Entering into the pH situation is the amount of calcium carbonate. Waters in tropical zones may be saturated or nearly so, and this plays an important ecological role in regulating the distribution of calcareous green and red genera. Hence such seas are dominated by these rather than by Phaeophyta. Coral or limestone reefs are constructed only in warm seas where *Lithothamnion* and *Halimeda* species are abundant.

It is not known how widespread among marine algae is the requirement for vitamin B_{12} especially. But culture studies have demonstrated that B_{12} is important to many plankters and to the red alga *Goniotrichum*. It well may be that the presence or absence of adequate B_{12} and/or thiamine is responsible for the distribution or occurrence of many species. Clearly B_{12} could be in significant concentrations only in certain localized zones — for example, in the vicinity of organic matter accumulation and bacterial decomposition.

The many trace elements found in marine algae may be of importance physiologically but are not deemed to be of ecological importance because apparently they are universally present or available. Subsequent studies, however, may show that trace elements are important determiners in distribution.

Marine Ecology: Temperature

As pointed out elsewhere, temperature is, in general, less important than light. Still, it is probably as important to marine algae as it is to fresh-water algae, though ranges and rates of change, however, are less in the former than in the latter. The freezing point of marine water is lower than that of fresh water. Temperature is important directly in respect to photosynthesis, and indirectly in a number of ways, such as its relation to the uptake of oxygen. Whereas the annual range may be from subzero to 15°C. in northern waters, the seasonal variation in the tropics is only 2 or 3°C. From Cape Hatteras to Newfoundland there is a winter-summer variation of 18°C. In the Mediterranean the variation is 7 to 14°C. Seasonal variations are greater in coastal waters than in open water, and have little direct or indirect effect in deep water. Besides variations in (latitude) insolation that bring about temperature changes, ocean currents also induce changes, or produce ecological situations that determine floristic characters. The main ocean currents are clockwise in the Northern Hemisphere, and counterclockwise in the Southern. Accordingly, the warm waters of the tropics are moved along western coasts of the continents, whereas cool waters from the polar regions sweep along the eastern coasts. Surface temperatures, through high insolation, may induce a thermocline so that lower zones are stagnated and there is no circulation of nutrients and oxygen into lower levels. In some sections seasonal overturns bring nutrients liberated at the bottom by bacterial decomposition into the upper photosynthetic zone.

Another factor that is indirectly related to ecology is the direction of prevailing winds, which mostly coincide with the direction of the cold currents. One of the indirect effects is that of inducing upwellings of subsurface or even deep water which in some circumstances is enriched in nutrients.

As in other physiological adjustments, algae vary in their temperature requirements and the temperature range within which they can operate. For most marine algae, 30 to 35°C. seems to be the upper limit of tolerance for both growth and reproduction, although some Supralittoral species have been shown to withstand 40°C. (*Bangia* and *Urospora*). *Bangia* can survive even at 42°C. when grown subaerially in a relative humidity of 17.2%, but cannot withstand 35°C. when submersed. Sublittoral plants are more sensitive to low temperatures than are Littoral. Some can withstand a drop to −2.0°C. whereas others die at 1 to 3°C.

Temperature has indirect effects that play a role in the selection of species and in productivity. One is the effect on the uptake of CO_2 for photosynthesis and O_2 in respiration. More light is needed to maintain the compensation point (the point at which oxidation is balanced by photosynthesis) when temperature rises from 10°C. to 20 or 30°C., because such a rise induces a rapid depletion (oxidation) of food substances. The compensation at 10°C. may require 250–300 Lux, but at 16°C. the compensation level requires 350–400 Lux. Oxygen-content is less of course in warm than in cold water and this is related to the fact that the largest algae and the most abundant beds develop in the colder waters of the temperate zones.

Some species respond to temperature changes by varying their time of development. In the same locality there may be a northern type of flora in the winter, but a subtropical one at the same level in the summer. Or a species may grow in the same station at different levels throughout the year.

Another adjustment which some "selected" species can make is that of maintaining high osmotic pressure and a physiology that can withstand low temperatures. Some species in the Arctic can have 80% of their water frozen without complete stoppage of metabolism (or at least only with a temporary interruption).

Setchell, in one of his earlier studies, recognized groups of species related to 10, 15, 20, 25°C. isotherms, and called attention to the fact that most species are confined to one selected zone; that a lesser number could occupy two zones; and that a few have a distribution in three zones. A relatively scant number are indiscriminate; but when the temperature of water where they live drops or rises 5°C. from the norm the plants enter a dormant or otherwise modified existence. In general, plants that have a wide geographic distribution carry on vegetative growth at one temperature range and reproduce at another.

In some localities temperatures drop so that ice is formed. This in turn limits the development of perennial species in Littoral zones, although below the ice a fairly rich flora may develop in the Sublittoral.

Marine Ecology: Light

Reference has been made elsewhere to the all-important role of light in algal ecology (p. 281). As with fresh-water algae, light determines a photosynthetic zone in the oceans — in general the upper ten to 15 meters. This is approximately the upper 3% of the mean depth of the sea.

The amount and quality of light available to plants in the marine environment is subject to many variables: reflection, scattering, absorption, the amount of suspended matter, amount of turbulence, amount of dissolved matter, latitude (angle of incidence), and depth.

It has been determined that on days when there is choppy water the maximum photosynthesis occurs only at or just below the surface, whereas on calm days the best photosynthetic rate is at five meters. One study showed that only 4% of incident light was reflected from a calm surface, whereas in turbulence, 25% or more was reflected, and that in any event at 25 meters only 25% of incident light was available (see, however, percentages for fresh-water algae, p. 283). It is well-known that benthic algae cannot grow at extreme depths when they occur in regions where water is continuously choppy. *Macrocystis* was found growing to a depth of 70 feet in turbid water, whereas nearby in clear water it occurred at 100 feet. Because shore waters are often turbid, especially near the mouths of rivers, as much as 99% of incident light may be lost in the upper 30 feet.

In northern seas the average depth limitation for algal growth is about 50 meters, whereas in tropical seas it is at 100 meters; in the Mediterranean 130 meters, and off the Minorca coast 180 meters. The maximum depth seems to be 200 meters (see Zonations, p. 300). Measurements show that below ten meters there is an abrupt drop in the percentages of available sunlight. At 50 meters there is only 5% available, and of this amount the blue and green waves account for almost all.

Because different light waves are absorbed and/or eliminated at different levels as they pass through water, vertical zonations of algae result. The Chlorophyta have their maximum absorption and most efficient photosynthesis rate in the red sector of the spectrum (420–500 mμ). Since the long waves (red, yellow, orange, violet) are absorbed first in the water, Chlorophyta are relegated to the upper levels. Many brown and red algae are also found in upper water zones, while the green algae for the most part drop out below 30 meters. The maximum absorption of the brown algae is from the green sector (440–470 mμ. with two peaks of absorption) and accordingly can exist down to the limits of penetration of green waves. Many species of the Rhodophyta have a maximum absorption in the blue sector (440–520–560 mμ., with two peaks of absorption) of the spectrum, or the short waves. Accordingly, the red algae are the ones which occur in abysmal depths, reached only by the waves of the blue sector. It is known that phycoerythrin not only functions directly in photosynthesis but that the pigment acts as a receptor, passing energy on to chlorophyll molecules. It is noteworthy that the same species at great depths contain more abundant amounts of red pigments than they do near the surface.

There is no absolute correlation between pigments and light intensity, for some green algae can exist in weak light and many red species can adjust to intense light. As many as 40 different pigments have been identified within different groups of algae, functioning either as transmittors of energy to photosynthetic pigments, or directly in the process. The phenomenon of complementary colors (as previously mentioned, p. 136) seems to be related to photosynthetic activity of light. This constitutes a striking example of the manner in which physiology acts in ecology by determining vertical distribution of species.

The use of light of different intensities for photosynthesis is closely allied to temperature. For each species there is an optimum temperature or temperature range. Therefore, favorable light received in waters of unsuitable temperature would not induce the most efficient (or necessary) assimilation. The assimilation rate is reduced by nearly 50% with a drop of 5°C. below the specific optimum.

Whereas obtaining efficient light of the right quality is a problem, so is adjustment to intense illumination. Many algae are inhibited by strong light; cf. *Delesseria*, which is not able to withstand light stronger than 100 foot-candles. It is noteworthy that plants existing in the Littoral are adjusted to strong light more successfully than plants (even the same species) living within the Sublittoral. This is to be expected because if Littoral plants lacked such an ability to adapt they long since would have been eliminated.

Plants in the Arctic and Antarctic which must survive long periods of darkness have a low respiratory rate as well as an ability to store unusual amounts of food as in *Fucus*. It even has been suggested that arctic algae are adapted to the long dark period by using dissolved organic substances in the medium.

Habitats

F̲ʀᴇsʜ-ᴡᴀᴛᴇʀ Pʟᴀɴᴋᴛᴏɴ ᴀɴᴅ Pʀᴏᴅᴜᴄᴛɪᴠɪᴛʏ

The degree of successful response of organisms to ecological factors and the interactions involved determine, finally, what may be termed *production*. The term has shades of meaning relative to individual points of view and definition. First, production may mean the total quantity (bulk) of plant life supported in a lake (or other body of water) at any one time. This may be determined by aliquot weighing, or by statistically evaluating counts of organisms. Production may refer to the amount of organic matter produced by plant metabolism during a selected measure of time. This is sometimes determined by measuring the amount of chlorophyll, or by measuring photosynthesis by the C^{14} uptake method. Production may refer to amount (bulk) of fish life (or all animal life) supported by the primary photosynthesizers within a body of water. This evaluation is often made statistically. The ability of a body of water to support quantities of life is its productivity (productiveness). The life which it supports is its production.

Productivity is directly related to ecology, some factors of which have been outlined (see Chart 8.1). Ecological factors determine the kind and amount of the primary producers which in turn determine the amount and kind of production. In a eutrophic lake, for example, where perch and pike are often abundant, the phytoplankton may be considered as an index of fish productivity because of the rather direct relationship of plankters

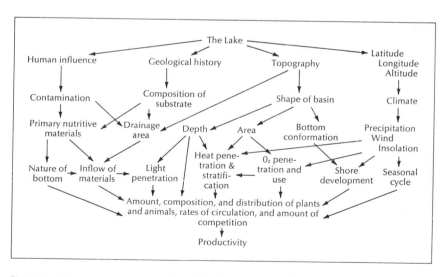

CHART 8.1   Trophic Nature of a Lake (modified from Rawson)

TABLE 8.4   Some Characteristics of a Productive, Eutrophic Lake*

BOTTOM DEPOSITS	DEPTH	NUTRIENT INDEX	NO₃	FREE NH₃

Gyttja
Organic silt
Over 2 million
  bacteria per cc
Aquatic plants
  abundant
	5-20 meters
	Large volume
	  in contact
	  with bottom
	Stratification
	  with seasonal
	  over-turn
		20.1	0.03-0.37
			ppm
				.008 ppm

P and P_2O_5	K	Ca	Fe	pH
0.025-0.77 ppm	4.9 ppm	24-50 ppm	13.3 ppm	7.2-8.0

PHYTOPLANKTON

10-20 million organisms per
  liter, including especially
  Microcystis, Coelosphaerium,
  Aphanizomenon, Anabaena,
  Melosira, Asterionella,
  Stephanodiscus
50-100 kg/hectare standing
  crop
Nygaard compound index above
  3.0
Myx-Chlor-Centrales-Euglen

  Desmids

* Figures based on averages of a number of analyses of eutrophic lakes.

to the food chain. Here, blue-green algae and diatoms dominate, particularly *Microcystis aeruginosa*, *Aphanizomenon flos-aquae*, *Coelosphaerium Kuetzingianum*, *Gloeotrichia echinulata*, *Asterionella formosa*, and *Melosira* spp; *Dinobryon* spp and *Synura uvella* in the Chrysophyceae; *Pediastrum* spp, *Sphaerocystis Schroeteri*, and *Botryococcus Braunii* in the Chlorophyta. Several of the species mentioned are associated in profuse growths, whereas some or another of the cyanophytes may occur in bloom proportions. Reference has been made to the ability of some bloom-producing plankters to upset the biology of a body of water. Lakes which have the ability to produce blooms have the characteristics shown in Tables 8.1 and 8.4.

Conversely, soft-water lakes with few electrolytes (oligotrophic) are poor producers, for they are low in nitrates and phosphates and lack half-bound carbonates. Trout *(Salmo fario)* is characteristic of such habitats. Countless studies have been made to show the relationship between lakes well-supplied with these substances and productivity. Similarly, many experiments in the field have shown that an increase in productivity results when fertilizers containing N, P, Mg, and Fe are added. Both organic and inorganic fertilizers can be used to modify the chemistry of a lake and so initiate a food chain which results in greater production of fish, the customary and popular index of a lake's productivity. Fe is a stimulator of primary plankton production when it occurs in an unoxidized form. This is especially true in respect to diatoms, which develop blooms when and if there is an abundance of iron and especially in early spring and late fall, when the pH is low. Manganese is known to be important for cyanophytes and seems to be related to their ability to take up sufficient iron (although they require less than diatoms). The critical point for blue-greens seems to be between 0.1 and 0.2 mg./L of manganese.

One of the immediate visible effects of a pulse development in the phytoplankton is an upsurge in zooplankton (usually occurring in spring and late summer or fall). Innumerable studies have shown that high counts of zooplankton occur following phytoplankton pulses. Many direct observations show that zooplankters are predators of algae and that predation is one of the causes of phytoplankton periodicity. Phytoplankton pulses not only initiate zooplankton pulses, but also lead to increased reproductive rates in microfauna. Edmondson, et al. (1962) found that egg-laying activities increased in three species of Copepoda following a dense phytoplankton population. Besides providing nutrition for primary consumers (microfauna) phytoplankton may be consumed directly by larger animals such as the gizzard shad.

Marine Plankton

The myriads of motes which drift in the photic zone and cloud the upper layers of the seas, small though they are, by sheer force of astronomical numbers exert a tremendous influence in aquatic biology. Their economic importances, often not appreciated, cannot be over-emphasized. This nomadic population, known as plankton, is comprised of mostly microscopic animals (zooplankton) and plant-like organisms (phytoplankton). But macroscopic organisms also are included, for there are many which drift or which cannot swim against currents (cf. coelenterates, a few fish, some seaweeds). In respect to size of plankters, one system of classification recognizes the following:

Ultranannoplankton   Organisms less than 2 μ. in diameter
Nannoplankton   Organisms 2–20 μ. in diameter
Microplankton   Organisms 20–200 μ. in diameter
Mesoplankton   Organisms 200–2000μ. in diameter
Megaplankton   Organisms 2000 μ. or more in diameter

Usually, however, nannoplankton refers to organisms which pass through an ordinary silk bolting cloth net (Nos. 20 or 25); such organisms would then be 2–5 μ. or less in diameter. Nannoplankton (and ultranannoplankton) are sometimes greater in bulk than the larger (5–20 μ. in diameter) and hence play a correspondingly important role in productivity.

Because the seas are the birthplace and the nursery of life, it is not impossible that some elements of the plankton universe represent forms closely related to those early elaborations of protoplasm which appeared some three billions of years ago. The phytoplankton, with which this outline is concerned, includes representatives of all algal phyla but Rhodophyta, Phaeophyta, and Euglenophyta (except for a few species of the latter). It is the Pyrrhophyta and the Bacillariophyceae (with other chrysophytes) which comprise the overwhelming bulk of marine phytoplankton. Included also are many coccolithophorids. These groups, as mentioned previously, constitute the "pasturage of the sea," for these are the energy-storing organisms which occupy a fulcrum position in the food-chain of aquatic animals. Abundant though plant life may be along the coasts and continental shelves, it does not constitute the source of food. Only rarely do fish even nibble on seaweeds, and shellfish cannot make use of sea lettuce. The fact is that the large animals of the sea (except possibly the plankton-straining whale) consume smaller animals, and the small animals feed only on microscopic animals and sometimes phytoplankton, whereas zooplankton depends on phytoplankton and organic debris produced by them. Hence, sea food for Man and for all the animals of the oceans is derived from the algae. Even vitamin D of cod liver oil has been passed along through the food chain from its initial fixation when the sun shone on some diatoms. Abundant as phytoplankton may be in the ocean water, "blooms" do not appear as frequently or as obviously as in fresh water.

The factors which regulate the distribution and composition of phytoplankton are, of course, the same as those which play roles in the ecology of other marine plants (temperature, nutrients and salinity, currents, light). Algae must occupy the upper layers of water (mostly the upper 15 meters) but within this zone there is a selectivity of species with pigments that make it physiologically possible for some plants to live in intense light;

that exclude some from strong light at the surface; and that allow others to adjust to an existence in feeble light down to about 50 meters. It is known also that some plankters (some nannoplankton, e.g.) can exist in the absence of light and metabolize by heterotrophy. It has been determined that chlorophyll can absorb blue light as deep as 50 meters. The greater concentration of short light waves in the lower latitudes accounts for the greater production (in general) of plankton in northern latitudes. The compensation point for plankton varies tremendously as related to light penetration. In the Sargasso Sea the compensation point is at 100 meters; in the Gulf of Maine, at 24–30 meters.

Phosphates and nitrates, relatively scant in the oceans, may be an important factor in plankton distribution as well as in productivity. For some reason phosphates are in general more abundant in tropical waters than in higher latitudes. There is less variation in amount where and when plant growth and decomposition proceed more continuously and at the same rate than in waters subject to seasonal changes. Sea water may produce 26.8 million diatoms for each 0.03 mg. of P consumed.

Much of the N and P in the sea is reassimilated, perhaps many times through the year. It was found, for example, that 93% of the phosphorus in the surface zone of water in the Gulf of Maine was organic. N and P can be recirculated by decomposition within the water, in addition to bacterial action at the bottom alone.

Dissolved nutrients of a sufficient amount to support a dense population disappear as they are taken up by phytoplankton. Further production is thereby automatically inhibited. The deterioration and decomposition of plankters in a pulse population returns nutrients to solution, and this serves to support another plankton increment of the same or (more often) another group of species. It has been noted that there is a cycle of plankton developments in the sea wherein carbohydrate-producing forms are followed by fat- and oil-storing algae.

The influence of nitrates and phosphates is noted in the "blooms" that develop especially along coasts, after heavy rains inland have led to a great inflow of nutrient-bearing water. The Red Tides (dinoflagellates) in the Gulf of Mexico, along the California coast, and along the New Jersey coast are related to periodic increase in nutrient-content (see p. 361). Also the upwelling of nutrient-bearing bottom water caused by wind and water currents induces the development of blooms. Limitation of plankton production may be determined indirectly by insolation. If surface waters warm sufficiently, a thermocline is established (at various depths) which limits circulation of nutrient-bearing waters from below.

In warmer and temperate waters there are usually two seasonal blooms or upsurges in plankton quantity, spring and autumn. Naturally the spring development is related to increase in insolation and to rise in temperature. This is followed by rapid reproduction, an increase in number, and a reduction in amount of nutrients. The thermocline (when present) prevents replenishment of nutrients from below. As the plankton decreases (with the lack of nutrients), decomposes, and passes into the hypolimnion, there is an increase in nutrient substances there. Then when the thermocline disappears, circulation of water in the fall makes possible another peak development of plankton which may be the same as or different from the algae in the spring pulse.

At least from culture studies it is known that plankters can assimilate nitrates and phosphates during darkness and in the absence of photosynthesis, and thus are able to maintain themselves even in areas where nutrients are in low supply.

Other determiners include vitamin B_{12}, carbonates as a source of CO_2, and Fe. These may be more important in the determination of quantity than of quality. Certainly the waters of the sea are amply supplied with all the elements necessary for an even greater productivity than exists.

The Silicoflagellates, often tremendously abundant, and the diatoms require silicon, which may be a limiting factor for these groups. Obviously silicon is abundant enough in most ocean waters to provide luxuriant floras. In some areas, however, it may be of such low quantity as to regulate productivity. In waters low in silicon the cell wall is thin; the genus *Attheya*, for example, has scarcely any silicon and is preserved with difficulty.

Plankton distribution is determined by surface currents, as concentrations of organisms drift across the ocean like floating, greenish meadows. Because of the relation of fish to the food chain, fishermen know from experience that their best takes come when they follow close upon these "pastures."

Because phytoplankters are consumed by zooplankters, a pulse of the former is usually followed by an upsurge in numbers of animals (see p. 316). Their predation reduces the algal population, forcing a drop in zooplankton, and, subsequently, another pulse in phytoplankton species (possibly quite a different flora than previously). Phytoplankton may occur in quantities as high as 40,000,000 per liter, but this number can be quickly reduced. One *Chilodon* is known to consume 30 algal cells within 24 hours.

Because of such factors as turbidity and distribution of nutrients (their concentration), plankton populations have different composition in different locations. For example, we can recognize neritic (coastal or tychoplanktonic) associations, and oceanic groups of species. The former is composed mostly of heavy individuals, and of forms which frequently use cysts in their life cycle. These are algae which physiologically demand richer concentrations of nutrients. Conversely, oceanic species drift in water of low nutrient concentration and pass their life history entirely at sea. As a result they often possess modifications of form as aids in flotation.

Due to the tremendous area occupied by the seas and their currents that cast organisms about, and because of the relative paucity of surveys, actually very little is known concerning plankton distribution and composition. But some generalizations can be made. For example, when Dinoflagellata are abundant diatoms are in much reduced numbers, and vice versa. A sample analysis of Atlantic plankton shows that dinoflagellates constitute 27% of the flora in October, with an increase to 64% in November. This pulse is followed by diatom increase so that by December this element occupies 90% of the flora. This percentage is maintained throughout the winter and recedes as phosphorus is depleted. There is then a new upsurge of dinoflagellates, followed by a late spring rise in diatoms. The latter may come to constitute 100% of the phytoplankton. Such a development is accompanied by increased insolation. A late summer and early fall pulse of dinoflagellates completes the periodic cycle.

Periodicity in plankton floras is related in part to the liberation of antagonistic metabolites. Laboratory cultures show that *Nitzschia* (a diatom) drastically inhibits the growth of *Chlorella*. Expanding research is producing more and more information on the control of one organism over another, or over a class of organisms.

Plankton species in the Antarctic are circumpolar because there are no land masses to interfere with dispersal by currents, whereas in the Arctic there are relatively few circumpolar species. Temperatures here range from 1.77 to 3.49°C.; the salt concentration is 32.61 to 34.5%. These features therefore serve to delimit diatoms and dinoflagellates to such an extent that there are northern sea associations and tropical-subtropical floras. A species such as *Ceratium tripos*, which is shade-seeking, occurs in deep water in the Tropics, but becomes a surface species in northern waters. In general, high temperatures are more conducive for a greater number of *Ceratium* species than northern and polar waters. Some species are confined to high temperatures (19 to 25°C.) whereas other *Ceratium* species adjust to a wide range, and by currents may be carried into cold water where at least they exist even if they do not multiply in large numbers. By analyzing the diatom flora, Braarud, Gaarder, and Grantved (1953) were able to divide the North Atlantic into 16 zones as determined by the flora composition.

Some studies indicate that production in warmer waters is not as great as that in upper latitudes. This is regarded as not necessarily true, however, because in the tropics the zone of productivity is much deeper and the overall production is about equal to that in cooler waters.

Soil

As previously indicated, the distribution of algal species is related to a combination of several edaphic factors and to physiological characteristics of the plant. These characteristics either accept or reject environmental conditions depending upon their suitability. The capabilities of algae to adjust to such combinations account for what is referred to as *niche associations*. These do not support the same species nor the same combination of species because of the simple fact that no two niches or habitats are the same, and because the factor of chance dispersal enters to an undetermined extent.

Because algae are primarily aquatic it seems almost paradoxical that there should be a relatively luxurious soil flora. Ordinarily this is neither as varied nor as abundant as in aquatic habitats, yet in some well-aerated, fertilized soils there may be as many as 1,000,000 algal cells per gram. The same species may occur in unfertilized soils, but in few numbers. In general, acid soils (pH 3.7–4.8) favor chlorophytes (desmids, *Chlorococcum*, *Zygogonium*, *Fritschiella*). Alkaline and calcareous soils (pH 6.8–8.4) are dominated by cyanophytes and diatoms (*Oscillatoria*, *Phormidium*, *Porphyrosiphon*, *Nitzschia*). Agricultural loam soils are much occupied by *Stichococcus*, *Hormidium*, *Euglena*, *Chlorella*, *Navicula*. The composition includes not unique organisms, but present (almost entirely) are species found elsewhere in water, and which are able to adjust to a soil habitat (see Table 8.5).

Naturally all soils do not contain the same kinds nor the same quantity of organisms because of variations in: (1) soil texture (physics); (2) soil chemistry (nutrients such as phosphates, nitrates, vitamins); (3) moisture; (4) temperature; and (5) light. These factors all play a role in determining the entire biology (including the higher plants).

The soil flora, consisting of both ephemeral and perennial species, collectively is often referred to as *edaphophytes* and includes representatives from most of the algal phyla. Sometimes the surface flora is known as the *saphophytes*, the subterranean as *cryptophytes*. Surface forms can also be called *epiterranean*, and subsurface, *subterranean*. In addition there are *casuals* which are incidentally present.

Occasionally the flora is conspicuous when plants occur as gelatinous films (*Phormidium*, *Anabaena*, *Microcoleus*, *Stigonema*) or as colored felts (*Porphyrosiphon*). But numerous forms are unicellular and distributed mostly throughout the upper six inches. Some unicellular green algae and diatoms have been collected from as deep as three meters. Moore and Karrer (1919) found *Protoderma viride* and *Hantzschia amphioxys* as deep as 100 cm. by culturing soil samples; in all, they found 14 species of algae growing between 20 and 100 cm. below the surface. Many species found in subterranean situations are those which have been carried there incidentally by percolating water or by earthworms, and do not maintain themselves. Some algae reach subterranean positions by their own movements. Obviously it is only in the surface forms and in those which exist within the upper centimeter or two that plants are actively photosynthetic. Subterranean forms are in a dormant state, whereas some can exist saprophytically. Table 8.5 shows the distribution of some of the more common genera found on or just under the soil surface. This list also includes the genera that are found in the psammon of sandy beaches. Akiyama (1961) reports 45 species from the soil near Hanshu, Japan, exclusive of diatoms. These were mostly green and blue-green algae, with a few Xanthophyceae.

One of the chief problems that soil algae must solve is that of intermittent and erratic dessication. This factor probably accounts for the abundance of blue-green algae on and in soil as compared with other forms. Their gelatinous film adsorbs water which aids in survival during a dry period, and their lack of cell vacuoles has an important bearing in respect to fatal plasmolysis. The fact that the cell wall is in contact with the protoplast is important because such water as can be imbibed reaches the cytoplasm directly.

In almost all instances, tropical soils harbor more cyanophytes than other algae, and, in general, have a richer flora than soils in temperate latitudes. In fact subaerial and terrestrial habitats the world over are characterized by cyanophytes. *Vaucheria* and *Botrydium* (Chrysophyta), on the other

TABLE 8.5 Genera of Algae Found in and Beneath Soil

EUGLENOPHYTA	CYANOPHYTA	CHRYSOPHYTA	CHLOROPHYTA
Euglena	Chroococcus	Navicula	Chlamydomonas
Trachelomonas	Gloeocapsa	Hantzschia	Chlorella
	Oscillatoria	Caloneis	Chlorococcum
	Porphyrosiphon	Botrydium	Stichococcus
	Lyngbya	Vaucheria	Hormidium
	Microcoleus		Oedocladium
	Phormidium		Fritschiella
	Nostoc		Netrium
	Stigonema		Roya
	Scytonema		Cylindrocystis

hand, are rare in subaerial habitats of the tropics. Those algae which can quickly assume an encysted form are naturally better adapted to a soil habitat. The classical report of Roach (1919) showed the ability of such cyanophytes as *Nostoc muscorum* and *Nodularia Harveyanum* to remain viable after 70 years of desiccation in stored soil. Students of exsiccatae know that very old, dried specimens of blue-green algae frequently can be revived and cultured.

Temperature changes in the terrestrial habitat are more drastic than in the aquatic environment. That is, the changes are more rapid and the extremes of high and low are greater and in many instances are held for longer periods of time. Accordingly the temperature factor plays an important role in determining the composition of the soil biota. Blue-green algae in general seem to be more adaptable to temperature changes and extremes than are chlorophytes and diatoms. This is probably related in part to the colloidal sheath of mucilage with which cyanophytes are invested. Mucilage-coated desmids, such as *Cylindrocystis*, and euglenoids which can encyst readily also are well-adjusted to a soil existence. Diatoms seem to be more sensitive to prolonged high temperatures than cyanophytes. Experimentally it has been shown that, on the other hand, diatoms can survive eight days at $-80°$C., and for 13 hours at $-192°$C. Such an adaptability explains the success of diatom floras in frigid waters.

Soil algae are important biologically and economically directly or indirectly. Often they are pioneer colonizers of barren, volcanic, or denuded areas. In such areas they form an erosion-preventing crust that retains moisture and provides a substrate for the germination of spores and seeds of other plants. By their own activities algae add organic matter to soil. Blue-green algae are especially advantageous because of the ability of some species to fix atmospheric nitrogen, a process which is particularly useful in the water-logged soils of rice fields. The nitrogen content of soil may be increased by as much as 400% where there is a dense growth of algae (see pp. 138, 337, Physiology). The association of algae with fungi to form lichens provides another type of soil pioneer. In addition, the production of antibiotics; the uptake of nutrients that otherwise might be saved by higher plants; the creation of films and crusts — all are examples of the many ways in which algae become involved in soil biota.

Cameron (1960) and Durrell (1962) have reported a surprisingly abundant soil flora in the desert where species take advantage of slightly moist surfaces beneath rocks, especially quartz, through which some light passes.

Qualitative and quantitative analyses of soil floras are difficult to make in a meaningful way. Direct examination and counts give only a myopic idea. Culturing of aliquots provides a more nearly complete analysis because it brings into activity dormant forms (cells and spores) otherwise overlooked, although algal cultures give misleading notions as to relative abundance of species. Many plants become active under culture conditions which would lie dormant and not contribute significantly to soil biology.

Symbiosis

Symbiosis among algae, from commensalism through epiphytism to outright parasitism, presents some situations which are curious, intriguing, and for the most part unexplainable, meriting considerable study. The ability of one organism to live with or upon another demands highly refined mutual adjustments, both morphological and physiological. What chemical changes are required; what enzymes are involved; what modifications are produced in the metabolism of both host and guest? In their symbiotism the organisms involved may be closely related taxonomically (*adeloparasites*) or not at all related (*alloparasites*). The association with animals, sometimes pathological, is seldom parasitic and is usually harmless to the host. In many instances the association is specific; in others the invader can select from a wide range of hosts.

Advantages of symbiotism include: (1) protection; (2) facilitated nutrition; (3) increased gas supply; (4) provision for dispersal (by animal host).

Marine Algae

Marine algae offer more examples of symbiotism than do fresh-water species. This may be explained by the fact that marine algae are older geologically, and also by the fact that overcrowding in the coastal belt provides more opportunities. Tokida (1960) listed 285 species of epiphytes on Laminariales alone, with *Laminaria* itself supporting 106 of these (mostly Rhodophyta and mostly specific). The Rhodophyta seem to be more parasite-oriented than any other group. In many instances epiphytism seems to be of a specific nature: *Dictyosiphon Eckmanii*, for example, has been found only on *Scytosiphon*, *Bangia ciliaris* on *Chaetomorpha*, and *Kylinia* seems to prefer an endophytic existence in *Porphyra*.

Colacopsis and *Choreonema* have highly reduced thalli, living almost entirely embedded in other mucilaginous red algae. Many members of the brown algae (especially the filamentous Ectocarpales and Sphacelariales) are both epiphytic and endophytic on the Rhodophyta (*Phloeospora braciata* on *Rhodymenia*, e.g.). Whereas many red algae are incidentally epiphytic or partly endophytic, a few, such as *Ceratocolax*, which penetrates deeply into the thalli of *Phyllophora*, is practically parasitic (see p. 233). The parasite often takes the form of gall-like or cancerous growths. A green alga endophytic in members of the Gigartinaceae is *Endophyton ramosum*, a branched filamentous form. In some instances endophytic algae simply grow within the walls of cells (cf. species of the Ectocarpales in the walls of *Cystoseira*). When red algae parasitize other Rhodophyta it is noteworthy that both host and invader are mutually able to form secondary pit connections.

FRESH WATER

In non-marine situations most of the symbiotism seems to occur among aerial or non-aquatic species, living on and in higher plants. These are epiphyllous (on leaves) or on bark (epiphloeophytes). *Rhodochytrium*, for example, is a chlorococcalean, branched, thread-like organism which grows within the leaves of such seed plants as *Ambrosia* and *Ceratophyllum*. *Phyllosiphon Arisari* forms mats just below the epidermis of various members of the Araceae and produces discolored, pathological areas on stems and leaves. In the same family (Phyllosiphonaceae) is *Phytophysa*, a siphonaceous, tubular alga that produces lemon-green galls on *Pilea*, a member of the nettle family. *Chlorochytrium Lemnae* is a well-known inhabitor of the duckweed *Lemna trisulca*, where it produces dark green "spots" that appear prominently when the host pales.

Semiparasitic forms are found among the Trentepohliaceae. *Cephaleuros virescens* produces discolored spots on *Magnolia*, *Oleander*, and other tropical and subtropical leaves such as banana and citrus. This is the species which causes so much economic loss in the tea industry by parasitizing young leaves of plants in Ceylon and Indian plantations. *Stomatochroon* is a member of the same family, a much-reduced filamentous plant growing within the stomatal chambers of leaves of higher plants. Thirty-three species of seed plants are known to serve as hosts. One species of alga endophytizing another is illustrated by *Coleochaete nitellarum*, which grows within the wall of *Nitella* where it occurs as a spreading, branched filament of irregularly shaped cells. Some interesting members of the Xanthophyceae, such as *Rhizolekane*, are epiphytic and endophytic in *Sphagnum*. *Endocladia* grows and spreads through walls of *Rhizoclonium*.

Among the Cyanophyta are to be found many instances of symbiosis. The most widely known is the commensal association of various species of blue-greens with various species of fungi to form lichens. (Many lichens involve such green algal species as *Trebouxia* and *Trentepohlia*.) Ahmadjian (1958) has listed 48 different species of algal components of lichens. It is noteworthy that *Nostoc* is involved with Basidiomycetes, whereas most lichen fungi are Ascomycetes. Other common components of lichens are *Cephaleuros*, *Coccomyxa*, *Urococcus*, *Prasiola*, and *Phycopeltis*. In lichen symbiosis there is both outright parasitism of the fungus on the alga, and a mutualism wherein the alga receives moisture and gases from the fungus in exchange for carbohydrates and proteins released from the photosynthetic member.

Anabaena cycadearum lives in the cortex of *Cycas* roots and *A. Azollae* occurs in the water fern *Azolla*. *Nostoc pruniforme* lives in the petioles and stems of the tropical, huge-leaved *Gunnera*, whereas other species are invariably found in the thallus cavities of liverworts such as *Anthoceros* and *Blasia*. The *Nostoc* colonies do not seem to have any organic connection. Some studies have shown, however, that the host may gain from the nitrogen-fixation of the blue-green algae. *Nostoc* from *Gunnera* has been found capable of growing without light in culture.

Some of the most curious combinations are *Gloeochaete* and *Glaucocystis*. The former consists of a colorless, tetrasporine cell containing blue-green protoplasts; the latter, a colorless *Oocystis* with numerous, vermiform protoplasts. Another curiosity is *Cyanella*, existing in colorless *Palmella*-like cells. And again, the unusual *Peliaina* is a flagellate, duplex form.

The adjustment of plants to protoplasm and the chemistry of animals must call for some special adjustments, especially when algal cells live within animals. Yellowish Zooxanthellae live in sea anemones, corals, and other invertebrates. Similarly *Chlorella conductrix* (Zoochlorella) and *C. parasitica* inhabit the cells of protozoans such as *Paramecium*, *Ophrydium*, and *Stentor*. *Gymnodinium adriaticum* (dinoflagellate) lives in *Cassiopeia* as a zooxanthella. It is thought that this is a mutually beneficial symbiotism. There are other close associations, such as *Chlorella* among sponge spicules, which then produce the familiar green sponge of fresh-water habitats. *Gongrosira* (Chlorophyta) and *Aphanocapsa* (Cyanophyta) also are involved in green sponges. Likewise green *Hydra* is colored by endozoic *Chlorella*.

It is paradoxical that some colorless blue-green algae (*Anabaeniolum*, *Oscillospira*, *Simonsiella*) are characteristically found in the digestive tract of mammals, including Man, and, in the case of *Alysiella*, in fowls. Here they live as saprophytes but assume an autotrophic existence when they are cultured in light. There are said to be 14 species of the Oscillatoriaceae that inhabit the digestive tract of higher animals.

Although not entirely specific there is a good biological reason why *Basicladia* invariably grows on the back of snapping turtles, or other turtles with rough carapaces. *Colacium* (euglenoid) and *Chlorangium* (Volvocales) are always found on the back or appendages of microcrustacea and some species of *Characium* seem to be confined to crustacea or insect larvae; *Characiopsis* occurs on the microcrustacean *Branchipus*.

Stigeoclonium has been found growing epizoically (if not parasitically) in the nose of fish. *Chlorella* or *Chlorella*-like cells occur under the scales of some fish. An unidentified chlorococcalean alga was found to be the cause of spots on *Mugil poecilus*, a character which previously had been used to separate it from the clear-skinned *M. troscheli.*

Oodinium limneticum and *Apodinium* are curious dinoflagellates that parasitize a number of fresh-water fish externally, whereas *Blastodinium* is an endoparasite of crustacea and worms. *Apodinium* is a sac-like cell with a thread-like attaching organ, and *Oodinium* is a globular body that has rhizoidal extensions which penetrate the host.

An unusual association exists between *Cyanoderma bradypodis*, a red alga, and *Trichophilus Welcheri* (Plate V, Fig. 69), a green alga living among the hair scales of the sloth in tropical South and Central America. A species of *Platymonas* (once thought to be *Carteria*) is known to live symbiotically with species of the worm *Convoluta*, where it loses many of its identifying characteristics. The cells develop processes that push in between the cells of the animal.

CRYOVEGETATION

A remarkable adjustment is made primarily by a number of Chlorophyta to an existence in snow and ice (cryovegetation or cryoplankton). This type of habitat well illustrates the selectivity of species because cryoplankters consist of relatively few species which, however, are practically the same the world over (Switzerland, Norway, the Andes, western United States and Alaska, Japan, Poland). The marine diatoms of ice fields of the Arctic, however, are different from those in the Antarctic.

Permanent snow banks may be colored red, green, yellow, or even black, and glacial ice sometimes is purplish-brown. The latter condition is produced mostly by desmids such as *Ancylonema Nordenskioldii* and *Mesotaenium Bergrenii* var. *alaskanum*. Red snow is commonly produced by *Chlamydomonas nivalis* (Bauer) Wille along with *Chionaster nivalis* (Bohl.) Wille, *Ulothrix flaccida* Kuetz., *Scotiella* spp, *Trochiscia* spp, and *Raphidonema* spp. Black snow is produced by species of the latter. In addition to the cryoplankters, there are many transient species, including some 22 genera of Chlorophyta, eight genera of Cyanophyta, at least one genus of Dinoflagellata, and a few Cyanophyta (such as *Gloeocapsa* and *Phormidium*). Many forms occur as cysts, red with haematochrome, and appear so much alike that culture methods are required to make identification.

The compositions of snow floras and variations among them are determined by light intensity, pH, available nutrients, and by what can generally be called time and circumstance; whims of weather often determine degree of permanency of a snow field, and air currents determine distribution of species. Altitude is only of incidental importance in that it determines degree of permanency. Green snow, for example, has been reported from as low an altitude as Nebraska's.

Whether because of temperature or availability of nutrients, there is a group of species which can grow only on ice, some which occur only on snow, a few that can grow in either situation. Nutrients are derived from wind-blown matter which must be in solution and readily available; there is no bacterial decomposition (or very little) within snow to release nutrients from particulate organic substance. Possibly because of the CO_2 supply, most cryoplankters develop in regions affected by calcareous rock (at least in Europe), although the pH of surface snows in Alaska was found to be 6.0–6.5.

In the Greenland ice field, at elevations of from 1800 to 2800 feet, curious cryoconite holes occur. These are as much as one meter in diameter and up to 60 cm. deep, and are very troublesome to vehicular movements. The holes are produced by cryoconite composed of algae, rotifers, and fungi. It has been suggested that rays of light re-emitted as long rays after photosynthesis are responsible for the melting and, thus, for the gradual formation of pockets. The flora includes species of *Plectonema* and *Calothrix* (Cyanophyta); *Trochiscia*, *Ancylonema*, and *Cylindrocystis* (Chlorophyta).

Vaucheria is sometimes found as an inhabitor of ice. At least one species (*V. Jonesii*) has been collected in pockets of water in winter ice where it was vegetatively vigorous and reproducing actively. It is intriguing that more than a few plankters (especially nannoplankton) can exist beneath ice and snow cover for long periods of time. It has been suggested that these forms, or some of them, can live saprophytically or even phagotrophically. Chrysophyceae such as *Chrysolykos* and the chlorophyte *Nannochloris* exist throughout the winter under ice in the Arctic.

Hot Springs

Just as low temperatures are selective of a limited number of species for existence in ice and snow, high temperatures determine a thermophilic algal flora. Hot springs and geyser basins in widely separated regions (Iceland, Spitzbergen, New Zealand, Japan, western North America) support a more or less similar algal flora. The Cyanophyta comprise practically all thermophilic species, although a few diatoms occur (mostly below 40°C although rarely at 50.7°C.). The limitation of hot spring floras to the Cyanophyta is responsible for the inference that blue-greens, having had an evolution during geological time when water was hot and sulphureous, are adapted to high temperatures. Whereas thermophilic algae include many which occur nowhere else, perhaps most species are plants of ordinary temperatures which possess a range of adaptability that permits them to live equally well in hot water.

The adaptability of blue-green algae is related to their protoplasmic structure; that is, to their lack of vacuoles, lack of chondriosomes, and lack of a nucleus. No nucleated organisms, in fact, are known to exist in highly thermal waters.

In Yellowstone Park hot springs, for example, the majority of blue-green algae live in temperatures between 35 and 70°C., but a few occur in water as hot as 85.2, and bacteria at 88°C. Those springs which have the majority of species possess a pH range of from 7.0 to 9.4, although the complete range for all springs containing algae is from pH 2.65. It must be noted that because of elevations in the Park the boiling point of water at 8000 feet is 91.0°C.; at 6000 ft., 92.5°C., rather than 100°C.

Thermal algae are predominantly calcareous and occur in encrustments which may be as much as ten centimeters thick. Concretions of marl, tufa, and travertine, often pastel colored, are laid down by blue-greens, with as much as five centimeters a year being deposited. Although many species are planktonic, a large percentage are epiphytic, partly because of the narrow zones of optimum temperature into which algae are crowded.

Hot springs are usually highly mineralized, rich in calcium, silicon, and sulphur, and often contain many gases. Thus water chemistry as well as temperature plays a role in determining species selectivity. Unicellular, colonial, and especially filamentous growth forms occur in hot water: cf. Chroococcus, Microcystis, Oscillatoria Plectonema, Phormidium, and Scytonema, to mention a few common genera. A number of genera known only from hot springs include Colteronema and Heterohormogonium.

Chapter 9

Laboratory culturing of algae using a shaker. (Reproduced from Algal Culture from Laboratory to Pilot Plant. Washington, D.C.; The Carnegie Institution)

Physiology

The physiology of algae is a facet of their biology to which generous attention has been paid, and to which an ever-increasing amount of interest is directed. One reason for this is that answers to general physiological problems of living matter can be found by using algae — organisms which readily lend themselves to culture. Much of what is known about photosynthesis, for example, has been learned from algal cultures, and it is in this area that more and more research is invited. The many economic importances of algae, their ecology, their reproduction and genetics, their morphology and hence their taxonomy all involve physiology.

Physiology includes, among others, such biological activities and processes as: (1) photosynthesis; (2) elaboration and recombination of storage products; (3) respiration and energy transfer; (4) osmosis and the maintenance of osmotic pressures; (5) elaboration of wall materials; (6) elaboration of pigments; (7) construction of chloroplasts and the synthesis of other organelles; (8) production and secretion of metabolites (including toxins); (9) motility; (10) nitrogen-fixation; and (11) elaboration of hormones (and possibly vitamins). It will be recognized immediately that most of these are activities carried on by any and all plants. Because of the relation of ecological factors to the performance of these processes, the former determine whether it is possible for an organism to live and reproduce in a habitat; i.e., they determine selectivity. Reference has been made to many of these relationships, especially in connection with ecology (p. 279). A few aspects only can be considered here.

Nutrition

In their nutrition and in storing reserve food, algae employ different processes, each type involving a particular biochemical reaction. The majority of chlorophyll-bearing plants are of course *phototrophic*, using light to produce organic carbohydrates from carbon dioxide and water.

331

Such phototrophs are said to be *autotrophic* or *holophytic*. Some organisms employ organic substances and are said to be *heterotrophic*. Experimentally, it has been shown that soil algae *(Spongiochloris* and *Bracteococcus)* can grow well as heterotrophs in the dark when glucose-salts such as sodium acetate arabinose or glucose plus phosphate are included in the medium. Flagellates in culture were found to grow best when the ratio of monovalent to divalent inorganic constituents was between 24 and 16. If heterotrophs or autotrophs also require, in part, organic growth stimulators (e.g., vitamins) they are said to have an *auxotrophic* nutrition. Organisms which employ inorganic compounds as a source of energy, especially chlorophylless species, and those which are dependent upon metabolites of an organic nature *(Dinobryon* growing in subdued light, e.g.) are *chemotrophic*. Hydrogen sulphide can be used as an energy source by some blue-green algae, an example of what is known as *chemolithotrophy*, wherein inorganic compounds are chemically broken down. Some species are able to alternate in their nutrition, photosynthesizing by day and synthesizing nutrients chemically at night. Animals primarily, along with a few algae, ingest particulate matter (organic or inorganic) and internal enzyme action induces energy release. This is a *holozoic* or *phagotrophic* nutrition, used by a few euglenoids (especially colorless members), by *Ochromonas*, and by *Oxyrrhis* (a dinoflagellate). Some plants may be in part holophytic (autotrophic) and in part *saprophytic*, digesting organic substances (dead organisms or substances thrown off by living organisms) and absorbing the dissolved material for internal digestion. Such a nutrition is sometimes referred to as *mixotrophic*. Parasitic nutrition involves the external digesting of organic matter within or upon another living organism.

These processes result in the accumulation of organic storage compounds which are peculiar to different phyla (as mentioned in connection with specific groups). Such compounds are the substances which are of primary importance when algae are used as food by Man and other animals.

In the Chlorophyta there are starch carbohydrates such as amylose and amylopectins. In the Euglenophyta a starch-like compound called paramylum is concentrated to form large or small grains shaped differently according to genus (see p. 189). This is considered to be a glucose residue. In the Cryptophyta and Pyrrhophyta the carbohydrate reserve is starch or starch-like, although oil also occurs in Pyrrhophyta. The Cyanophyta store food as a starch-like "glycogen," as indicated by staining. Chemical tests of blue-green algae show the presence of arabinose and glucose and, in some, the disaccharide trehalose. The latter also occurs in the Rhodophyta (abundant in some species), where floridean starch (a glucose residue) is the most abundant and common reserve. Some "sugar alcohols" also have been identified in the Rhodophyta.

An entirely different form of food storage is found in the Phaeophyta, in which most reserves are in solution. One of the most abundant of these reserves is the alcohol mannitol, which, however, varies in amount according to season and habitat, especially in reference to salinity.

Food reserves also consist of simple sugars, glycosides, and such glycopyranose residues as laminarin. The latter is thought to originate from what has been termed laminariose, another disaccharide. Leucosin (chrysolaminarin, chrysose) is formed in the Chrysophyta, suggesting thereby a phylogenetic relationship to the Phaeophyta. Oily residues also occur in some Chrysophyta, especially the Bacillariophyceae. Fatty foods actually occur in certain members of most phyla. Sterols such as fucosterol occur in both brown and green algae whereas fucosterol, cholesterol, and sitosterol are abundant in some red algae, but these vary within the same genus geographically. Chondrillosterol has been identified in *Scenedesmus* and lipids occur in the membranes surrounding the pseudovacuoles of the Cyanophyta cell. Lipids may constitute a large percentage of the total content of brown algae — as much as 4.9% in *Pelvetia*, for example. Proteins in the form of amino acids are similar to those produced in higher plants and involve nitrogen metabolism. Organic acids which have been identified include citric, malic, and ascorbic, some of which are extruded as extrametabolites, or, in the blue-green algae especially, as polypeptides. Enzymes employed in the concentration of food reserves are carbohydrase, maltase, protease, lipase, and oxidase.

Inclusions and Composition

In addition to nutritional storage products, some of the many other substances found in algae include those involved in wall structure. These vary from group to group, but in the main are various carbohydrates, including, in some species, cellulose. Polysaccharides such as galactose, mannose, glucans, xylans, and uronic acid, appear in the fibrils of the inner wall (see p. 18). Some forms such as the siphonaceous *Bryopsis* and *Caulerpa* contain callose and pectic compounds in lieu of cellulose.

Algin, a salt derivative of alginic acid, is abundant in the walls of many Phaeophyta (*Laminaria, Nereocystis*), and carrageenin is often so in the walls of red algae. Agar, another carbohydrate mucilage or gel common in several genera (*Gelidium, Gracilaria*), has been identified as a sulphated component from galactose. In addition, other cell wall constituents in the red algae include carbohydrates (furcellarin, porphyrin, iridiophycin) isolated primarily from particular genera.

There are many other mucilages such as fucoidin (in *Fucus* especially) which are also sulphated polysaccharides. Mucilage analyses of some representative genera are listed in Table 9.1. There is an extensive and readily available literature on the composition of algae, especially those which are economically important, but even so, there is a need for continuing research in this area by the biochemist for both practical and purely scientific objectives.

Requirements

For the elaboration of the above-mentioned substances, algae require the same essential elements and salts used by higher plants (if not by all protoplasms). These include K, Mg, Ca, Na, C, S, O, H, P, N. Such elements are used in metabolism and in the formation of wall-building materials. Calcium, for example, helps to erect the plasma membrane. Sodium is not widely used but is critically important for at least some marine blue-green algae which apparently take this element from NaCl. Also, trace elements may be highly critical and just as important, even though needed in minute amounts. Such elements are Fe, Si, Zn, Cu, Co, Mb, Bo, and, rarely, vanadium. Iron is necessary in chlorophyll construction and in the photosynthetic process, but minimal requirements are not known, especially in marine algal metabolism. Iron may be critical if it is not present in the medium 0.1 ppm. (see p. 290). When critical trace elements are lacking, another or others may be substituted as shown by culture studies.

Silicon is important for members of the Chrysophyta, especially Bacillariophyceae. But demands for this or that element vary greatly according to genus or species. *Chroococcus* and *Anabaena*, for example, require a rich supply of sodium but little potassium. Plants which demand the latter in large quantities usually are those with a low growth rate, and there is a low photosynthetic productivity if there is a deficiency of this element. A deficiency of sulphur results in an inadequate chlorophyll elaboration. Calcium salts are at least useful, as shown by culture work wherein it has been found that concentrations of 0.25 to 1.75% (in culture media) increase the growth of a plant such as *Coelastrum*.

Nitrogen

High on the list of critical elements is nitrogen, which enters into metabolism in a number of ways. The quantity of nitrogen available and the form in which it occurs may be a presence-absence determiner of algal species. Nitrogen is essential in protein synthesis and in pigment construction. The protein composition in algae fluctuates with nitrogen availability and hence population density may rise and fall. This is partly because the construction and action of enzymes are hampered, especially those involving the formation of DNA. In photosynthesis nitrogen may function as an alternate H-receptor.

TABLE 9.1   Mucilage Content of Representative Genera of Algae*
                              (in percentages)

PORPHYRA TENERA (Rhodophyta)

Water: 4.57
Pentosan: 3.79
Methyl-pentosan: 0.30
Cellulose: 2.50
Sugars: glucose, fructose,
   galactose, pentose

GELIDIUM CARTILAGINEUM
(Rhodophyta)

Water: 13.0
Pentosan: 3.35
Methyl-pentosan: 0.91
Cellulose and sugars: fructose,
   galactose, pentose

LAMINARIA JAPONICA (Phaeophyta)

Water: 4.20
Pentosan: 8.12
Methyl-pentosan: 0.84
Cellulose: 12.33
Sugars: glucose, methyl pentose,
   fucose, pentose

LAMINARIA sp (Phaeophyta)

Water: 7.8
Soluble salts: 8.6
Inorganic insolubles: 4.4
Mucilage, water solubles: 47.4
Cellulose: 10.9
Intercellular substance
   (tannic acid): 19.0

CYSTOPHYLLUM FUSIFORME (Phaeophyta)

Water: 15.15
Pentosan: 10.87
Methyl-pentosan: 1.37
Cellulose: 26.16

ECKLONIA BICYCLIS (Phaeophyta)

Water: 11.56
Pentosan: 5.33
Methyl-pentosan: 1.06
Cellulose: 14.08
Sugars: none reported

UNDARIA PINNATIFIDA (Phaeophyta)

Water: 9.22
Pentosan: 6.40
Methyl-pentosan: 0.25
Cellulose: 9.23

ENTEROMORPHA COMPRESSA
(Clorophyta)

Water: 14.17
Pentosan: 7.37
Methyl-pentosan: 16.52
Cellulose: 5.30
Sugars: glucose, fructose,
   rhamnose, pentose

* Content varies in different plants after hydrolysis.

Nitrogen accumulates in varying amounts and in different forms in different algae. In the large vacuoles of siphonaceous green algae one analysis disclosed nitrogen to be 200 times the concentration in sea water, and in some marine algae the ratio of nitrogen to carbon to phosphorus was found to be 7:42:1. In the open sea water the ratio of nitrogen to phosphorus has been estimated to about 20:1. Chlorophyta in culture show 6.5–8.3% of their ash-free dry weight might be nitrogen. This element, together with phosphorus, is highly important in determining the productivity of plankton, in its relation to blue-green blooms and the development of Red Tides. It was noted by Gerloff and Skoog that production in Microcystis was decidedly reduced when the nitrogen content of the cells became less than 4% of the dry weight.

As in higher plants, the source of nitrogen is mostly nitrates. Nitrogen, however, can also be obtained from ammonium salts, from organic nitrogenous compounds, glutamic and aspartic acid, and from the fixation of free nitrogen. Some species select ammonium over nitrite nitrogen as a source, and there is considerable variation among different groups and within groups of algae in respect to the uptake mechanism. It has been determined many times that molybdenum is essential for nitrogen metabolism and that ammonium is the form in which nitrogen finally enters metabolism.

As mentioned elsewhere, nitrogen (and phosphorus) are relatively low in sea water (although somewhat more plentiful near shore than in open water). When in especially low concentration there is a drastic reduction in beds of Laminaria and Fucus. In fact the seasonal or periodic reduction in these nutrients by phytoplankton uptake seems, in some instances, to regulate the abundance of large marine, littoral algae.

Another source of nitrogen is through an as yet little-understood process of nitrogen-fixation. When supplied with carbohydrates a few cyanophytes make use of this process. Interestingly enough, it is only filamentous cyanophytes which possess heterocysts that are able to fix nitrogen. Trichodesmium (lacking heterocysts) is an exception. Other genera known to fix nitrogen are Nostoc, Anabaena, Cylindrospermum, Tolypothrix, Mastigocladus, Calothrix, and Nostoc (marine). There well may be other blue-green genera not yet studied which are nitrogen-fixers. Thus far no chlorophyte genus has been found with this capability, although there is the questionable instance of Chlorella.

This process is highly significant in the biology of the organism involved and directly or indirectly it is economically important. Nitrogen-fixation by blue-green algae, as by certain bacteria, reconditions agricultural soil, and increases crop productivity. This is especially valuable in the rice fields of Asia, where commercial fertilizers are not readily obtained. Such habitats are highly suitable for these algae, and their nitrogen-fixing metabolism permits repeated use of soils for crops year after year.

Nitrogen-fixation has been studied experimentally and much has been learned about the chemistry, although many facets, such as the role of enzymes and their kind(s), are not well understood. In the laboratory *Nostoc* was able to fix 151.7 mg. of nitrogen in 97 days within a 2% sucrose-mineral culture medium. Also it has been found possible for the plant to fix, in the dark, 5.44 mg. of nitrogen per mg. of sugar supplied. Figures from another experiment indicate that 480 pounds of nitrogen per acre per month could be fixed by *Anabaena* sp. Drewes found *Anabaena* spp and *Nostoc* (in pure culture) to grow successfully in nitrogen-free media, in two months fixing as much as 3 mg. of nitrogen for each 250 cc. of media. Additional experiments have shown that nitrogen will not be fixed if there is an unlimited or fully adequate supply of CO_2 or of hydrogen. Hence the conclusion that nitrogen-fixation in nature proceeds only under certain variable conditions.

PHOSPHORUS

Like nitrogen, phosphorus plays an important role in metabolism and in nutrition. Its source is orthophosphates in solution. The importance of phosphorus (and nitrogen) in metabolism and in population production is illustrated by increments in phytoplankton development following fertilization of lakes. For example, a fertilizer containing 10% nitrogen, 6% phosphoric acid, and 4% potassiu ı (applied 100 pounds to the acre every three weeks) brings about a substantial increase in total plankton. In some instances, available phosphorus is related to the ability of the plant to assimilate nitrogen from nitrates or from other nitrogenous compounds. The demands vary tremendously. Ketchum and Redfield (1949) found that some chlorophytes require as much as 2–3% of their dry weight in phosphorus. For the blue-green algae (in general) a minimum of 0.03 ppm. is critical, whereas the optimum concentration is around 0.45 mg./L. Some species (*Asterionella* sp, e.g.) in culture have shown that there is an interaction of factors which determines the importance of phosphorus in metabolism, or in the amount required; hence it is appropriate to have an open mind when generalizations relative to the role of phosphorus are attempted for algal metabolism in nature. It is well-established that blue-green algae thrive in waters enriched with nitrogen and phosphorus. For other algae, such as *Chara* spp, phosphorus is limiting, for these plants thrive in lakes where it is 4–6 mg./L., but seem unable to grow where the concentration is more than 20 mg./L. Cultured *Microcystis* grows best when the N:P ratio is 20:1. Unproductive lakes (for fish) are brought into productivity by adding phosphates and nitrates, which, however, at times produce highly objectionable secondary effects. (Dense mats of filamentous algae may develop, or there may be a dense growth of aquatic plants which upon decay reduce the oxygen to a dangerous, sometimes fatal, winter-kill level.) Species of algae which are limited in development by availability of phosphorus have a high content of the enzyme alkaline phosphatase. In some green algae phosphorus may become highly concentrated (850,000 times the concentration in the surrounding water).

Silica

As previously indicated, silica is particularly critical for those members of the Chrysophyta and the Silicoflagellata in which the wall contains silicates. Diatoms require minimum concentrations which vary from genus to genus. Because natural waters in general contain concentrations as high as 77 mg./L. (or usually 4.0–27 mg./L.) most habitats are suitable for silica-demanding species (other factors being adequate). In general, a minimum of 0.5, 0.8, or 1.0 mg./L. (or rarely 500 mg./L.) are necessary for many species of diatoms. In culture media lacking silica, however, it has been found that these plants (soil or sedentary species) can continue to multiply for some time as naked protoplasts. One adjustment to silica-content is seen in the thickness of the wall, the same species exhibiting marked differences according to availability. *Skeletonema* spp, for example, appear to multiply relatively successfully when the Si-concentration is very low, but form weakly silicified walls. Sometimes long spines occur on diatom frustules when the silica supply is ample.

The silica-content of natural waters rises and falls with fluctuations in the number of diatoms. Usually there is a peak development of such plants semiannually, one in the spring and one in the fall. At the height of diatom populations, and immediately afterward, the silica content may decrease to as little as 30 mg. per cubic meter in a habitat. This acts as a critical limiting factor in further increment, leading to a decline in the population which (in general) is low throughout the summer months.

Silica occurs in both a soluble and insoluble state in diatom walls. Whereas there is possibly a recycling of silica in nature, approximately 50% appears to be rendered insoluble and hence becomes unavailable to succeeding generations. Accordingly there must be a continuing replenishment in natural waters. The insoluble silica eventually leads to mountainous accumulations of diatomaceous material in lake and sea bottoms (see diatomite, p. 336). Many diatoms have relatively sparse quantities of silica. As a result the walls are very delicate and their shells do not appear in the deposits at abysmal depths, the silica having been dissolved out after the death of the cell.

VITAMINS

Reference has been made elsewhere to the need of vitamins in algal physiology, and to the stimulus that certain vitamins give to productive rates and population explosions (especially Red Tide organisms). The importance of vitamins to larger marine algae is mostly inferred from knowledge obtained from culturing microscopic species, partly because of the difficulty of securing bacteria-free cultures of larger plants. But some of the filamentous marine algae have been stimulated in culture by using vitamin B_{12} (0.1 mg./L.).

A review of literature dealing with the detection of vitamins and their roles reveals that species representing all of the phyla require vitamin B_{12}, thiamine, and biotin. Some species use only one; others two. In the Pyrrhophyta and the Chrysophyta 30 species are known to need all three vitamins. Some marine cyanophytes need B_{12} especially. There are doubtless other "factors" which conceivably might be termed vitamins among the extracellular substances found to be stimulants in algal metabolism (auxotrophic nutrition, and to this extent heterotrophic).

Although all algal species studied have not been shown to be vitamin-demanders, about 60% of those investigated have proven to be, and perhaps the percentage will increase as more and more taxa or strains of species are cultured. Here there is indeed an opportunity for biochemical research which would be highly rewarding. Considerable work, for example, has been done on *Ochromonas*, which requires all the vitamins in addition to amino acids. This unusual alga is one of several species known to ingest particulate matter, and hence is phagotrophic as well as partly autotrophic. It is noteworthy that a large percentage of species which demand rich vitamin sources are members of those phyla in which phagotrophism or heterotrophism are common.

Of the known vitamins involved in algal nutrition thiamine (or fractions such as pyrimidine) is the most widely used. At times, however, glutamic acid, when available, is substituted. Unlike thiamine, in which there are two components, thiozole and pyrimidine, vitamin B_{12} has several analogues, some of which are important for certain species but not for others. This sensitivity of species to particular vitamins permits the use of algae to perform assays. By refined culture techniques strains of algal species can be isolated which are reactive to particular components of vitamins and amino acids. Unfortunately it is only by inference that much of the information on vitamin demands can be applied directly to problems of algal productivity in nature.

It is possible that vitamins used by algae may be produced and liberated by the organisms, themselves, as well as derived from organic compounds resulting from bacterial action. Thiamin, however, has been determined in cultures of Coccomyxa, and it must be remembered that some of the unknown extrametabolites thrown off by some algae (some being growth promoters) may be vitamin in character. Algae used in food for animals are said to add vitamins to the diet.

In addition to vitamins, algae, particularly cultured, colorless flagellates, may require amino acids and lipids (lecithin and cholesterol). These requirements may vary with temperature levels. Available amounts of several classes of lipids have been studied in Chlorella and in other species which lend themselves to culture. The latter includes phospholipids, sulfoquinovosyl diglyceride, and galactolipids, all highly complex and containing fatty acids. Culture studies have also determined that certain organic substances such as ascorbic acid, glycine, and niacin are stimulators. Their importance has been indicated by showing the relation of seasonal content in plants to the growth periods.

Photosynthesis

The principal activity involved in the nutrition of chlorophyll-bearing organisms is photosynthesis, the subject of long and exhaustive study. This is a highly complex process within the green cells of the plant world whereby inorganic matter is converted to organic. Much of our knowledge of photosynthesis accrued during the past two or three decades especially has been gleaned from the algae. Research into some of the as-yet-unexplored aspects of photosynthesis is continuing with an increasing intensity. The biochemistry and the many factors involved are discussed by a number of authoritative writers in the volume Physiology and Biochemistry of Algae (Academic Press, 1962).

Photosynthesis in algae is, in general, quite similar to, and involves the same factors as, the process carried on in other green plants. The whole series of chemical operations has to do with three general, recognized phases. The first involves the liberation of hydrogen atoms from molecules of water, thus forming molecules of oxygen (O_2). Second, compounds produced in the first phase are broken down by light energy so that the H atoms can be transferred and, in a third phase, united with carbon dioxide to form carbohydrates. This process is often expressed (overly simplified) as: $6CO_2$ plus $6H_2O$ plus energy (light) plus chlorophyll equals $C_6H_{12}O_6$ plus $6O_2$ (with energy stored in the sugar).

The most important "factors" (if any can be regarded as more important in this highly interacting series of processes) are: (1) light — especially red rays; (2) pigments — chlorophyll and sometimes others as well; (3) raw materials — CO_2 and H_2O; (4) chemical agents (enzymes, for example) in the cell which regulate the process of energy transfer and the elaboration of secondary compounds from the primary photosynthetic products. Also entering the process, directly or indirectly, are such factors as temperature, pH of the medium, and the availability of elements necessary for the construction and maintenance of chlorophyll.

The process is known to involve as many as 20 chemical reactions and many intermediary substances between the raw materials and the finished product. Whereas the process is rather uniform throughout the algal phyla, it is noteworthy that there are important variations in the amount of energy stored and the rate of production. These variations are related to pigment qualities in the various algal phyla, to the response of these pigments to different qualities and intensities of light, and to different enzyme systems. For example, plants representing two different phyla of the algae growing in the same light intensity (at the same water depth, for example) will show different photosynthetic rates according to the abundance of secondary pigments possessed by one organism which are capable of functioning in the photosynthetic process. In each group, as might be expected, there is a different set of variations in the operational pathways. And, as might be expected, there is a difference in the enzymes, resulting in an accumulation of different forms of reserve material produced from the photosynthetic sugar (as mentioned before). These materials can appear as oils, fats, proteins, or various polysaccharides, such as starches.

Elements of Photosynthesis
Carbon

The carbon which enters the photosynthetic process in building carbohydrates is derived variously. Much of the carbon dioxide released by respiration becomes an important source, as is true also for the free carbon dioxide dissolved in plant-inhabited water. Only in acid water (soft water lakes), however, is there an adequate supply of free carbon dioxide. In hard water and marine habitats, where there are high concentrations of calcium and magnesium, carbon dioxide combines to form either bicarbonates $(CaHCO_3)_2$ or insoluble carbonates. The amount of available CO_2 is related to water temperature, with more held in solution at high than at low temperature ranges. Thus tropical and subtropical waters contain more than do north temperate or frigid seas. (This is the converse of the solubility levels for O_2.)

Apparently most algae (especially phytoplankters) find a suitable supply of CO_2 constantly available through the natural dissociation of bicarbonates in the reversible process, wherein CO_2 plus H_2O react to form H_2CO_3. This in turn dissociates to form H plus HCO_3, and then to form H and CO_3 and some CO_2. It has been thought that the removal of CO_2 from carbonates is responsible for the deposition of lime (calcite) about such plants as the coralline red algae and *Chara*. But it is a matter of common observation that calcium deposition does not occur in certain plants living in the same habitat with those on which lime collects. It is clear that the availability of carbon is regulatory and stimulatory, for when in unlimited supply, other factors being suitable, the development of superabundant plankton blooms is possible. This accounts for the appearance of such profuse growths in hard water and never in soft water lakes.

LIGHT AND PIGMENTS

As pointed out elsewhere (pp. 280, 311) in relation to ecology, pigments of algae are selective of different light intensities and different light qualities. Chlorophylls are active and more efficient in using red light (420–500 mμ, or at 675–680 mμ; brown pigments are active in green (440 mμ and at 520–560 mμ, although some shade-loving species can thrive using wave lengths between 5 and 250 mμ). It may not be universal, but experimentally it has been shown, that algae use only about 20% of the available energy of red light.

Chlorophyll-a is the primary pigment, but it is known that carotenoids and the phycobilins (phycoerythrin and phycocyanin), under some conditions at least, function in the photosynthetic process. From 80 to 100% of the light absorbed by secondary pigments is transferred, especially by phycobilins and fucoxanthin. Otherwise, secondary pigments of some algae (fucoxanthin, for example) act to absorb energy which rather than functioning directly in the process, is then transferred to the active chlorophyll. Chlorophyll-a is thought to exist in two forms, each absorbing slightly different waves. The relative abundance of chlorophyll and xanthophyll in some algae fluctuates with daily light intensity, the chlorophyll being more abundant in midday. Conveniently, chlorophyll concentration is increased in some deep water species, thus accommodating them to and compensating for weak illumination. This is true also for the phycobilins in the red algae, which also can use yellow light for photosynthesis. It is obvious that deep-water algae are either (1) capable of absorbing great (or sufficient) quantities of such light as does reach them, or (2) able to make photosynthetic use of feeble quantities of light.

As long ago as 1893 Englemann determined that supplemental phycobilins could be used photosynthetically by umbrophilic algae. It is not known how universally true this is, but at least one experiment shows that chlorophyll-b and -c are more efficient in light absorption than chlorophyll-a which is, of course, the pigment common to all algae. From a phylogenetic point of view it probably is more nearly the fundamental pigment of the plant world.

It is now known that photosynthesis can take place in two phases, light and dark. In the light phase, adenosine triphosphate and triphosphopyridine are formed as the first identifiable photosynthetic products. These are used up or they may enter into a whole series of catalytic and enzyme actions which operate at night (the dark phase), whereby CO_2 is assimilated into the formation of carbohydrate sugars. In the light phase, after light has been absorbed by pigments, the energy is transferred by one or two chemical processes directed by phosphate (riboflavin) and by vitamin K to form adenosine triphosphate. Thus chemical energy, in the form of pyrophosphate bonds, is produced from light energy. The behavior of electrons from the energized molecules of chlorophyll (or sometimes other pigments) induces a series of oxidizing and reducing processes. These involve a phosphorylation of adenosine phosphate to adenosine triphosphate. The final liberation of O_2 comes about with the photophosphorylation in which an atom of H from water reduces triphosphorpyridine nucleotide.

This very involved system of cyclic and non-cyclic reactions and photophosphorylations can be expressed equationally by:

$$ADP + 2H_2O \longrightarrow ATP \text{ (a cyclic photophosphorylation)}$$
$$NADP + 2H_2O + 2\,ADP + aP \longrightarrow NaDPH_2 + O_2 +$$
$$2ATP \text{ (a non-cyclic phosphorylation)}$$
$$CO_2 + 2NADPH_2 + n.ATP \longrightarrow (CH_2O) + H_2O +$$
$$2NADP + n.ADP + n.P$$

This multiple equation when reduced gives the summarizing expression:
$CO_2 + H_2O \longrightarrow CH_2O + O_2 + H_2O$ (including 112,000 cal. per mol. (per gram molecule) where

ATP = Adenosine triphosphate
ADP = Adenosine diphosphate
NADP = Triphosphopyridine nucleotide
$NADPH_2$ = Triphosphopyridine nucleotide reduced

Cytochrome-f and vitamin K have been found in *Chlorella*, and it is supposed that at least this genus makes use of phosphorus in light to bring about chemical energy conversion. Information about photosynthetic reactions in the dark period has been gained from use of activated carbon as a tracer in cultured *Chlorella*. By this technique it has been possible to identify at least two sugar phosphates that are intermediary in the formation of the final photosynthetic carbohydrates. The light-dark photosynthetic cycle may exist in such an established rhythm that the two phases continue to express themselves even if algae are given continuous illumination.

Some algae (in four different phyla) are known to have the enzyme hydrogenase which enables the cell to use hydrogen rather than water to reduce carbon dioxide. This enzyme seems to be called into operation when illumination is not intense. Light increased above a norm leads to a reduction in the hydrogen uptake, followed by a return to the more customary photosynthetic process. In the process involving hydrogenase much less oxygen is released than in usual photosynthesis.

Each species has its optimum light intensity requirement but this varies with a number of factors including temperature. *Chlorella*, for example, can be grown in light intensity of 3000 ft-c when maintained at a high temperature; whereas if the temperature is dropped to 25°C. the same species fails to photosynthesize in light of 1000 ft-c. Again whether these relationships hold in nature is not known.

Respiration

Respiration, the process by which food (glucose, for example) is "burned" and energy released, is measured by oxygen-uptake and by carbon dioxide release. Oxygen under the influence of oxidizing enzymes, therefore, brings about an analytic process which fractures the substance produced by the synthetic mechanism of photosynthesis. The carbohydrate is reduced to carbon dioxide and water. One mole of glucose oxidized by six moles of oxygen will yield 690 kcal. (kilogram cal.), most of which (410 kcal.) accumulates as adenosine triphosphate.

The general process of respiration involves, however, the formation of intermediate organic substances such as fructose-diphosphate, phosphoglyceric acid, and pyruvic acid. In addition to oxidases are other enzymes which seem to be similar to those employed in higher plants. Of the various processes involved in respiration, one known as a tricarboxylic acid cycle is apparently used in all groups of algae to break down pyruvic acid. As we have mentioned, the rate of respiration which just balances productivity by photosynthesis is said to be at the "compensation point." This varies with amount of light, depth, and other ecological factors.

Oxygen tension leads to reduced respiration, as does low temperature. But decrease in respiration at low temperature is greater than the decrease in photosynthesis, so that oxygen output is relatively greater even at temperatures which are not optimum for the photosynthetic process. This relationship may explain the relative abundance of brown-pigmented algae in the Arctic and Antarctic which seem to maintain high photosynthetic rates.

The rate of respiration is also effected by pH, thus making the latter a possible ecological determiner. Reazin (1954), for example, found that the maximum uptake of oxygen in *Ochromonas* occurred at pH 5.0; at pH 3.5 the uptake is reduced or inhibited (also at pH 8.5 in an alkaline medium).

Blue-green algae in general are able to exist in water with an oxygen content lower than that for all other groups. They can occur, for example, in stagnant waters and at deep levels where oxygen is low. But photosynthetic organisms are automatic producers of an oxygen supply. A few algae (*Scenedesmus*, *Chlorella*, for example) under culture and in abnormal situations can respire anaerobically when provided with carbohydrates such as glucose in a fermentation process. *Chlorella* produces acids and alcohols, and *Scenedesmus* forms hydrogen and lactic acid.

Antibiotics and Extrametabolites

There appears to be no end to the discoveries of substances produced or liberated by algae. The potentials of these substances stimulate the imagination. In any event extrametabolites are of at least great biochemical interest, and are of significance in explaining a number of algal behaviors such as periodicity and the response of one species to another when growing in close proximity, or in mixed culture. A substance from one species may be inhibitory to the growth of another (or even self-inhibiting), whereas it may be stimulating to a third species. It is not possible at this time to differentiate exotoxins (see p. 361) from all extrametabolites (or extrametabolites from antibiotics) through behavior alone; only chemical analyses, in addition to a knowledge of effects produced, can give precise understanding.

Analyses of extrametabolites are difficult because of problems involved in separating organic substances one from another or from components in the medium. Much has yet to be learned about their chemistry. In their behavior extrametabolites may induce specific reactions or modify specific physiological activities of another species either positively or negatively. At the same time, stimulators may be merely increased amounts of the nutrients to which an organism is normally exposed, or may be growth-exciting substances to which the organism is not normally subjected.

Extrametabolites are varied chemically and can be either carbohydrates (polysaccharides), polypeptids, or amino acids. The antibiotic produced by *Chlorella* (chlorellin) is apparently composed of a number of fatty acids which upon analysis give 77.35% carbon, 11.66% hydrogen, and 10.99% oxygen. It is thought likely that at least some extrametabolites are substances which are intermediates in metabolic processes within the cell. These diffuse to a point at which there is an equilibrium between the substance within and without the cell. Eighteen species of *Chlamydomonas* are known to release such carbohydrates as galactose, arabinose, and others; whereas *Chlorella* gives off glycolic acid (derived from the ribulose diphosphate used in one phase of the photosynthetic process). This extrametabolite has been found in fresh water to be as much as 0.2 milligrams per liter.

Numerous examples can be cited of inhibitory extrametabolites and their effects. The marine volvocoid *Dunaliella* inhibits the growth of *Chlorella stigmatophora*, whereas extracts of *Chlorella* culture inhibit the growth of *Dunaliella*; and extracts from each inhibit the growth of the bacterium *Staphylococcus aureus*. Likewise, *Microcystis* is inhibitory to *Staphylococcus* and *Clostridium*, and conceivably might function as a substitute for penicillin.

The dinoflagellate *Katodinium* produces an antibiotic which was found to be inhibitory to nine species of marine bacteria, but stimulated the growth of 18 others, changed the morphology of four, and had no effect on five. *Nitzschia* (a diatom) and *Chlorella* are mutually inhibitory as shown by mixed and separate cultures on comparison — another example of an interaction which can explain periodicity of algal flora composition. Chlorellin (mentioned above) is a stimulant for some organisms at low concentrations, but inhibitory at high. *Haematococcus pluvialis* and *Chlamydomonas Reinhardii* were found to be mutually inhibitory, even though closely related. Substances named for the genera secreting them (pandorine, microcystine, scenedesmine, phormidine, etc.) have been found inhibitory or lethal to *Pediastrum*, *Cosmarium*, and other algae. Some algae such as *Nostoc* are known to produce an auto-inhibiting substance in culture.

It appears that antibiotics interfere with oxidation of nutritive substances and also inhibit the behavior of chlorophyll. Extracts from marine algae (*Ascophyllum*, *Laminaria*, *Polysiphonia*, and others) include antibiotics that inhibit bacteria, but these substances may not be extrametabolites in the usual sense. Washings from the diatom *Nitzschia* are extrametabolite in character and are inhibitory to the growth of other organisms.

One of the obvious suggestions arising from these interactions is that extrametabolites may be used in the control of parasites. In this connection it should be mentioned that viruses may be used to control objectionable algae. At least it is reported by one investigator that a virus isolated from a sewage oxidation pond will attack *Lyngbya*, *Plectonema*, and *Phormidium*. How many more anti-alga viruses occur in nature will be determined by future research.

Algae provide highly suitable organisms for determining the production of and the responses to organic stimulators, and antibiotic inhibitors. All manner of organic and inorganic substances have been introduced to culture media with many reactions involving: (1) production of cellular substances within algae (sometimes not normally produced in nature); (2) increase or inhibition of cell division rates; (3) stimulation or retardation of sexuality and other facets of reproduction. A few of these will be outlined.

At least 30 species of algae in their development are known to make use of some 72 dissolved organic substances, including carbohydrates, aldehydes, alcohols, fatty acids, organic acids, and proteins. Reference has been made to the stimulating effect of vitamins, including B_{12}. This vitamin very clearly acts (along with other critical factors) to trigger the development of blooms of cyanophytes, and also profuse populations of Gymnodinium in the sea. The important element in the vitamin is apparently cobalt, an element which may also be obtained elsewhere. It is thought that cobalt is involved in the process of nitrogen-fixation by blue-green algae.

In many cultures it has been shown that gibberellic acid acts as a stimulant as it does for higher plants. Twenty ppm. added to a medium in which Scenedesmus was cultured increased reproduction by 30%, and the length/width dimension ratio by 32.5%/39.7%.

Many other organic substances produce significant reactions which are at least important in algal culture. Kinetin, a fraction of DNA, is known to have a decided growth stimulating effect on mitosis, doubling the rate in various algae as well as in some animals. Also benzedine stimulates cell division (Polytoma uvella). B-indol-acetic acid at various concentrations, especially at 1×7^{10} mol proved to be highly stimulating to some species of algae (Stichococcus sp), in respect to both number of cells and cell size. The effects of acetic acid on several different species varied; at some concentration these effects were even inhibiting.

A growth regulator very similar to indol-acetic acid has been isolated from the meristematic region of Laminaria. Rather oddly, it was found that the sea lettuce Ulva would not develop a normal thallus when grown in a bacteria-free culture and indol-acetic acid and other organics were required to induce normal growth. This suggests a dependency on some extrametabolite produced by bacteria.

Organics such as streptomycin and terramycin are inhibiting to several genera of blue-green, green, and diatomaceous genera. The pigments and chloroplasts of Euglena are destroyed by streptomycin. The antipernicious anemia antibiotic has produced permanently colorless strains of Euglena.

The blue-green alga Gloeotrichia produces an extrametabolite which is stimulating to the reproductive rate of microfauna such as Cyclops and Daphnia, whereas extracts of Microcystis are inhibiting to these zooplankters. Also filtrates from other cyanophytes, Phormidium and Oscillatoria, have been found to increase the cell division rate of Cosmarium (a desmid).

Chapter 10

A diatomite quarry in California. (Courtesy
Johns-Manville Products Corp., Lompoc, California)

Economics

Although Man has turned to the sea for food and material throughout his history, it is only in relatively recent times that he has given really serious consideration to this storehouse. This is partly because several persons have been able to project the world's food and population problem into the future and to appreciate the possibility that the sea subsequently can take care of additional food needs. Man has also begun to exploit resources of the sea to find materials which can be produced more economically than can those from terrestrial sources. Further, there is an interest in algae as a possible food source in anticipated space flights.

In some parts of the world, Man has used the sea out of necessity, especially to supplement his diet. This is particularly true for the maritime peoples in the crowded countries of the earth. Perhaps the earliest reference to the use of algae as food occurs in the poetic literature of the Chinese, about 600 B.C. Chinese literature also refers to the use of *Gracilaria* and *Laminaria*.

At present there are a number of industrial companies and research organizations, such as the Seaplant Chemical Corporation, the Marine Colloid Company, and the Scottish Seaweed Reseach Institution, actively developing marine products.

Food

The indirect importance of algae as food for man and other animals needs only a reminder. The boundless supply of fish, shellfish, and sea mammals is witness to the degree of Man's dependency on marine and fresh-water algae by virtue of the food chain (see Chart 10.1). But in many coastal regions algae are used directly for human food. Over 100 species appear on the diet list of Polynesians and Orientals. By nature, algae do not store sufficient quantities of energy-yielding substances to make feasible their transportation to great distances. Marine algae have

349

their greatest value in the minerals and vitamins with which they are amply supplied. Carbohydrates and proteins are present, but much of the carbohydrate material, abundant in the cell walls, has been found largely indigestible, especially when a person is first introduced to an algal diet. Later, as a proper and special bacterial flora develops in the digestive tract, digestibility increases.

For food, marine algae are mixed with rice and fish, served as a base for soups and condiments, or used alone as salads. In Hawaii algae for food are known as *limu*, of which there are 75 species. The word "alga" in Chinese (in dialect at least) is *tsao*, a word which is used adjectively to describe beauty or excellence. In Tahiti, the word for edible algae is *rimu*.

The larger brown algae are little-used as food by Man, mostly because of their texture and their undigestible components. Mucilage from them is used as emulsifiers, however, and as stabilizers in various foodstuffs. Phaeophyta, especially kelps, are converted to fodder for cattle, and chopped for sheep and chickens in Great Britain, France, Scandinavia, and along the Pacific coast of the United States. Here *Macrocystis* spp are used, being rich in vitamins E and A. Egg-yolks of fowl fed on chopped phaeophytes are rich in carotene and in iodine. *Rhodymenia* (Rhodophyta) is also used for cattle food in France. *Pelvetia* is a choice ingredient in cow feed, and when supplied to cattle, increased milk production by 10%. In Japan, laminarian food (from stipes) is called *kombu*; food from *Alaria* is called *sarumen*. Stipes of some of the larger brown algae are cut, washed in fresh water, boiled and seasoned with preserving fluids, making a tasty substitute for watermelon pickles or for citron.

Analyses of brown algae show contents of food value: for example, 6.15% protein, 1.56% fat, and 57.04% carbohydrates (mostly in wall material). Fatty substances may be from 1 to 9% in *Pelvetia*, for example. From 5 to 37% dry weight of some brown algae is mannitol, depending upon the species. The mannitol forms an odorless powder which has one-half the sweetness of sucrose, leading to the suggestion that this could be used by diabetics. Experimentally it has been shown that ten grams of mannitol per day has no injurious effects on the kidneys. About 36% dry weight of the brown algae is laminarin which is a glucan (20 B-D-glucopyranose units) that becomes glucose when injected intravenously. No digestion experiments have been performed. In the cell wall are B-D-mannopyruronic acid residues which are digestible by rats and presumably by Man. Cellulose, which is 1 to 9% of dry weight, while digestible, does add bulk which may have advantageous effects in digestion. At least 50% of algin in brown algae is indigestible.

Of proteins in the brown algae, 17 are amino acids; and land plants contain a similar amount. It is known that from 32 to 80% is digestible. For every ton of algal protein produced there is required 1.1 tons of potassium nitrate and 0.75 tons of ammonium sulphate.

Minerals are variable, but may account for 50% of the ash of brown algae and of course are a desirable diet supplement, along with vitamin B carotene, thiamin, and subflavin.

Among the many red algae used widely throughout the world is *Rhodymenia palmata*, both as food and as a salty confection known as *dulse*. This is a dried or partly dried seaweed used by fishermen (especially) on both sides of the Atlantic (called *dillick* in Ireland) for long-time chewing.

Porphyra (*laver*), another red alga, is a common item of diet in Korea, Japan (*amanori* or *nori*), China (*tsats' ai*), and Great Britain (as *sloke*). It is very rich in vitamins B and C. In Japan alone 65 million pounds a year are used and the plants are cultivated on bamboo frames in the water to meet the demand. Fully 25% of the daily diet of Japan is seaweed. North Pacific Indians use *Porphyra* to salt their meats. In Great Britain *Porphyra* is grilled on toast and, according to personal notions, tastes like oysters. Nori is a Japanese paste made from *Porphyra*.

The gelatinous carbohydrates from many red algae are used for puddings (blancmange, eaten with milk or sometimes mixed with fruit) and are processed for ingredients of frozen desserts, including ice cream (as stabilizers). They are also used as a clearing agent in beer preparation. The most famous of these carbohydrate mucilages is carrageenin, named for the Irish village Carragheen. Probably the bulk of this mucilage comes from *Gigartina stellata* and *Chondrus crispus* (Irish moss). The mucilage contains a galactose-sulphuric acid and other carbohydrates in varying quantity. In the United States from Maine alone, in one year 1,643,607 pounds of Irish moss were harvested (mostly by hand) at a value of $40,070. A total of 15 million tons a year are taken in the whole United States. From the Maritime Provinces of Canada in 1957 25,948,000 pounds of Irish moss were collected (used in industry as well as for food).

Among the carbohydrates found in the red algae (as well as in some browns) are sugar alcohols such as dulcitol and sorbitol in *Bostrychia*, and glycerol. Floridean starch, the food storage product of the Rhodophyta, is a glucose compound. Gels produced by Marine Colloids Company are much used in packaged whipped cream, pie fillers, etc.

A few Chlorophyta are used as salads or relish (Ulvales, *Codium* spp). *Monostroma* (*aonori*) is harvested in Japan. Scarcely any of the Cyanophyta are suitable for food, but a terrestrial form of *Nostoc* is used in the Orient (China, as *fat choy*, and Java), and in Ecuador (at one time at least) *Nostoc commune* was eaten as a food called *yuyucho*. Other freshwater algae, however are rarely, if ever, used for food.

Chlorella is a genus which is cultured both in pilot plants and industrially as a possible source of food. The capacity for *Chlorella* to produce is illustrated by culture plants turning out 100 pounds per acre per day, or the equivalent of 17.5 tons per acre per year. Several species of this genus are high producers of both lipids and proteins; as much as 85% dry weight may be lipid content. Chlorella has been harvested and used for flour from which crackers and biscuits have been made more or less on an experimental basis. Although deficient in sulphur amino acids, the protein has all the essential amino acids, and is thus being cultured in aeronautical research laboratories as possibly useful in space flights. Of the amino acids present, 1.15% is methionine. It is estimated that the average man in space flight would require 510 gs. dry weight for daily energy requirements or 537 gs. to balance off the indigestible portion of Chlorella.

From a mixed culture of Scenedesmus and Chlorella (dried) there was produced 41.8% protein, 27.4% carbohydrates, 7.2% fat, 19.1% ash. Other analyses of Chlorella alone show the production of 15% lipids, 30% proteins (about equal to that of cottonseed meal), 30% carbohydrates, and 5% ash. At present the efficient digestibility of Chlorella is a problem, and the production of the antibiotic chlorellin may be a source of discouragement for its use by human beings. Chlorellin is considered to be a decay product of Chlorella.

Indirectly algae provide food to man through their position in the food chain. In both marine and fresh water, plankton especially feed animals which in turn feed larger animals (see Chart 8.1).

> All the animals on land and in the sea, including man, are but a small brood of parasites living off the great body of the plant kingdom. . . . Each year the plants of the earth combine about 150 billion tons of C, 25 billion tons of H and set free 400 billions tons of O. . . . Few are aware, incidentally, that perhaps as much as 90% of the grand chemical industry is carried on under the surface of the sea by microscopic algae.[1]

The fresh-water gizzard shad takes from 70 to 100% of its food directly from plankton. Steeman-Nielsen found that plankton in a Danish lake produced 1300 gs. of glucose per sq. m. each year, with a maximum of 9.5 g. per day. Diatoms alone yielded 60 cal. of organic matter per sq. m. per hour in the surface waters. The ratios of primary food producers to primary feeders (see Chart 10.1) to secondary feeders was expressed 70.3:7.0:1.3 cal. per sq. cm. In a Wisconsin lake 25,920 pounds of plankton annually (or 2592 pounds per acre) produced 295 pounds of fish per acre. And in another lake it was found that 1622 kg. of plant life supported 244 kg. animal life per hectare.

---

[1] E. I. Rabinowitch, "Photosynthesis," in The Scientific Reader, 1953.

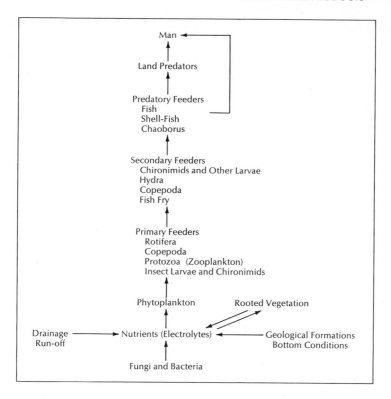

CHART 10.1   The Food Chain and Algae

It is estimated that marine plankton produces 126 billion tons of organic carbon annually as compared with 20 billion tons produced by terrestrial flora. This equals 340 tons per sq. km. in the sea — 160 tons on cultivated land.

A single fish consumes 1.2% of its weight every 24 hours, of which 50% is from bottom fauna that feeds directly on primary producers (algae). Laboratory experimental studies have given evidence on the direct feeding of animals on plankton. A single *Chilodon*, for example (as mentioned previously in another connection), consumes 30 diatoms each day and *Oxytricha* can consume 90 *Navicula* cells. The size of the predator of course determines the size of the plankter selected for food.

Commercial Products

A complete inventory of the industrial and medicinal importances of algae would make a very impressive account, with the list growing continually.

RHODOPHYTA

Some of the same substances useful as food are also the basis for many commercial products. Among these perhaps none is more important or better known than agar-agar. This mucilage is obtained from Gelidium primarily or from Hypnum, Gracilaria, and Ahnfeltia. Although harvested on the North American coast, most of the tonnage comes from Japan and southeast Asia. The substance is a gel involving galactose and a sulphate, melting between 90 and 100°F. and becoming solid at lower temperatures. This explains its universal use as an easily handled base for bacterial and fungal media. As such it was first used by Koch as long ago as 1881. A tabulation of the annual amount of agar-agar used in the United States alone gives an idea of its importance in commerce.

As a laxative base	100,000 lbs.
As a culture medium	100,000 lbs.
In baked goods	100,000 lbs.
In confections	100,000 lbs.
In dentistry	75,000 lbs.
Meat industry	50,000 lbs.
Emulsifiers (dairy products)	50,000 lbs.
Cosmetics	25,000 lbs.
Miscellaneous	50,000 lbs.

The latter includes lubricant for tungsten wire, photographic film, coating of pellets of nitrogen-fixing bacteria for soil seeding, and activation of sprays.

Agar-producing species are gathered from rocks at low tide or by diving. The plants are dried, washed, and, especially for some uses, bleached and cleared. After this the mucilage is boiled for a few hours and then is passed through several filters, poured into frames as a jelly, and frozen, thus forming the bulk or bar kanten which is convenient for storage and shipping.

Carrageenin from Chondrus crispus (as much as 70% of the dry weight; see p. 351) has innumerable uses as a component of tooth pastes, deodorants, cosmetics, and paints. It is employed in the leather-finishing industry and as a clearing agent for liquors, beet sugar, juices, etc. Gloiopeltis furcata is the source of a glue known in Japan as funori; 45 million pounds of this material are used in one year both for sizing paper and cloth as well as for an adhesive.

One well-known brand, Seakem Stabilizer from Chondrus crispus and Gigartina mamillosa, is a high-weight (100,000 to 500,000) molecular polymer negatively charged with properties that cannot be duplicated by other hydrocolloids. Within the extract are two components, a kappa and a lambda carrageenin which have different combinations of sulphated D-galactose units. Such stabilizers can be mixed with sugar, starches, and other carbohydrates, with gums such as tragacanth, guar, and locust bean, with milk, eggs, and gelatine, and with water-soluble salts. Chocolate milk is a good example of a stabilizer use. The Marine Colloids Company uses ten million pounds of carrageenin for miscellaneous products.

PHAEOPHYTA

Alginic acid and alginate derivatives account for many of the uses of Phaeophyta. Algin, first discovered in England in 1884, is a carbohydrate originating in the cell wall (as much as 40%) with a formula of $(C_6H_8O_6)n$. This formula involves polymeres of d-mannuronic acid, the soluble salts of which are known as algin. The insoluble extract is known as alginic acid; when treated so that a soluble compound is formed it is known as sodium alginate. Alginates are prepared by a rather complex process which includes maceration of the seaweed in acid and the addition of calcium chloride so that calcium alginate is produced. Other alginates are salts of potassium and magnesium. Of these sodium ammonium alginate is highly viscous. From these alginic acid is precipitated. As a British product sodium alginate in excess of one million pounds is exported to many other countries.

The best producers are Laminaria spp (Macrocystis spp, Ascophyllum nodosum, and Fucus spp in North America, and Eklonia and Eisenia in Japan). The content in plants varies throughout the year and from place to place; in general, however, it has been found feasible to carry on most harvesting during the late fall months. In addition to harvesting by hand (grapple hooks and hauling nets) various mechanical means are employed, including submerged moving knives on barges. Along the Pacific coast in the sections where there are dense beds, the harvested seaweeds are processed in floating factories aboard ship. It is estimated that there are 100 sq. miles occupied by Macrocystis off the coast of California.

Among the many uses of alginates, one that is highly important is in the treatment of latex for manufacturing rubber tires. Alginates are also used in paints, as a binding medium for coal briquettes, in ice cream, and as fillers for confections. When mixed with resin they are used for binding panel boards; when mixed with copper they are used for antifouling paints. They can also be spun into various fibers, although in this connection there has not been complete success. Sodium alginate is further used in asphalt paints, and copper alginate is used to treat canvas to prevent mildew.

In coastwise countries many brown algae are used as fertilizers on agricultural fields. In India Turbinaria is used especially around palm trees.

Liquid extracts from algae can be used as fertilizers and also as insecticides.

At different times (especially during wars) brown algae are a source of potash and iodine, and the U.S. government has surveyed and mapped the Pacific algal beds for such use. Potash is obtained by a fermentation of calcium acetate. Bromine is also obtainable, mostly from such red algae as *Rhodomela* and *Polysiphonia*, in which it may occur in quantities as large as 3 to 6% of the dry weight. From the New Hebrides 20,000 tons of algal ash are produced for commercial purposes each year.

DIATOMS (BACILLARIOPHYCEAE)

Small though they are, diatoms by virtue of their astronomical numbers and their ubiquity take a place in human economy. Reference has been made to their role in the food chain of aquatic animals. A seldom appreciated importance of living diatoms is the success with which they take up and store life-giving nutrients from water along continental shelves. Water from land pours into the sea millions of tons of nutrient-bearing silt. Much of this would be lost to the food cycle if allowed to settle in the abysmal depths of the sea. But photosynthetic diatoms and dinoflagellates gather these essential elements and retain them in the food chain (see p. 316).

Diatoms from Cretaceous and Tertiary deposits are economically important because of their siliceous, indestructible walls and because of their tremendous numbers which, over many millions of years, collected (and are still being collected) on the floors of lakes and seas. Underwater currents sweep shells along, as the plants die and fall to the bottom, together with other detritus. The particles settle out according to their specific gravity with the result that dunes of diatoms are formed on the ocean floor (diatomaceous earth or Fuller's earth). With the warping of the earth's crust and during submarine uplifts, the sea bottom becomes exposed and, as is well known, fossil beds and diatomaceous deposits are brought to light. Some dunes dating from the Jurassic are 300 feet or more high and may be a mile or longer in length. Tertiary deposits 2000 feet deep are known. The largest deposits are in western United States (California, Oregon, Wyoming), and there are many other sizeable deposits in New Hampshire and Maritime Canada and in Tripoli (which accounts for the name Tripoli Earth). Perhaps the most extensive deposit of all is at Lompoc in Santa Barbara County, California (see Text Figure 10.1).

Diatom accumulations are white (or yellowish if intermixed with iron oxide), firm, but usually soft and light. The deposits can be quarried, cut into great blocks, or scooped by power shovels. The material is known as diatomite or *Kieselguhr* and varies in composition according to age, degree of purity, and origin (fresh water or marine). When dry, diatomite will float, having a specific gravity of less than 1.0, and averages about ten or 12 pounds per cubic foot (sometimes as much as 34 pounds per cubic foot). Sample analyses of some deposits are shown below.

	From South Africa (17 species involved)	From Lompoc, California
Silicon dioxide	95.33%	88.68%
Magnesium	0.38%	1.30%
Aluminum (Alumina oxide)	1.96%	2.68%
Iron oxide	0.82%	trace
Lime	....	1.61%
Moisture	1.51%	5.54%

At present more than 87,000 tons are produced annually in the United States, of which 95% comes from California. One New York company alone uses 100 tons of diatomite each year for silver polish.

Diatomaceous deposits in lakes are never as deep or as pure as those formed in the oceans. In lakes with suitable limnological features sufficient quantities of diatoms have accumulated to make recovery feasible. Suction dredging removes bottom deposits which are spread out to air-dry. The sludge is then cut into blocks and burned to remove the organic matter, leaving the retrieved siliceous material as a white or gray powder. Lakes in Florida have supplied considerable quantities of diatomite; the advantage here is that this somewhat limited supply is nearer the processing and manufacturing centers, and thus is obtained more economically than shipping the light but bulky material from the West Coast.

The economic importances of diatoms and diatomite may be summarized:

1. Each diatom is a capsule of stored food (oil especially) and of a size suitable for ingestion by zooplankters. Because of their tremendous numbers diatoms (along with dinoflagellates) constitute the basis of the food chain of fish and other aquatic animals.

2. Also in their abundance, diatoms are efficient conservers of nutrient materials (as mentioned previously) which are continually washed from the land into the sea and which would be carried in the form of colloids beyond the continental shelves and lost in the abysmal depths of the oceans. Diatoms trap life-providing nutrients and keep them in circulation, thus performing a distinct service in one of the economies of nature.

3. Cod- and halibut-liver oil and its vitamin D is the oil which originally was stored in diatom cells, activated by sunlight, and finally

passed along through the food chain to become concentrated in fish livers.

4. Diatomaceous earth has numerous uses in industry and commerce. A few are: car and silver polishing powders (especially using fresh-water deposits which are more resistant); insulating material for hot and cold pipes; hollow tile brick for construction of constant temperature rooms; Berkfeld and other filters (such as aeration elements for aquaria); with bakelite to form switch and fuse boxes; filler for paints and gutta percha, papier maché and many other commercial products; clearing agent for fluids; manufacture of waterglass (sodium silicate); absorbent for commercial fertilizers; bleaching powders; tops for salt shakers to keep salt dry; etc.

5. Nitroglycerine or sulphuric or other acids can be poured into diatomaceous earth, thus rendering the former much safer for handling and shipping.

6. Diatomite sprinkled generously over walls and floor of coal mine tunnels reduces the danger of secondary explosions when great quantities of dust are thrown into the air by a smaller, primary explosion.

7. It is generally agreed (although with some beliefs to the contrary) that an unknown but significant percentage of the world's oil supply is of diatom origin. Each diatom cell has as much as 11% volume in oil droplets (occasionally much more). Oil which is unused when the cell dies, not being immiscible in water, collects with billions of other droplets and under proper geophysical conditions is thought to collect in pockets. The theory is that marine rather than fresh-water diatoms are responsible for oil because the latter undergo less complete deterioration. At least oil deposits in California are considered to have originated from Tertiary diatoms. On the other hand, it is also thought that much of our present-day supply of oil comes from the decomposition of marine animals. Even this, however, nevertheless establishes the diatom as indirectly responsible for the oil. The location and extent of diatomaceous layers are used by oil drillers in determining feasibility of putting down wells.

8. At one time (and to a certain extent now) a species of *Pinnularia* was used as a standard test object to check the resolution efficiency of high magnification microscope lenses.

9. In the Middle East diatomaceous earth has been used, unfortunately, as an adulterant to give bulk to dwindled flour supplies in times of famine (much to the detriment of the consumer).

Medicine

Because of their high iodine content (20,000 times the concentration in sea water) brown algae are used in various goiter medicines, either mixed or alone as a powdered weed. For example, *palcoto*, obtained from kelp meal, is used as a goiter check by South American Indians. Kelp Ore water is made by extracting salts from pockets of seaweeds buried in ancient sand banks. This brown soil is rich in iodine said to have been discovered in the ash of algae by a Frenchman in 1811.

Physicians sometimes treat for prolapsed stomach condition by placing the patient on a diet that includes dried agar-agar. This expands so greatly after a few glasses of water that the distended stomach regains a normal position.

Experimentation and testing algae for antibiotics are still in a preliminary stage, but much can be expected, judging from the advances that have been made already. Antibiotics (chlorellin from *Chlorella* and others) are known which inhibit several species of bacteria, and are effective against other algae. It is claimed that a species of *Nitzschia* can reduce the number of *Escherichia coli* in water and filter systems.

Agar-agar is used in making many kinds of pharmaceutical products such as pills and ointments. Also it is used as a base for several types of laxatives. Of special interest is the ability of carrageenin extract to act as a blood coagulant. Other genera besides *Chondrus* have the same property.

Extracts from *Alsidium*, *Corallina*, *Codium*, *Durvillea*, and *Digenea* (30 to 35% dry weight agar) contain an effective vermifuge, and the herb doctors of the Orient use many kinds of algae for the treatment of kidney, bladder, and lung diseases.

Reference has been made to the use of *Euglena* in medical research. It is sensitive to B_{12} and can be used diagnostically when grown in comparison with a culture in which there is blood of a suspected anemia patient.

Objectionable Features

Whereas the many positive qualities of algae place them on the black side of the ledger, others must be listed in red as liabilities (see Table 10.1).

Water Supplies

Plankton algae, especially cyanophytes, in lakes and reservoirs used for domestic supply, are rendered unfit by superabundant growths. When alive *Microcystis*, *Aphanizomenon*, *Dinobryon*, *Synura*, and many diatoms impart disagreeable tastes and odors to water. But when highly proteinaceous plants die and decompose there is no odor quite so revolting. Lakes are often described as "smelling fishy," but this is because of oil-producing plants rather than fish. The many objectionable effects of algae, particularly the blue-greens, can be traced to the following characteristics:

1. Their rapid rate of multiplication.
2. Their pseudovacuoles, which cause them to float high in the water and to concentrate at the surface where they are destroyed in intense light.
3. Their mucilaginous sheaths, which are sticky and cause plants to clot and to form floating mats.
4. Their high protein content, responsible for offensive odors and tastes.
5. Their ability to produce and give off antibiotics and toxins.

Profuse growths often are annoying and cause economic loss by clogging screens and sand filters in water systems. This is especially true in the case of diatoms. Their resistant walls form layers over sand, thus facilitating the collection of organic matter and the development of a thick mat of filamentous algae (*Aufwuchs*) which completely closes the filter.

If algae do not ruin drinking water, they can and do ruin recreational sites because of their odors and dense, matted growths. Boating, swimming, and fishing are ruined by algae and many a resort area has found it necessary to close down because of algal pests.

TABLE 10.1   The Algal Ledger

DEBIT	CREDIT
Water spoilage, both domestic and industrial	Food for Man: marine algae; *Chlorella*
Recreational sites spoiled	Food for fish; support of the food chain
Water filters clogged	Commercial products; seaweeds and diatomaceous earth
Pulp and paper industry interference; slime-formation	Medicinal products
Animal deaths; toxin effects (cattle, sheep, hogs, horses, fowl)	Nitrogen-fixation and soil conditioning; soil conservation; soil pioneers
Fish death, by toxins and by suffocation	Sewage oxidation ponds
Human deaths, fish and shellfish poisoning	Pollution research; indices
Human ailments: skin allergies, pulmonary disease, digestive complaints	Oxygenation for space and submarines; purification of streams
Parasites on higher plants: tea, citrus, banana	Assay of biologicals in research
	Cancer research
	Limnological and oceanographic research
	Evolution of Life; problems and research
	Paleontological research.
	Oil industry
	Lime deposits
	Aesthetic properties

Algicides such as copper sulphate or other organic salts can control the growth of objectionable algae in water supplies, especially if applied at the right time and in the correct amounts. Although a poison, copper sulphate (blue vitrol) can be used in such minute amounts that it can eliminate algae without injury to fish or Man. About two pounds of the crystals per million gallons of water are (in general) effective in control. Somewhat greater amounts of algicides are needed for basic waters. For large city reservoirs this control is expensive but copper sulphate is probably the most effective and least costly of any of the algicides available. (Other algicides are available but they are more dangerous and more expensive.) Because of the relationship of high nitrogen- and phosphorus-content to the development of objectionable blooms of algae, control measures should include elimination of pollution wastes. In fact some very serious conditions have been completely remedied by diverting effluents from sewage treatment plants.

Death of Fish

Abundant plankton may lead to death of fish either directly or indirectly. Toxins liberated into the water can kill at least some kinds of fish, and evidence is at hand indicating that by-products of algal decay (protein derivatives such as hydroxylamine) are poisonous to fish. Crappies and perch were killed when placed in an aquarium with *Aphanizomenon*, although oxygen was maintained at 8.0 ppm. Two of the common species of *Microcystis* were found to produce extrametabolites lethal for *Gambusia*.

Dinoflagellates are infamous perpetrators of fish and shellfish deaths, often leading to the death of human beings as well. Guilty species are *Gymnodinium veneficum*, *G. brevis*, *Gonyaulax catenella*, *G. Tamarensis*, and *Pyrodinium phoneus*. Spectacular deaths of marine fish occur in the Red Tide. Whole schools of fish are killed when they swim into areas in which *Gymnodinium* spp are in bloom condition. The toxin is concentrated enough to kill fish within many square miles (Gulf of Mexico, New Jersey coast). The dinoflagellates occur in quantities as high as 60,000,000 per liter of sea water during summer months and especially when water becomes suitably enriched with nutrients (phosphates, nitrates, vitamin B_{12}). It is thought that vitamins are supplied by the bacteria which have been isolated from the dinoflagellates. The tides are known to occur along the coasts of several continents, but in the Western Hemisphere they develop especially along Florida, New Jersey, California, and in the Gulf of California and Gulf of Mexico. It has been estimated that in eight months one-half billion fish were killed in the Gulf of Mexico alone. A secondary objectionable effect results when great masses of dead fish wash onto beaches. Air which blows landward from Red Tide waters produces respiratory ailments among human beings.

Laboratory experiments have shown the toxin of *Gymnodinium* to be lethal for 23 species of test fish. The toxin seems to act by depolarizing membranes over which nerve impulses pass, hence affecting both nerves and muscles. The general result is similar to that produced by curare; that is, it inhibits the response of skeletal muscles to acetylcholine. *Gymnodinium veneficum* is known to be toxic also to mussels along the California and Washington coasts.

An indirect way by which algae cause death of fish is suffocation. Dense algal blooms develop to a peak in warm water, when oxygen content is low in any event. At night, with photosynthesis stopped, the continuous respiration of a great mass of plants leads to oxygen depletion, 0.3 ppm to almost zero. This triggers a series of upsets which ends in the death of every single organism in the lake. Death of one group of animals leads to increased bacterial decomposition which accordingly lowers the oxygen content still further. Algae therefore become arch destroyers, even to themselves.

Death of Animals

As a result of their exotoxins and endotoxins, blue-green algae can bring about the death of farm animals. The most noxious of these are the exotoxins produced by *Microcystis* spp, although *Nodularia*, *Anabaena*, *Gloeotrichia*, and possibly *Aphanizomenon* are also known to be toxic. Significantly, perhaps, the species which produce lethal toxins are those which contain pseudovacuoles. Domestic animals such as horses, cattle, sheep, hogs, and even birds are killed or made seriously ill by drinking alga-infested waters. Death results within one to 24 hours. In one instance 700 Franklin gulls in Iowa were killed by a toxin produced by *Anabaena*.

In South Africa repeated blooms of *Microcystis toxica* in the shallow lakes (pans) of the grazing range cause the death of thousands of cattle annually. The symptoms include loss of weight, weakness, liver pathology, and abortion. The phycocyanin, passing through the liver, is carried to the skin by the blood stream and is sensitized by light so that an internal burning occurs and the skin peels from the animal.

Laboratory experiments with extracts from *Microcystis*, *Anabaena*, and *Aphanizomenon* have been performed on laboratory animals. Tests include intravenous, intraperitoneal, and oral exposure, with death occurring within three minutes to as much as 48 hours. It has been learned that toxins vary according to strains of the species, some being non-toxic. Whether these variations are related to a genetic quality or simply to the time within the life cycle of the alga (spore-production, etc.) has not been determined for certainty, and much more research is indicated. There is a VFD (very fast death factor, operating within three minutes); an FDF (fast death factor, killing within two hours); an SDF (slow death factor causing death within four to 48 hours or not at all; see Table 10.2).

The toxin from Microcystis has been found to be a non-volatile, acidic compound with great absorption qualities. It is a peptide composed only of amino acids and behaves as a neurotoxin. Components include D-serine, L-ornithine, and aspartic and glutonic acid (dicarboxylic acids). The effects produced in animals are much the same as those caused by the fungus Amanita phalloides in human beings. There is an enlargement of the liver, a failure of blood to clot, and congestion within the spleen. An extract of Microcystis toxin which was analyzed by electrophoresis showed that five components are involved, each of which gives a positive peptide reaction and one of which is toxic. This latter contains the following acids:

TABLE 10.2   Death-Inducing Algae

Algae	Lypholized Cells Intra-Peritoneally Administered To White Mice, 40-60 mg/kg Of Body Weight			Ducks Birds	Sheep	Cattle	Fish
	VFDF 1-10 Min	FDF 1-2 Hrs	SDF 4-48 Hrs				
Anabaena flos-aquae	5*		2	+	+	+	
Anabaena circinalis							+
Anabaena limnetica			3				
Anabaena Scheremetievi			2				
Anabaena inaequalis							+
Anabaena Nadsonii							+
Aphanizomenon flos-aquae			5	+		+	+
Aphanothece nidulans			2				
Aphanothece cyanea			9				
Gloeotrichia echinulata			1				
Lyngbya Birgei			1				
Microcystis toxica						+	+
Microcystis aeruginosa		8	11		+	+	+
Nodularia spumigena			1		+	+	
Scenedesmus sp			1				
Chorella sp	5	2	3				
Gonyaulax catenella							+
Gymnodimium brevis and other spp							+

*Strains or number of times positive reaction.

aspartic, glutamic, leucine, serine, valine, ornithine, and alanine. It is noteworthy that toxicity is reduced after a *Microcystis* bloom begins to subside; hence the toxin is not released from dead cells.

DEATH OF HUMAN BEINGS

Deaths or poisoning resulting from the consumption of fish and shellfish are actually caused by dinoflagellates, at least indirectly. These algae are the chief source of food for many marine animals and one especially, *Gonyaulax catanella*, contains an endotoxin. Although the toxin is harmless to the fish and shellfish themselves, it accumulates in human tissues, especially the liver, and is capable of causing severe illness or death (in about 75% of the cases). At times *Gonyaulax* may be present in amounts of 40,000,000 per liter during summer months. The toxin (an alkaloid)

TABLE 10.3 Toxic Dinoflagellates

ORGANISMS	TOXIN	CHEMICAL CHARACTERS	PHYSICAL CHARACTERS	INTER-MEDIARY	EFFECT ON MAN
Gonyaulax catenella	Paralytic toxin Endotoxin	Alkaloid similar to strychnine	Soluble in water and alcohol. Insoluble in ether. Heat stable in acid, not in alkaline	Shellfish	Paralysis. Liver path. Respiratory failure. Death in 2-12 hrs.
Gonyaulax catenella or possibly a blue-green algal plankter	Tetraodontoxin	$C_{16}H_{31}NO_{16}$	Hygroscopic white powder	Fish	Numbness Nausea Paralysis Death in
Gonyaulax Tamarensis	Exotoxin			Fish Death	1-24 hrs.
Gymnodinium brevis flavum mikimotoi veneficum	Exotoxin		Water-borne Vapor	Fish killed. Also other marine animals	Vapor causes respiratory ailments
Pyrodinium phoneus	Exotoxin			Fish killed	

is acid-stable, non-volatile, and water soluble, and can be stored for many months without losing its strength. The poison is estimated to be ten times more potent than strychnine, and its effects are not unlike those of botulina poisoning. As an indication of its potency, one millionth of a gram is fatal to a mouse when injected.

Tetraodontoxin (from the puffer) is thought to be caused by a toxin from Gonyaulax (and perhaps other dinoflagellates). Apparently the puffer and other fish consume great quantities of the plankton when it is in bloom status. The toxin (referred to as ichthyosarcotoxin) has been given the tentative formula of $C_{16}H_{31}NO_{16}$. Symptoms are dizziness and nervous disorders, beginning about 30 minutes after eating, and death usually follows within 24 hours. It is said that whole companies of Japanese soldiers in the South Pacific were killed during World War II from poisonous fish (see Table 10.3).

Chapter 11

Devonian Algae. (American Museum of Natural History, New York)

Phylogeny and
Fossil Algae

If for no other reason, the past is of interest because a knowledge of what has gone before helps in an understanding and an explanation of the present, and possibly provides a view into the future. Hence speculations are many as to the historical development of the algal groups, their possible relationships to one another, and their ancestry. The characteristics used to group or to separate alga phyla have already been outlined. Many, if not all of our notions and ideas concerning the evolution (phylogeny) and systematics of the algae are derived mostly by inference from study of the taxonomic criteria of extant species. This means that we are considering the ultimate twigs of the evolutionary "tree(s)"; present day expressions of algae (as of all organisms) represent the culmination of all the changes in physiology and morphology that have occurred throughout natural history. It is intriguing therefore to speculate on the sequence of developments which have brought algae to their present status.

As mentioned elsewhere, the almost universal appearance of flagellated cells, vegetative, reproductive, or both, in the several phyla has given rise to the postulation that all groups possess a flagellated ancestral stem. This was first suggested in printed form by Klebs in 1893, enlarged upon by Blackman in 1900, by Blackman and Tansley in 1902, and considered by Luther, Borzi, Bohlin, and Pascher. The similarity of zoospores and motile gametes produced by non-motile algae to flagellated algal cells is of course highly suggestive. Further, the fact that some predominantly flagellated phyla contain a few non-motile, filamentous, and "higher" morphological expressions emphasizes the possible (if not probable) trends of similar evolutionary development that run throughout so many of the phyla. That is, evolution appears to have followed somewhat the same pathways in the several different groups. For, admitting parallel evolution of alga phyla from the great unknown pool of primitive Life (see Chart 11.1), it is interesting to note the similarities of form and habit which appear in the respective groups.

At present it is generally believed that form and behavior in organisms are determined by genetic mechanisms. Hence, the cytological, physiological, and morphological similarities between groups bespeak a common genetic blueprint — a pattern that guides the response of different protoplasms to environment in somewhat similar fashion. For example, within the Chrysophyceae, Xanthophyceae, Chlorophyta, and a few Rhodophyta there are many counterparts. A number of these similarities are listed below:

I. Motile Unicells
   Chrysophyceae: **Chromulina, Amphichrysis**
   Xanthophyceae: None
   Chlorophyta: **Pyramimonas, Chlamydomonas, Pedinomonas**
II. Non-motile Unicells
   Chrysophyceae: **Apistonema**
   Xanthophyceae: **Botrydiopsis**
   Chlorophyta: **Desmococcus; Ourococcus**
   Rhodophyta: **Porphyridium**
III. Simple Motile Colony
   Chrysophyceae: **Syncrypta**
   Xanthophyceae: None
   Chlorophyta: **Pandorina, Gonium**
IV. Gelatinous Non-motile Colony
   Chrysophyceae: **Chrysocapsa, Naegeliella**
   Xanthophyceae: **Gloeochloris**
   Chlorophyta: **Tetraspora**
V. Indefinite Filament
   Chrysophyceae: **Sphaeridiothrix**
   Xanthophyceae: None
   Chlorophyta: **Geminella, Radiofilum**
   Rhodophyta: **Asterocystis**
VI. Definite Filament
   Chrysophyceae: **Chrysomeris**
   Xanthophyceae: **Tribonema, Bumilleria**
   Chlorophyta: **Hormidium, Ulothrix**
VII. Branched Filament
   Chrysophyceae: **Phaeothamnion**
   Xanthophyceae: **Monocilia**
   Chlorophyta: **Stigeoclonium, Microthamnion**
   Rhodophyta: **Erythrotrichia**
VIII. Siphonaceous Filament
   Chrysophyceae: None

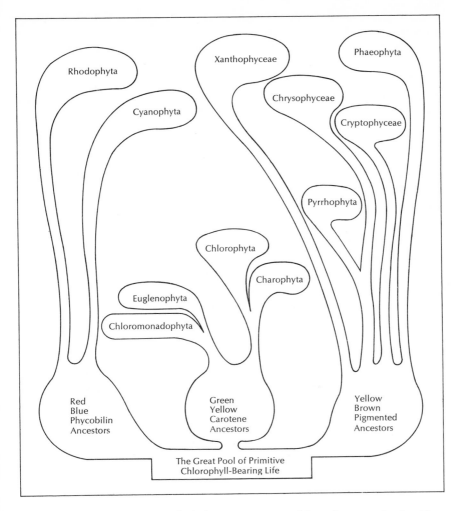

CHART 11.1   Suggested Phylogenetic Lines of Development in the Algae

Xanthophyceae: **Vaucheria**
Chlorophyta: **Dichotomosiphon**
IX. Coccoid Cells
Chrysophyeae: **Epicystis**
Xanthophyceae: **Goniochloris**
Chlorophyta: **Characium**

In addition to inferential theories regarding the phylogeny of algae, somewhat more concrete ideas concerning their history can be derived from evidence left in fossilized algae. Considering the perplexing length of time in geological history, the number and amount of fossil remains are relatively few. This is true partly because most algae do not lend themselves well to fossilization; their structures are too soft and can be too readily decomposed. Another reason is that there is relatively little exploration with fossil discovery in mind, notwithstanding the constant boring and gouging of the earth's crust by Man. Mines, quarries, well-drillings, and erosion have yielded some fossil records, however, especially of those algae which have siliceous walls, calcareous walls, or cellulose walls impregnated with decay-resisting properties. Included in the fossil record, therefore, are the calcareous Rhodophyta and Chlorophyta, the diatoms, the dinoflagellates, the Silicoflagellata and some Coccolithophoridae. In addition imprints of supposed algae have been found in the most ancient of rock, as well as calcareous concretions built by algal metabolism (ooliths).

The Cyanophyta are considered the oldest of the algae because of their relative simplicity (even today), and because of similarities with imprints in Precambrian, Archaeozoic rock. Imprints are two or possibly three billion years old, and while there are no structural remains the impressions resemble those which would have been made by minute, globular, or thread-like organisms. Egg-like or biscuit-shaped calcareous masses show concentric zones as though having been laid down by repeated, lime-depositing actions of colonial Cyanophyta such as *Microcystis, Gloeocapsa, Aphanothece,* or *Rivularia.* This type of concretion is well-illustrated today by the production by thermophilic algae of calcareous deposits (especially travertine and calcite) around hot springs and geyser basins. The fossil records of such blue-green algae occur in Ontario and British Columbia, Canada, in Montana and other sites in the montane of western United States. Other examples are *Collenia* and *Cryptozoon,* both of uncertain origin and classification. Calcareous beds in which such remains occur may be many hundreds of feet deep, such as those known from the Proterozoic and Upper Cambrian.

The idea that Rhodophyta may be related to Cyanophyta is suggested by the fact that these two groups share some of the same pigments (phycocyanin and phycoerythrin). They both have a primitive type of pigment-bearing body, although one which is scarcely developed in the Cyanophyta. Present in at least some genera of both are interconnecting wall pores. These two groups are examples of phyla which have no motile cells, and for which there are no known motile ancestors. Other algal phyla supposedly do have such ancestors. In any event the lack of motile cells is a reminder that conversely some of the flagellated phyla include non-motile, strictly plant-like, "higher" algae (cf. filamentous forms in the Pyrrhophyta).

The Rhodophyta today include many forms which are easily fossilized because of their habit of encasing themselves in lime. Many of the fossils are clearly identifiable with, or are closely related to, extant forms. Fragments of such algae were thought for a long time to be animal in origin and were later called nullipores. Finally they were identified as remains of coralline algae. Rhodophyta fossils occur in the Ordovician of the Paleozoic, an age during which several of the algal groups left their records. Such algae, already highly developed, must have had a beginning during the aeons prior to the Ordovician and, indeed, their exact age is not known. The appearance of so many algae during this period (*Dalyia, Bosworthia, Wahpia*) in the Laurentian of the Archaeozoic has earned for it the name Age of Rhodophyta.

The record of the red algal past is well-known from the impressive accumulations laid down during the Eocene and Miocene of the Cenozoic, when deposits, thousands of feet thick, of *Lithothamnion* and other coralline algae were formed. *Corallina* and other members of the Corallinaceae are known also from the Cretaceous of the Mesozoic. That period saw the building of calcareous deposits by a now-extinct class of algae known as the Solenoporaceae.

In all Rhodophyta groups which include filamentous genera there appears to be an evolution from the heterotrichous to the homotrichous habit of growth; i.e., from the part-prostrate, part-erect thallus to the completely erect plant. Further, there is a tendency to develop from an isomorphic to a heteromorphic life cycle. The most primitive life cycle, and one which is unknown for the red algae, involves a unicellular gametophyte alternating with a one-celled sporophyte (zygospore). In another expression a multicellular gametophyte alternates with a unicellular diploid (zygospore). This is the simplest type of life history known for the Rhodophyta which reproduce sexually. As outlined previously, evolutionary developments in the red algae have resulted in highly involved life histories in which multicellular gametophytes alternate with multicellular sporophytes (sometimes with intermediate diploid stages).

Chart 7.1 (page 244) presents a suggested phylogenetic arrangement of the orders within the Rhodophyta.

Whereas the Phaeophyta have no members motile in the vegetative state there is an almost universal employment of zoospores and motile gametes. We can therefore infer that the phylum has had a motile ancestry, though such forms are no longer extant. The Phaeophyta have similarities of pigmentation with some of the yellow-brown phyla in which there are many motile organisms, and it well may be that similar forms might be involved in the origin of the brown algae. Phaeophyta fossils from the Triassic, like many of the Chrysophyta, have fucoxanthin, and there is present laminarin which is similar to chrysolaminarin. These two phyla have heterokont flagellation almost throughout. Rather curiously, but of no phylogenetic significance, the Phaeophyta and Euglenophyta possess the same carbohydrate-splitting enzyme.

The present lack of calcium-depositing forms in all Phaeophyta except *Padina* probably reflects a similar absence of such forms in geologic time, and explains the paucity of fossil records of them. They seem to have had an origin in the Algonkian of the Proterozoic, and the geologic timetable definitely places them in the Silurian of the Paleozoic — again indicating that their actual beginnings are much further back in time. Forms recognized from this age are *Fucus, Cutleria, Ectocrapus, Dictylota,* and others.

Chart 6.1 (page 231) presents a suggested phylogenetic arrangement of the Phaeophyta.

Like the Rhodophyta, a number of genera in the Chlorophyta are lime-depositors (especially in the Siphonales and Siphonocladiales). The most conspicuous of these are in the families Codiaceae and Dasycladaceae; e.g., *Codium* and *Halimeda. Chara* in the Charales, also a lime-depositor, has representatives as well as related genera in fossil history. The Chlorophyta undoubtedly had their beginning with the motile order Volvocales (or with the ancestors of that order). Like the Rhodophyta, the Chlorophyta first appeared in the Ordovician period, during which time very elaborate and highly ornate, branched forms evolved in the Dasycladaceae (*Primicorallina, Palaeodasycladus, Dimorphosiphon,* e.g.). These were abundant in the Permian and Jurassic but curiously became reduced in number in the Cretaceous. Of interest in the fossil history of the green algae is Boghead Coal (Scotland) formed by *Botryococcus* (*Pia*), an oil-rich form which was very abundant in Permian seas.

The Characeae, represented in fossil history by forms dating from the Ordovician and Silurian, show even then an advanced state of morphological complexity. The oogonia (oospores), known as gyrogonites, especially are represented in the fossil record together with sections of stem (especially nodal regions). Many of the fossil remains have been assigned to the genus *Clavator.*

Because of their active deposition of lime *Chara* are responsible for the formation in lakes of deep beds of marl and tufa. Even since the last glaciation in central North America old lake bottoms have been layered with enough marl to make it feasible for cement plants to establish operation in the vicinity of the lakes.

The Charophyceae (Charophyta of some authors) possess many Chlorophyta characteristics: pigmentation, food reserve, flagellation, and dominant gametophyte generation. The inclusion of the Charophyceae under the Chlorophyta seems to be a reasonable association. And yet the fossil history of the two groups, and the lack of any interconnecting forms (either living or fossil), leave considerable doubt. The Charophyceae are known from the Silurian; the other Chlorophyta (as such) from the Precambrian, with some of the present-day orders having representatives in the Ordovician (the Dasycladales in the Permian, for example). (See Chlorophyta, Chart 2.1, p. 43.)

The Euglenophyta have the same chlorophyll-*b* possessed by the Chlorophyta. Some students recommend uniting these two phyla on the basis of this pigment similarity. But the food reserve and flagellation, in addition to other basic cytological characteristics, are so vastly different that to do so would point up many inconsistencies.

In the Chrysophyta and Silicoflagellata, forms were readily fossilized. The diatoms were abundant in the Silurian and Devonian, and were, interestingly enough, primarily the Centricae. It is claimed that *Pyxidicula* is the oldest fossil diatom, dating from 190 million years ago. Judging from accumulations of siliceous shells, the diatoms seem to have had their peak development during the Tertiary.

The Pyrrhophyta, abundant and varied in the plankton today, have existed for many millions of years in both fresh and salt water. Because of the cell wall, with its calcareous and siliceous inclusions, especially when the cells encyst, the Pyrrhophyta lend themselves well to fossilization. The dinoflagellates with siliceous impregnations are known from as far back as the Jurassic, and cysts have been found in New Zealand that are so characteristically formed and so well-preserved that taxonomic identification to many genera is possible.

Eodinia and *Lithodinia* are two fossil genera. Other forms with calcareous impregnations are *Biecherella* and *Calcisphaerella*, found in the Jurassic of France, as well as *Bicarinellum* from the Eocene (France). Other genera have been found in Australia, New Zealand, and, from the Miocene, in Algeria. Cookson and Eisenack have described a number of species of both naked and thecate dinoflagellates from the Cretaceous in Victoria, Australia, taken from as deep as 4499 feet. Other dinoflagellates have been found in the chalk deposits of Germany and France.

That the immediate ancestors of the Pyrrhophyta are motile is a foregone conclusion. At the same time, in the evolution of this group of predominantly swimming organisms, palmelloid, sedentary, cyst-like and filamentous expressions have developed. *Dinothrix* and *Dinoclonium* have been mentioned previously (Plate XIV, Figs. 210 and 211) as examples of the alga form of growth, a reminder of the inadequacy of the artificial division of Life into "plant" and "animal" categories.

The Pyrrhophyta share some features in common with the Phaeophyta such as abundant carotenoids, chlorophyllic, and lateral or subapical flagella. But there seems to be no phylogenetic relationships.

Mostly because of uncertainties relative to a suitable classification, the Cryptophyceae (Cryptophyta), a protozoan-like group, have usually been included with the Pyrrhophyta. The somewhat similar pigmentation of the two groups and their remotely similar flagellation seem to justify such a grouping. But even though reasonable from a few points of view, and even though convenient, the assignment of the Cryptophyceae to the dinoflagellates creates more taxonomic problems than are solved. Small and relatively unknown though the group is, it is excusable to elevate the group to a phylum status (i.e., the Cryptophyta) and thus recognize their unique characteristics.

Chapter *12*

Culturing of Algae

Algae are placed into artificial cultivation for a number of reasons, including the following:

1. To trace the life cycle of a species and to learn the morphological and genetical phases of the life cycle.

2. To study manner of gamete-formation, gametic union, and the ecological factors related to reproductive phases.

3. To determine morphological and reproductive characteristics as aids in establishing taxonomic criteria and in developing phylogenetic relationships.

4. To provide specimens for cytological and ultra-microscopical examinations of cell structure, organelles, and cell division.

5. To study the physiology of algae (and to apply information to other plants); photosynthesis (its mechanism and its products); elaboration of ergastic substances; respiration; nutrition requirements; response to light (quantitative and qualitative); and temperature. Culture for physiological studies may involve either organic or inorganic media or a combination of both.

6. To study the elaboration of extrametabolites; endo- and exotoxins; and antibiotics.

7. To determine the chemical composition of algae for both scientific and practical purposes.

8. To study production and the productivity rate, and their relationships to limnology, to the food chain of aquatic animals, and as food for domestic animals, and for Man.

9. To study and test algicides, their effects on different species and their use in various concentrations.

10. To study relationships of algae to water quality or sanitation.

A voluminous literature is readily available describing various techniques and media to be employed in culturing fresh-water and marine algal species. A few selected references are listed in the bibliography.

One must be on guard not to misinterpret or to misapply results of algal cultures. Culture techniques and media seldom, if ever, can duplicate the natural habitat. Hence it is only to be expected that in adapting to an artificial situation organisms would exhibit morphological, physiological, and reproductive characteristics unlike those they would exhibit in nature. For example, two, three, or more species belonging to one genus when cultivated often lose the morphological characteristics which have been used to differentiate them. They may show a number of characteristics in common to the extent that the observer is led to postulate that such species are all one and not separable. It is only to be expected that species belonging to a particular genus would have similar genetic characters that well might appear when placed under abnormal conditions — characteristics which are recessive or which do not appear when plants are growing in nature.

By experimentation and by trial and error, scientists have been able to determine culture methods, ingredients of artificial media, and necessary controlled conditions. They have also studied the degrees to which media, light, temperature, etc., must be varied for the proper growth of different algal groups or even species. Either salt water or synthesized sea water, sometimes highly modified, is used for marine algae.

All the various techniques and media employed attempt to do one of two things: either to duplicate natural conditions as nearly as possible, or to provide a set of artificial conditions which are suitable for growth and which can produce desired results. Flasks, tubes, bottles, and Petri plates with appropriate media are used for minute or microscopic algae, whereas basins, glass vats, or tanks must be employed for macroscopic algae, especially the larger marine forms. The culture vessels, both large and small, may be connected (either singly or in series) with a continuous-flow nutrient supply and gas supply (O_2, CO_2, etc.). The culture vessels or tubes may be vertical or horizonal and so equipped that they receive nutrients at constant temperatures and under controlled illumination. In many instances culture vessels are maintained in a shaker device to provide a more nearly equal exposure of plants to medium and to light, and to prevent settling out of cells. Such a vibration is often desirable because agitation somewhat duplicates water movement in the natural habitat. In other experimentation, when possible, controlled, artificial brooks are constructed in the laboratory and provided with simulated rapids and quiet sections. Sometimes growth chambers or constant temperature rooms are employed.

In general, a temperature of 20°C. (28°C. commonly applied also), and a light source of from 800 to 1200 (or up to 2000) foot candles is used. For a host of fresh-water species, ordinary room temperature and the daylight from a north window are suitable for successful growth. Such cultures may be maintained in jars or batteries of lake water, or in soil-water culture media (see below). One difficulty with these cultures is that certain nutrients become exhausted, especially trace elements that are sometimes critical for particular species. On the other hand, even when trace elements are not optimum, a gross culture may become balanced, especially in exchange of gases, in a short time so that growth, death, and decomposition result in a cycling of elements, thus permitting a culture that may endure for years.

Depending upon the objectives of the culture study, types of cultures are established. For some purposes a mixture of algae (a *gross culture*) may be grown together in a balanced aquarium. In others, a plant may be isolated and placed in a medium to form a *unialgal* culture, either free from or with bacteria. In specialized studies a unialgal culture is developed using antiseptic (bacteriological) techniques to produce *bacteria-free* growths. Some cultures are established by isolating a single cell or a spore (zygospore, zoospore, or other) to initiate an *axenic* culture. Such an isolation is accomplished by using a pipette under a binocular microscope, or with a micromanipulator under a compound microscope. The axenic culture is especially necessary for studies to determine and isolate physiological or genetic clones or races.

In continuous-flow cultures the supply of nutrients, the temperature, and light can be regulated so that the growth rate and population development can be measured at a desired time, the cells or plants being all at approximately the same stage. This is referred to as a *synchronous* culture.

In many instances a study of parasitic, endophytic, or endozoic species requires a special medium and particularized growth conditions which are suitable for the host as well as for the invader.

Whereas the gross culture may be suitable for such purposes as class or incidental study, specialized methods must be employed to grow selected species. Perhaps the simplest is the soil-water extract method. Essentially, this method takes advantage of the nutrient elements and vitamins in soil. A layer (about one-fourth inch) of garden loam is placed in an Erlenmeyer flask, or about four centimeters in a test tube. The vessel is then nearly filled with sterile water, plugged with cotton and pasteurized in a steamer for three hours. This allows sufficient time to kill algae and other organisms present (except for bacterial spores). In some instances it may be desirable to include a kernel or two of some grain before soil is added, thus providing an additional amount of organic matter and a nutrient medium for subsequent bacterial action in the culture. After pasteurization and after the flasks have been cooled, desired amounts of algal material are added, the nature of the specimen determining the amount to be introduced. One cc. (or less) of a suspension of unicells or colonial forms is sufficient.

There are various modifications of the soil-water method. One involves pasteurizing the soil in water and then pouring off the liquid to be used as a base for a medium to which various selected ingredients are added. Another involves using the soil-water to make up an agar medium for Petri plate or slanted tube cultures if a surface growth of an alga is desired.

A standard medium of the inorganic mineral type is the well-known, so-called "A-Z" solution. The ingredients are (in grams):

$Al_2(SO_4)_3$	1.0	$MnCl_2.4H_2O$	7.0
$Ca(NO_3)_2.6H_2O$	1.0	$NiSO_4.6H_2O$	1.0
$CuSO_4.5H_2O$	1.0	$SnCl_3.1H_2O$	0.5
H_3BO_4	11.0	TiO_2	1.0
KBr	0.5	$ZnSO_4$	1.0
KI	0.5	LiCl	0.5

When dissolved in one liter of water this stock solution is then further diluted so that the above amounts of minerals are distributed through 18 liters of water for a stock supply. The solution obviously contains all the necessary plant nutrient elements (except vitamins and organic acids). One cc. of the above mixture (diluted) is added to a liter of water or to some other culture fluid to be used for the actual culturing of an alga. This solution is suitable for a great variety of algae (fresh-water) and for other plants. Experimentation will determine whether or how much additional organic matter is necessary to culture particular species.

An almost universally used and standard nutrient is known as Chu No. 10 (Chu, 1942), which is sometimes used with 10% soil extract solution. Chu's solution (with ferric citrate recommended in place of his original ferric chloride) is (in mg. per liter):

Ca	4.0	N	5.25
Cl	13.3	Na	7.5
Fe	0.18	P	0.89
HCO_3	12.0	Si	4.6
K	2.2	SO_4	20.0
Mn	0.01	Mg	5.0

or:

$Ca(NO_3)_2$	0.004%	$MgSO_4.7H_2O$	0.025%
$FeCl_3$	0.00008%	Na_2CO_3	0.002%
K_2HPO_4	0.001%	Na_2SiO_3	0.0025%

Modified by Rodhe (1948) and by others this solution may be prepared as follows (in mg. per liter):

$Ca(HCO_3)_2$	160.0	K_2HPO_4	5.0

MgSO$_4$	25.0	Ferric citrate and	
NaSiO$_3$	20.0	citric acid each	1.0
		MnSO$_4$	0.03

The ferric citrate and citric acid stock solution must be made up fresh about once each week. All the solutions listed above are used as stock, and from each the following proportions are added to one liter of water or nutrient medium:

Ca(HCO$_3$)$_2$ (as CaCO$_3$)	10 mg.	NH$_4$Cl	20 ml.
MgSO$_4$	25 ml.	Ferric citrate and	
NaSiO$_3$	20 ml.	citric acid	100 ml.
K$_2$HPO$_4$	5 ml.	MnSO$_4$	0.3 ml.

Rodhe (1948) discusses the use and efficiency of this and other media. The above combination is suitable for diatoms and for green algae; also for blue-green species when organic substances are added. McLachlan and Gorham (1961) offer a modified medium for the culture of the blue-green genus *Microcystis*. Another modification found to be especially suitable for blue-green algae is recommended by Gerloff, Fitzgerald, and Skoog (1950), in grams per liter:

CaCl$_2$.2H$_2$O	0.0359	NaCO$_3$	0.02
Citric acid	0.003	NaNO$_3$	0.0413
Ferric citrate	0.003	Na$_2$PO$_4$	0.0082
KCl	0.0086	Na$_2$SiO$_3$	0.250
MgCl$_2$.6H$_2$O	0.0209	Na$_2$SO$_4$	0.0146

A synthetic medium enriched with vitamins was used successfully by McLaughlin, *et al.* (1960), for the mass cultivation of dinoflagellates (*Katodinium* and *Gyrodinium*). This medium is:

NaCl	2.4 gm.	Biotin	1.0 µg.
MgSO$_4$.7H$_2$O	0.9 gm.	Thiamine HCl	0.01 mg.
KCl	0.07 gm.	Pyridoxine HCl	2.0 µg.
Ca (with chlorine)	30.0 mg.	Folic acid	2.0 µg.
NaNO$_3$	5.0 mg.	K$_2$HPO$_4$	0.1 mg.
NaSiO$_3$.9H$_2$O	1.0 mg.	Urea	0.1 mg.
P-II (metal mix)[1]	0.3 ml.	DL-alanine	5.0 mg.
Nitrilotriacetic acid	20.0 mg.	Na$_2$fumarate	5.0 mg.
B$_{12}$	1.0 µg.	(NH$_4$)$_2$SO$_4$	0.1 mg.
D-ribose	5.0 mg.	H$_2$O	100 ml.
Tris[1]	0.1 gm.	pH adjusted	7.6-7.8

[1] See J. A. McLaughlin and P. A. Zahl. Axenic zooxanthellae from various invertebrate hosts. Ann. New York Acad. Sci., 77(2): 55. 1959.

Pringsheim (1949) has recommended the following for the culturing of desmids (expressed in percentages of volume):

KNO_3	0.02	$CaCl_2.6H_2O$	0.00005
$(NH_4)_2HPO_4$	0.002	$FeCl_3$	0.00005
$MgSO_4.7H_2O$	0.001		

This solution is made up in a greater concentration and then diluted to give the desired percentages for culture. The pH of this and other solutions should be adjusted (usually to a slightly acid or neutral condition) by added KNO_3 (after titrating). (See Pringsheim, 1930, in reference to pH adjustment.)

Any one of the nutrient solutions mentioned above can be used with agar. After the agar mixture is sterilized, Petri plates are poured and allowed to cool. Then by use of bacteriological techniques (micropipette or sterile transfer loop or needle) the surface of the algar is streaked with inoculum from an alga culture (preferably from a unialgal culture). This permits the development of unicellular, colonial, or prostrate "creeping" algae in an isolated condition.

A medium suitable for *Volvox*, and probably for most volvocoids, is suggested by Moewus (1940): One kg. of garden soil in one liter of water is autoclaved (15 pounds pressure for one hour). After this cools the water is decanted. To 30 cc. of the soil-water one cc. of 5% KNO_3 and 300 cc. of distilled water are added to produce a culture liquid.

Unless one is located conveniently near the ocean the culture of marine algae usually requires the preparation of artificial sea water. Natural sea water for culture purposes, however, has been found unsuitable because some salts precipitate during sterilization in the autoclave. In general it has been found necessary to increase the amounts of certain salts in natural sea water to produce suitable media. Further, modifications of techniques, determined by experimentation, have been found necessary to make natural sea water successful as a culture medium. Provasoli, McLaughlin, and Droop (1957, p. 401) outline the enrichments and the techniques needed to prepare sea water properly.

In making up artificial sea water media it is necessary to include the proper salts and to have them in suitable proportions. Naturally, factors such as appropriate temperature, proper illumination, pH and oxygen-content must be considered. All of the above conditions are subject to variation in reference to the kind(s) of organisms to be cultured. Obviously the conditions under which respective species of algae exist in nature must be understood first.

An artificial sea water medium (ASP-2) reported by Provasoli, et al. (1957) and referred to (modified) by McLachlan (1959) for marine alga culture is designed to retard bacterial growth. The formula of the medium, found to be especially useful for phytoplankton, is as follows (in micromoles):

NaCl	410,000	$FeCl_3.6H_2O$	1.5
$MgSO_4.7H_2O$	24,000	H_3BO_3	185.0
$MgCl_2.6H_2O$	22,000	$MnCl_2.4H_2O$	7.0
$CaCl_2.2H_2O$	10,000	$ZnCl_2$	0.8
KNO_3	1,000	$CoCl_2.6H_2O$	0.02
K_2HPO_4	100	$CuCl_2.2H_2O$	0.0002
$Na_2SiO_3.9H_2O$	100	Sodium ethylenediamine-tetraacetate	30.0

These substances are all somewhat less in percentage than in normal sea water. McLachlan (1959) obtained some interesting results when he compared cultures of Dunaliella and Platymonas in artificial sea water with cultures in natural sea water, with and without the addition of soil extract. Other useful suggestions for the culturing of algae in sea water may be found in Foyn (1934); Hämmerling (1931, 1934); Schiller (1928).

Whereas the preparation of media for the successful culturing of algae, especially marine species, is often tedious and exacting, such studies are highly rewarding. Some of the objectives of culture investigations outlined above apply especially to marine algae, for in the sea there is an impressive number of genera for which life histories are still unknown or imperfectly so. Accordingly, the taxonomic position of many species is uncertain and the duplication of names for two different phases of the same plant await clarification. In addition to these aspects, the many details involving cytology of life cycle stages, and the anatomy of reproductive organs, pose a host of problems. Thus the student of the algae is offered ample opportunity to expand our information about these intriguing groups of ancient plants.

Bibliography

1. LITERATURE CITED

Ahmadjian, V., A guide for the identification of algae occurring as lichen symbionts. Bot. Not., 111(4): 632-644. 1958.

Akiyama, M., Aerial and terrestrial algae in San-in Region of Honshu, Japan. Bull. Shimane Univ., Nat. Sci., No. 10: 75-89. 1961.

Allen, C. E., Die Keimung der Zygote bei Coleochaete. Ber. d. Deutsch. Bot. Ges., 23: 285-292. 1905.

Blackman, F. F., The primitive algae and the flagellata. An account of modern work bearing on the evolution of the algae. Ann. Bot., 14: 647-688. 1900.

———, and A. G. Tansley, A revision of the classification of the green algae. New Phytol., 1: 17-24; 47-48; 67-72; 89-96; 114-120; 133-134; 163-168; 189-192; 213-220; 238-244. 1902.

Bliding, C., A critical survey of European taxa of Ulvales. Opera Bot., 8(3): 1-160. 1963.

Bourrelly, P., Phylogenie et systématique des Chrysophycées. 8th Congr. Inter. Bot., 1954: 117-118. 1954.

Braarud, T., K. R. Gaarder and J. Grotved, The phytoplankton of the North Sea and adjacent waters in May, 1948. Rapp. Cons. Explor. Mer, 1953: 133. 1953.

Bristol, B. Muriel, On the retention of vitality by algae from old stored soils. New Phytol., 18(3/4): 92-107. 1919.

Cameron, R. E., Communities of soil algae occurring in the Sonoran Desert in Arizona. Jour. Arizona Acad. Sci., 1(3): 85-88. 1960.

Chandler, D. C., Plankton entering the Huron River from Portage and Base Line Lakes, Michigan. Trans. Amer. Microsc. Soc., 58(1): 24-41. 1939.

Chapman, V. J., The Algae. New York: Macmillan Co. 1962.

Chu, S. P., See: 4. Physiology and Culturing.

Deflandre, G., Sur la structure des flagelles. Ann. Protistol., 4: 31-54. 1934.

Dawes, C. J., A light and electron microscope survey of algal cell walls. II. Chlorophyceae. Ohio Jour. Sci., 66: 317-326, 1966.

Drouet, F., Revision of the Classification of the Oscillatoriaceae. Monograph 15, The Academy of Natural Sciences of Philadelphia. 1968.

———, and W. A. Daily, Revision of the coccoid Myxophyceae. Butler Univ. Bot. Stud., 12: 1-218. 1956.

Durrell, L. W., Algae of Death Valley. Trans. Amer. Microsc. Soc., 81(3): 267-273. 1962.

Dutton, H. J., and C. Juday, Chromatic adaptation in relation to color and depth distribution of freshwater phytoplankton and large aquatic plants. Ecology, 25: 273-282. 1944.

Edmondson, W. T., G. W. Comita, and G. C. Anderson, Reproductive rate of copepods in nature and its relation to phytoplankton population. Ecology, 43(4): 625-634. 1962.

Feldmann, J., Recherches sur la végétation marine de la Méditerranée. La côte des Albères. Rev. Algol., 10: 1-339. 1937.

Foyn, B., See: 4. Physiology and Culturing.

Gayral, J., Monostroma Thuret, Alvaria Rupr. emend. Gayral, Ulvopsis Gayral (Chlorophycées, Ulotrichales): structure, reproduction cycles, position systématique. Rev. Gén. Bot., 72: 627-638. 1965.

Gerloff, G. C., G. P. Fitzgerald, and F. Skoog. See: 4. Physiology and Culturing.

Hämmerling, J., See: 4. Physiology and Culturing.

Hirose, H., and K. Yoshida, Genus Monostroma. A review of the life history of the genus Monostroma. Bull. Jap. Soc. Phycol., 12(1): 19-31. 1964.

Jacobs, W. P., Studies on cell differentiation: The role of auxin in algae, with particular reference to rhizoid-formation in Bryopsis. Biol. Bull., 101(3): 300-306. 1951.

Ketchum, B. H., Lois L. Lillick, and A. C. Redfield. The growth and optimum yield of algae in mass culture. Jour. Cell. Physiol., 33: 267-280. 1949.

Klebs, G., Flagellatenstudien. I. Zeit. Wiss. Zool., 55: 265-351. Ibid. II. Ibid., 55: 353-445. 1893.

Kreger, D. R., An X-ray study of Hydrodictyon cell walls. I. Kon. Neder. Akad. Wet. Biol. and Med. Soc., Ser. C, 63(5): 615-622. 1960.

McLachlan, J., See: 4, Physiology and Culturing.

McLachlan, J., and P. R. Gorham, See: 4. Physiology and Culturing.

McLaughlin, J. J. A., and P. A. Zahl, See: 4. Physiology and Culturing.

Moewus, F. See: 4, Physiology and Culturing.

Moore, G. T., and J. K. Karrer, A subterranean algal flora. Ann. Missouri Bot. Gard., 6: 281-307. 1919.

Nygaard, G., Hydrobiological studies on some Danish ponds and lakes. Part II. The quotient hypothesis and some new or little known phytoplankton organisms. Det. Kongl. Dansk. Vidensk. Selsk. Biol. Skr., 8(1): 1-293. 1949.

Okada, Y., A new classification of Conjugatae with special reference to desmids. Mem. Fac. Fish. Kagoshima Univ., 3(1): 165-192. 1953.

Palmer, C. M., The effect of pollution on river algae. Ann. N. Y. Acad. Sci., 108(2): 389-395. 1963.

Parker, B. C., Translocation in the giant kelp Macrocystis. Science, 140: 891-892. 1963.

Parker, B. C., and J. Bleck, A contribution to the ecology of Pelagophycus. Ann. Missouri Bot. Gard., 53: 1-16. 1966.

Pearsall, W. H., A suggestion as to factors influencing free-floating vegetation. Jour. Ecol., 9: 241-253. 1922.

Pringsheim, E. G., See: 4. Physiology and Culturing.

Provasoli, L., et al., See: 4. Physiology and Culturing.

Rabinowitch, E. I., Photosynthesis, In: The Scientific Reader, 1953.

Reazin, G. H., On the dark metabolism of a golden-brown alga, Ochromonas malhamensis. Amer. Jour. Bot., 41(9): 771-777. 1954.

Rodhe, W., See: 4. Physiology and Culturing.

Schiller, J., See: 4. Physiology and Culturing.

Shinke, N. and K. Ueda. A cytomorphological and cytochemical study of Oscillatoria princeps. Mem. Coll. Sci. Univ. Kyoto, Ser. B., 23(1): 101-104. 1956.

Schlichting, H. E., Viable species of algae and protozoa in the atmosphere. Lloydia, 24(2): 81-88. 1961.

Starr, R. C., A comparative study of *Chlorococcum* Meneghini and other spherical, zoospore-producing genera of the Chlorococcales. Univ. Indiana Pub. Sci. Ser., No. 20: 1-111. 1955.

Tiffany, L. H., A physiological study of growth and reproduction among certain green algae. Ohio Jour. Sci., 24(2): 65-98. 1924.

Tokida, J., Marine algae epiphytic on Laminariales plants. Bull. Fish. Hokkaido Univ., 11(3): 73-105. 1960.

Vlk, W., Über die Struktur der Heterokonten-geisseln. Bot. Centralbl., 48(1): 214-220. 1931.

Whitford, L. A., The current effect and growth of fresh-water algae. Trans. Amer. Microsc. Soc., 79(3): 302-309. 1960.

———, and G. J. Schumacher, Communities of algae in North Carolina streams and their seasonal relations. Hydrobiol., 22(1/2): 133-196. 1963.

———, Effect of current on respiration and mineral uptake in *Spirogyra* and *Oedogonium*. Ecology, 45(1): 168-170. 1964.

Wolken, J. J., and E. Shin, Photomotion in *Englena gracilis*. I. Photokinesis. II. Phototaxis. Jour. Protozool., 5(1): 39-46. 1958.

2. HANDBOOKS AND REPRESENTATIVE PAPERS DEALING WITH BIOLOGY AND ECOLOGY OF THE ALGAE

Aleem, A. A., Distribution and ecology of British marine diatoms. Jour. Ecol. 38: 75-106. 1950.

Boney, A. D., *A Biology of Marine Algae*. London: Hutchinson Educational Press, 1966.

Borzi, A., Studi Algologici. Fasc. 1: 1-112. Palermo, 1883.

———, Studi Algologici. Fasc. 2: 121-378. Palermo, 1895.

Chapman, V. J., *Seaweeds and Their Uses*. London: Methuen & Co., 1950.

———, Distribution of marine algae in relation to continental drift. 7th Pacific Sci. Congr., 5: 1-3 (Reprint). 1953.

———, Marine algal ecology. Bot. Rev., 23(5): 320-350. 1957.

———, *The Algae*. New York: Macmillan Co., 1962.

———, and C. B. Trevarthen, General schemes of classification in relation to marine coastal zonation. Jour. Ecol., 41(1): 198-204. 1953.

Dangeard, P., Traité d'Algologie. Encyclop. Biol. Vol. XI. Paris: Le Chevalier & Fils, 1933.

Fott, B., Algenkunde. Jena: Fischer, 1959.

Fritsch, F. E., *The Structure and Reproduction of the Algae*. Vols. I, II. Cambridge: Cambridge Univ. Press, 1935, 1945.

Godward, Maud B. E., *The Chromosomes of the Algae*. New York: St. Martin's Press, 1966.

Komarek, J., and H. Ettl, *Algologische Studien*. Prague, 1958.

Kylin, H., *Die Gattungen der Rhodophyceen*. Sweden: Lund, 1956.

Lewis, J. R., The mode of occurrence of the universal intertidal zones in Great Britain. Jour. Ecol., 43: 270-290. 1955.

Moore, H. B., *Marine Ecology*. New York: John Wiley & Sons, 1958.

Oppenheimer, C. H., ed., *Marine Biology II*. New York: Acad. Sci. New York, 1966.

Papenfuss, G. F., Progress and outstanding achievements in phycology during the past fifty years. Amer. Jour. Bot., 44(1): 74-81. 1957.

Round, F. E., *The Biology of the Algae*. New York: St. Martin's Press, 1965.

Scagel, R. F., The role of plants in relation to animals in the marine environment. Mar. Biol., Proc. 20th Ann. Biol. Colloq., 9-29. Corvallis, Oregon, 1959.

―――, Ecology of marine algae. A synthetic approach to some problems in marine algal ecology. In: Advances in Botany. 1961.

Schlichting, H., The role of waterfowl in the dispersal of algae. Trans. Amer. Microsc. Soc., 79(2): 160-166. 1960.

―――, Viable species of algae and protozoa in the atmosphere. Lloydia, 24(2): 81-88. 1961.

Southward, A. J., The zonation of plants and animals on rocky sea shores. Biol. Rev., 33: 137-177. 1958.

Smith, G. M., *Cryptogamic Botany*. Vol. I. New York: McGraw-Hill Co., 1955.

Stephenson, T. A. and Anne Stephenson, The universal features of zonation between tide marks on rocky coasts. Jour. Ecol., 37(2): 289-305. 1949.

―――, Life between tide-marks in North America. I. The Florida Keys. Jour. Ecol., 38: 354-402. 1950.

―――, Life between tide-marks in North America. III. A. Nova Scotia and Prince Edward Island: Description of Prince Edward Island: B. The geographical features of the region. Jour. Ecol., 42(1): 14-70. 1954.

Tiffany, L. H., *Algae. The Grass of Many Waters*. Springfield, Ill.: Charles C Thomas, 1938.

Ward, H. B., and G. C. Whipple, *Fresh-water Biology*, ed. W. T. Edmondson. New York: John Wiley & Sons, 1965.

Womersley, H. B. S., and S. J. Edmonds, Marine coastal zonation in southern Australia in relation to a general scheme of classification. Jour. Ecol., 40(1): 84-90. 1952.

―――, A general account of the intertidal ecology of South Australian coasts. Austral. Jour. Marine and Freshwater Res., 9(2): 217-260. 1958.

Young, E. G., and J. L. McLachlan, eds., *Proceedings of the Fifth International Seaweed Symposium, Halifax, Canada*. New York: Pergamon Press, 1966.

3. SOIL, SUBAERIAL, THERMAL, AND CRYOVEGETATION

Akiyama, M., Aerial and terrestrial algae in San-in region in Honshu, Japan. Bull. Shimane Univ. Nat. Sci., 10: 75-89. 1961.

————, Some soil algae from Japan. Bull. Shimane Univ. Nat. Sci., 13: 96-117. 1965.

Allison, F. E., L. R. Hoover, and H. I. Morris, Physiological studies with the Nitrogen-fixing alga, Nostoc muscorum. Bot. Gaz., 98: 433-463. 1937.

Anagnostides, K., Untersuchungen über die Cyanophyceen einiger Thermen in Griechenland. Inst. Syst. Bot. u. Pflanzengeogr. Univ. Thessalonikii. 1961.

Berggren, S., Alger fran Grönlands inlandsis. Oefv. Svensk. Vet. Akad. Förhandl., 1872: 293-296. 1872.

Bethel, E., Red snow in Colorado. Colorado Mag., 1: 159-162. 1924.

Bohlin, M., Snöalger fran Pite Lappmark. Bot. Notis., 1893: 42-46. 1893.

Bolyshev, N. N., The role of the algae in the formation of the soils. Vestn. moskov. Univ. Ser. Biol., Pochvoved., 16(2): 67-75. 1961.

Booth, W. E., Algae as pioneers in plant succession and their importance in erosion control. Ecology, 22(1): 38-46. 1941.

————, The thermal death point in soil inhabiting algae. Proc. Montana Acad. Sci., 5/6: 21-23, 1946.

Borzi, A., Alghe terrestri xerofile della Triolitania. Note biologiche. Boll. di stude i inform. del R. Giard. Bot. de Palermo, 1914: 91-130.

Brewer, W. H., On the presence of living species in hot and saline waters in California. Amer. Jour. Sci., II, 14:391-394. 1866.

Bristol-Roach, B. M., On the alga-flora of some desiccated English soils: an important factor in soil biology. Ann. Bot., 34: 35-80. 1920.

Brook, A. J., A note on the ecology of the terrestrial alga, Fritschiella tuberosa, in the Sudan. New Phytol., 55(1): 130-132. 1956.

Cain, Brother Joseph, Preliminary survey of the algal flora of soils of certain areas of Texas. Southwest Nat., 9: 166-170. 1964.

Cameron, R. E., Communities of soil algae occurring in the Sonoran Desert in Arizona. Jour. Arizona Acad. Sci., 1(3): 85-88. 1960.

Chantanachat, S., and H. C. Bold, Phycological studies. II. Some algae from acid soils. Univ. Texas Publ. No. 6218. 1962.

Chodat, F., and A. Chastain, Recherches sur le potential algologique des sols. Bull. Soc. Bot. France, 104(7/8): 427-451. 1957.

Chodat, R., Sur la neige verte du glacier d'Argentiere. Bull. Soc. Bot. Genève, 2(1): 294-298. 1909.

————, Sur les algues de la neige rouge dans le massif du Grand St.-Bernard. Bull. Soc. Bot. Genève, 13: 75-80. 1921.

Cholodny, N. G., Methods of direct observation of soil microflora. Microbiol. 4: 153-165 (Russian with English summary). 1935.

Conn, H. J., The Cholodnys technic for the microscopic study of the soil microflora. Centralbl. f. Bakter., 87 (2 Abt.): 229-233. 1932.

Copeland, J. J., Yellowstone thermal Myxophyceae. Ann. New York Acad. Sci., 36: 1-232. 1936.

Davis, B. M., The vegetation of the hot springs of Yellowstone Park. Science, 6: 145-157. 1897.

De, P. K., The role of blue-green algae in nitrogen fixation in rice-fields. Proc. Roy. Soc. London, B, 127: 121-139. 1939.

Deason, T. P., Phycological studies. I. Exploratory studies of Texas soil algae. Univ. Texas. Publ. No. 6022. 1960.

Durrell, L. W., Algae of Death Valley. Trans. Amer. Microsc. Soc., 81: 267-273. 1962.

————, Algae in tropical soils. Trans. Amer. Microsc. Soc., 83(1): 79-85. 1964.

———— and L. M. Shields, Characteristics of soil algae relating to crust formation. Trans. Amer. Microsc. Soc., 80(1): 73-79. 1961.

Engle, H. B., and J. E. McMurtrey, Effect of algae in relation to aeration, light and sources of phosphorus on growth of tobacco in solution cultures. Jour. Agr. Res., 60: 487-502. 1940.

Esmarch, F., Untersuchungen über die Verbreitung der Cyanophyceen auf und in verscheiden Böden. Hedwigia, 55: 224-273. 1914.

Forest, H. S., The soil algal community. Jour. Phyc., 1(4): 164-171. 1965.

Frémy, P., Algues du parc de l'établissement thermal de Bagnoles-de-l'Orne. Bull. Soc. Linn. Normandie, Sér. 9, 1: 197-212.

Fritsch, F. E., The role of algal growths in the colonization of new ground and in the determination of scenery. Geogr. Jour., 30: 531-548. 1907.

————, Freshwater algae collected in the South Orkneys. Jour. Linn. Soc. Bot. London, 40: 293-339 (Some snow algae). 1912.

————, The moisture-relations of terrestrial algae. I. Some general observations and experiments. Ann. Bot., 36: 1-20. 1922.

————, The terrestrial algae. Jour. Ecol., 10: 220-236. 1922.

————, and F. W. Haines, The moisture-relations of terrestrial algae. II. The changes during exposure to drought and treatment with hypertonic solutions. Ann. Bot., 38: 683-728. 1923.

Fukushima, H., Studies on the cryoalgae of Japan. 2. Cryoxenous algae from Japan. Nagaoa, 4: 31-35. 1954.

Fuller, W. H., R. E. Cameron, and N. Raica, Fixation of nitrogen in desert soils by algae. Trans. 7th Inter. Congr. Soil Sci. (Madison, Wis.), 2: 617-624. 1961.

Gain, L., La neige verte et la neige rouge des régions antarctiques. Resumé de l'étude de M. le Pr. N. Wille. Bull. Mus. Hist. Nat., 1911: 479-492. 1911.

————, La flore algologique des régions antarctiques et subantarctiques. Deuxième. Expéd. Ant. Franc., 1908-1910. Commandée par le Dr. J. Charcot, 1912: 1-218. 1912.

Gerdel, R. W., and F. Drouet, The cryoconite of the Thule area, Greenland. Trans. Amer. Microsc. Soc., 79: 256-272.

Gonzalves, E. A., The algal flora of the hot springs of Vajreswari near Bombay. Jour. Univ. Bombay, 16: 22-27. 1947.

Grintzesco, Jean, Contribution a l'étude de la microflore des sols de Roumaine. 14th Congr. Inter. Agric., Bucarest Actes, 4: 565-568. 1929.

Guarrera, S. A., Algas termales de la provincia de salta (Rep. Argentina). Bol. Soc. Argentina de Bot., 9: 199-215. 1961.

Györffy, I., Über den auf der nordlichen Seite der Belaër Kalkalpen in der "dolina Kepy" i. J. 1926 entdeckten grünen Schnee. Acta Soc. Bot. Poloniae, 4(2): 154-165. 1927.

Holm-Hansen, O., Isolation and culture of terrestrial and fresh-water algae of Antarctica. Phycol., 4(1): 43-51. 1964.

Holton, R. W., Isolation, growth, and respiration of a thermophilic blue-green alga. Amer. Jour. Bot., 49(1): 1-6. 1962.

Ikoma, Y., and S. Doi, The thermal algae of the hot springs in Tottori Prefecture. Bull. Jap. Soc. Phycol., 3: 36-41. 1955.

John, R. P., An ecological and taxonomic study of the algae of British soils. I. The distribution of the surface-growing algae. Annal. Bot., 6: 323-349. 1942.

Kadlubowska, J., The algae of artificial warm springs in Lodz and Pabiabice. Polsk. Arch. Hydrobiol., Warsaw, 8(21): 223-233. 1960.

Kobayashi, Y., and H. Fukushima, On the red and green snow newly found in Japan. I. Bot. Mag. Tokyo, 65 (765/766): 77-85: Ibid., II. Ibid., 65: 128-136: Ibid., III. Nagaoa, 2: 67-75. 1952.

————, and H. Fukushima, On the cryovegetation of the Ozegahara Moor and its environment. Sci. Res. Ozegahara Moor, 1954: 585-589. 1954.

Kol, E., Über die Kryovegetation der Hohen-Tatra. I. Folia Cryptogamica, 1: 613-621. 1928.

————, Kryobiologische Studien I. Verh. d. Inter. Ver. f. Theor. u. Angew. Limnol., 6: 275-285. 1933.

————, Biologie de la cryovegetation des Alpes valaisannes et du Massif du Mont-Blanc. Bull. Soc. Bot. Genève, Sér. 2, 25: 287-292. 1934.

————, Biological research on the snowfields and glaciers of Alaska, 1936. Explor. & Field Work, Smith. Inst., 1938: 69-74. 1938.

————, Some new snow algae from North America. Jour. Washington Acad. Sci., 28(2): 55-58. 1938.

————, Zur Schneevegetation Patagoniens. Ark. Bot., 29(A)(20): 1-3. 1939.

————, The green snow of Yellowstone National Park. Amer. Jour. Bot., 28: 185-191. 1941.

————, Vergleich der Kryovegetation der nördlichen und südlichen Hemisphäre. Arch. f. Hydrobiol., 40(3): 835-846. 1944.

————, Vergleich der Kryovegetation der Alpen und der Karpaten. Verh. Inter. Ver. f. Theor. u. Angew Limnol., 10: 243-246. 1949.

————, Blauer Schnee im Gebiet der Kleiner-Kukullo. Ann. Hist. Nat. Mus. Nat. Hungar., 6: 93-94. 1955.

————, Algological investigations in the ice-cave of the Sator Mountain. Bot. Közol., 47(1/2): 43-50. 1957.

————, The red snow of Greenland. I. West Greenland. Acta Bot. Sci. Hungar., 5(1/2): 57-70. 1959.

————, Cryobiological research in the Rocky Mountains, Arch. f. Hydrobiol., 60(3): 278-285. 1964.

————, and F. Chodat, Quelques algues nouvelles des sols et de la neige du Parc National Suisse, Engadine. Bull. Soc. Bot. Genève, Sér. 2, 25: 250-263. 1934.

Lanciani, G. D., and J. M. Kingsbury, Soil algae of forty ponds under construction at Ithaca, New York. Rhodora, 67: 242-254. 1965.

Lowe, C. W., and A. V. Moyse, An investigation of some Manitoba soils for the presence of soil algae. Trans. Roy. Soc. Canada, 28: 119-152. 1934.

Lund, J. W. G., Observations on soil algae. New Phytol., 44: 196-219; Ibid., 45: 56-110. 1945.

Mifune, M., H. Hirose, and K. Tsumura, The thermal algae in certain strong radioactive springs in Japan. Part I. The thermal algae of Ikeda Mineral Springs in Shimane Prefecture. Onsen Kagaku, 10(3): 60-64. 1959.

————, Y. Emoto, and H. Hirose, Studies on the thermal flora in Japan. XXXIII, The thermal algae in certain strongly radioactive springs in Japan. II. Onsen Kagaku, 16(3/4): 129-135. 1966.

Moore, G. T., and N. Carter, Further studies on the subterranean algal flora of the Missouri Botanical Garden. Ann. Missouri Bot. Gard., 13: 101-140. 1926.

————, and J. L. Karrer, A subterranean algal flora. Ann. Missouri Bot. Gard., 6: 281-307. 1919.

Mori, M., On the desmids of the rice-fields in the catchment area of Kuma River. Jap. Jour. Ecol., 13(3): 104-108.

Musaev, K. Yu., (Algae of irrigated lands and their significance for soil fertility). Tashkent, Inst. Bot. Akad. Nauk Uzbek, SSR (Russian). 1960.

Negoro, K. I., The diatom flora of the Nasu Hot Springs. Bot. Mag. Tokyo, 54: 63-65. 1940.

Okada, Y., On the Cyanophyceae in the hot springs of Sukayu, Mt. Hakkoda. Ecol. Rev., 5: 259-266. 1939.

Parker, B. C., and B. L. Turner, "Operational niches" and "community-interaction values" as determined from in vitro studies of some algae. Evolution, 15(2): 228-238. 1961.

————, and H. C. Bold, Biotic relationships between soil algae and other microorganisms. Amer. Jour. Bot., 48(2): 185-197. 1961.

————, H. C. Bold, and T. R. Deason, Facultative heterotrophy in some Chlorococcacean algae. Science, 133: 761-763. 1961.

Paryski, W. H., Coloured snow in the Tatra Mountains. Acta Soc. Bot. Polon., 21: 217-229. 1951.

Petersen, J. B., Studies on the biology and taxonomy of soil algae. Dansk. Bot. Ark., 8(9): 1-180. 1935.

Prát, S., Contribution to the physiology of the vegetation of thermal and mineral waters. Rapp. 8th Inter. Bot. Congr., Paris, 1954. Sec. 17. 1954.

————, and Sh. Kubin, Assimilation and respiration of thermophilic blue-green algae. Plant Physiol., 3(6): (mimeographed translation). 1956.

Quispel, A., A new method for the investigation of aerial and soil algae. Proc. K. Acad. Wetensch. Amsterdam, 41: 395-402. 1938.

Schwabe, G. H., Lagernildungen hormogonaler Blaualgen in thermalen und anderen extremen Biotopen. Verh. Inter. Ver. Limnol., 15(2): 772-781. 1964.

Shields, L. M., and L. W. Durrell, Algae in relation to soil fertility. Bot. Rev., 1964: 92-128. 1964.

Shtina, E. A., The algal communities of the main soil types of the USSR and their significance. Bot. Zhur. (Moskova), 44(8): 1062-1074. 1959.

———, Zonality in the distribution of soil algae communities. Trans. 7th Inter. Congr. Soil Sci., (Madison, Wis.), 2: 630-634.

Sieminska, J., Red snow below the Szpiglasowa Pass into the High Tatra. Acta Soc. Bot. Polon., 21: 231-233.

Singh, L. P., The algal flora of Vindhyan formation of the Mirzapur district, U. P. Proc. Indian Acad. Sci., Sec. B, 49(1): 66-73. 1959.

Skinner, C. E., Isolation in pure culture of green algae from soil by a simple technique. Plant Physiol., 7: 533-537. 1932.

Smith, F. B., Occurrence and distribution of algae in soils. Proc. Florida Acad. Sci., 7: 44-49. 1944.

Soriano, S., Método de observación directa de la microflora y microfauna del suelo en carmara humeda. Rev. Argentina Agron., 1: 39-48. 1934.

Starmach, K., and B. Kawecka, The yellowish-green snow in the valley Za Mnichem in the Tatra Mountains. Polska Akad. Nauk, Limnol. Conv. in Pol., 1965, No. 11: 75-80. 1965.

Stein, Janet R., and R. C. Brooke, Red snow from Mt. Seymour, British Columbia. Canad. Jour. Bot., 42: 1183-1188. 1964.

Stokes, J., The role of algae in the nitrogen cycle of the soil. Soil Sci., 49: 265-275. 1940.

Strom, K. M., Some algae from hot springs in Spitzbergen. Bot. Not., 1921: 17-21. 1921.

———, Snow algae (Cryoplankton) from the Sarek Mountains. Naturw. Unter. Sarekgebirges in Schwedisch-Lappland, Bot., 3(5): 522-524. 1923.

Suchlandt, O., Dinoflagellaten als Erreger von roten Schnee. Ber. d. Deutsch. Bot. Ges., 34: 242-246. 1916.

Taylor, Wm. R., The alpine algal vegetation of the mountains of British Columbia. Proc. Acad. Nat. Sci., Philadelphia, 80: 45-114. 1928.

Tchan, Y. T., L. N. Balaam, and F. Draette, Study of soil algae. IV. Estimation of the nutrient status of soil using an algal growth method with special reference to nitrogen and phosphorus. Plant and Soil, 14(2): 147-158. 1961.

Thomas, J., and E. A. Gonzalves, Thermal algae of western India. I. Algae of the hot springs at Akoli and Ganeshpuri. Hydrobiol., 25(3/4): 330-351. 1965.

———, Thermal algae of western India. II. Algae of the hot springs at Pali. Hydrobiol., 25(3/4): 340-351. 1965.

———, Thermal algae of western India. III-VI. Hydrobiol., 26(1/2): 21-71. 1965.

Treub, M., Notice sur la nouvelle flora de Krakatau. Ann. Jard. Bot. Buiten-zorg, 7: 221-223. 1888.

Vouk., V., Die Probleme der Biologie der Thermen. Inter. Rev. Hydrobiol. u. Hydrogr., 11: 89-99. 1923.

Vouk, V., On the origin of the thermal flora. Acta Bot. Inst. Bot. Univ. Zagreb, 4: 59-63. 1929.

Wailes, G. H., Notes on the flora and fauna of snow and ice in northwest America. Mus. & Art Notes, Vancouver City Mus., 8(Suppl. 1): 1-4. 1935.

West, G. S., On some algae from hot springs. Jour. Bot., 1902: 241-248. 1902.

Wille, N., Sur quelques algues des neiges antarctiques. Doc. Sci. Deuxième Exped. Antarct. Française, 1908-1910: 187-191. 1912.

Wilson, D., and H. S. Forest, An exploratory study on soil algae. Ecology, 38(2): 309-313. 1957.

Winter G., (The assimilation of nitrogen from the air by endophytic blue algae). Reitr. Biol. Pflanzen., 23: 295-335 (German). 1935.

Yoneda, Y., Studies on the thermal algae of Hokkaido. I. Acta Phytotax. & Geobot., Kyoto, 8: 101-107. 1939.

————, Studies on the thermal algae of Hokkaido. 3. Acta Phytotax. & Geobot., Kyoto, 9: 192-202. 1940.

4. PHYSIOLOGY AND CULTURING OF ALGAE ANTIBIOTICS, TOXINS, NITROGEN-FIXATION

Anonymous, Culture of algae in the laboratory. Ward's Nat. Sci. Estab., 1961. Mimeographed.

Accorinti, J., Inhibidores producidos en cultivos masivos. Trev. Mus. Argentina Cien. Nat., Buenos Aires, 2(6): 363-401. 1962.

————, Efectos de los indolacetico y giberelico sobre el crecimiento de "Scenedesmus obliquus." Univ. Nac. de La Plata, Rev. del Museo de La Plata, 9: 101-124. 1962.

Aleev, B. S., (On the nature of the organic substances given off by algae.) Biokhimia, 1: 94-100 (Russian with English summary). 1936.

Aleshina, E. S., (The obtaining of bacteriologically pure cultures of green flagellated halophilic algae.) Vestn. Moskov. Univ., Ser. Biol., Pechvoved., 16(4): 62-66 (Russian). 1961.

Algeus, S., Studies on the cultivation of algae in artificial light. Physiol. Plant., 4(4): 742-753. 1951.

Allen, E. J. and E. W. Nelson, On the artificial culture of marine plankton organisms. Jour. Mar. Biol. Assoc. U. K., 8: 421-474. 1910.

Allen, M. B., The cultivation of the Myxophyceae. Arch. f. Mikrobiol., 17: 34-53. 1952.

Allison, F. E., and S. R. Hoover, Conditions which favour nitrogen fixation by a blue-green alga. 34d Inter. Congr. Soil Sci., Oxford, 1935: 145-147. 1935.

————, S. R. Hoover, and H. J. Morris. Physiological studies with the nitrogen-fixing alga, Nostoc muscorum. Bot. Gaz., 98: 433-463. 1937.

Artari, A., Ueber die Bildung des Chlorophylls durch grüne Algen. Ber. d. Deutsch. Bot. Ges., 20: 201-207. 1902.

Bach, M. K., Mass culture of Euglena gracilis. Jour. Protozool., 7(1): 50-52. 1960.

Bachrach, E. and M. Lefèvre, Recherches sur la culture des Péridiniens. Rev. Algol., 5: 55-59. 1930.

Barkar, H. A., The culture and physiology of marine dinoflagellates. Arch. Ber. d. f. Mikro-biol., 6: 157-181. 1935.

Biebl, R. Protoplasmatische Oekologie der Meeresalgen. Deutsch. Bot. Ges., 57: (78)-(90). 1939.

Boalch, G. T., Studies on Ectocarpus in culture. I. Introduction and methods of obtaining uni-algal and bacteria-free cultures. Jour. Mar. Biol. Assoc., U.K., 41(2): 279-286; II. Growth and nutrition of a bacteria-free culture. Ibid., 41(2): 287-304. 1961.

Bold, H. C., Life history and cell structure of Chlorococcum infusionum. Bull. Torr. Bot. Club, 57: 577-604. 1931.

————, The cultivation of algae. Bot. Rev., 8: 69-138. 1942.

Braarud, T., Cultivation of marine organisms as a means of understanding environmental influences on populations. In: M. Sears, ed., Oceanography, pp. 271-289. 1961.

Bristol-Roach, B. M., Zuchtung von Bodenalgen in Reinkultur. In: S. A. Waksman. Methoden der mikrobiologischen Bodenforschung. Abder. Handb. Biol. Arb. Method., Abt. XI, Teil 3, Bd. 1: 815-821. 1927.

Brown, R. M., and H. W. Bischoff, A new and useful method for obtaining axenic cultures of algae. Phyc. News Bull., 15(4): 43-44. 1962.

Brunel, J., G. W. Prescott, and L. H. Tiffany, eds., The Culturing of Algae: A Symposium. Yellow Springs, Ohio: Antioch Press, 1950.

Burlew, J. S., ed., Algal Culture from Laboratory to Pilot Plant. Washington, D. C.: Carnegie Inst., 1953.

Chesnokov, V. A., V. V. Pinevich, N. N. Verzilin, and A. M. Stepanova, Some results of mass culture of unicellular algae. Vestn. Leningrad Univ., 15(9): 29-36. (Transl.). 1960.

Chodat, R., Monographies d'algues en culture pure. Matér. pour la Flore Crypt. Suisse, 4(2): 1-266. 1913.

Chu, S. P., The influence of the mineral composition of the medium on the growth of planktonic algae. I. Methods and culture media. Jour. Ecol., 30: 284-325. 1942.

Colinvaux, L. H., K. M. Wilbur, and N. Watabe, Tropical marine algae; growth in laboratory culture. Jour. Phyc., 1(2): 69-78. 1965.

Cooke, Paul M., Chemical engineering problems in large scale culture of algae. Indust. & Eng. Chem., 43(10): 2385-2389. 1951.

De, P. K., The role of blue-green algae in nitrogen-fixation in rice fields. Proc. Roy. Soc. London, B, 127: 121-139. 1939.

Droop, M. R., A note on the isolation of small marine algae and flagellates for pure cultures. Jour. Mar. Biol. Assoc., U. K., 33(2): 511-514. 1954.

————, Some chemical considerations in the design of synthetic culture media for marine algae. Bot. Mar., 2(3/4): 231-246. 1961.

Eyster, C., The micro-element nutrition of Nostoc muscorum. Ohio Jour. Sci., 58(1): 25-33. 1958.

Fogg, G. E., The Metabolism of Algae. London: Methuen & Co.

————, Algal Cultures and Phytoplankton Ecology. Madison: Univ. of Wisconsin Press. 1965.

————, and G. T. Boalch, Extracellular products in pure culture of a brown alga. Nature, 181: 789. 1958.

Foyn, B., Lebenszyklus, Cytologie und Sexualität der Chlorophycee. Arch. f. Protistenk., 83: 1-56. 1934.

Gayral, P., Algues d'eau douce du Maroc en cultures purés. Bull. Soc. Phys. Maroc, 37: 83-87. 1957.

Gerloff, G. C., G. P. Fitzgerald, and F. Skoog, The isolation, purification and culture of blue-green algae. Amer. Jour. Bot., 37: 216-218. 1950.

Grintzesco, J., Recherches expérimentales sur la morphologie et la physiologie de Scenedesmus acutus Meyen. Publ. Univ. Genève Lab. Bot., Sér. 6, 1: 217-288. 1902.

Gross, I., Beiträge zur Entwicklungsgechichte der Protophyten. VII. Entwicklungsgechichte, Phasenwechsel und Sexualität bei der Gattung Ulothrix. Arch. f. Protistenk., 73: 206-234. 1931.

Gross, J. A., T. J. Jahn, and E. Bernstein, The effect of antihistamines on the pigments of green protista. Jour. Protozool., 2(2): 71-75. 1955.

Hall, R. P., Certain culture reactions of several species of Euglenidae. Trans. Amer. Microsc. Soc., 56: 285-287. 1937.

Haemmerling, J., Entwicklung und Formbildungsvermögen von Acetabularia mediterranea. Biol. Zentralbl., 51: 633-647. 1931.

————, Über die Geschlechtsverhältnisse von Acetabularia mediterranea und Acetabularia Wettsteinii. Arch. f. Protistenk., 83: 57-97. 1934.

Harries, R., An investigation by cultural methods of some of the factors influencing the development of the gametophyte and the early stages of the sporophyte of Laminaria digitata, L. saccharina and L. cloustoni. Ann. Bot., 46: 893-928. 1932.

Hoffman, G. A., Contribution a l'étude des algues unicellulaires en culture pure. Bull. Soc. Bot. Genève, 3: 73-104. 1911.

Hollenberg, G. T., Culture studies on marine algae. Amer. Jour. Bot., 45: 653-656. 1958.

Holm-Hansen, O., G. C. Gerloff, and F. Skoog, Cobalt as an essential element for blue-green algae. Physiol. Plant., 7: 665-675. 1954.

Hopkins, E. F., and F. B. Wann, Relation of hydrogen ion concentration to growth of Chlorella and to the availability of iron. Bot. Gaz., 81: 353-376. 1926.

————, Iron requirement for Chlorella. Bot. Gaz., 84: 407-427. 1927.

Hoyt, W. D., Some toxic and antitoxic effects in cultures of Spirogyra. Bot.

Contr. Johns Hopkins Univ. No. 29, Bull. Torr. Bot. Club, 40: 333-360. 1913.

Hutner, S. H., L. Provasoli, et al., Assay of anti-pernicious anemia factor with *Euglena*. Proc. Soc. Exper., Biol. & Med., 70: 118-120. 1949.

Ketchum, B. M., L. Lillick, and A. C. Redfield, The growth and optimum yields of unicellular algae in mass culture. Jour. Cell. Comp. Physiol., 33: 267-280. 1949.

————, Some physical and chemical characteristics of algae growth in mass culture. Jour. Cell. and Comp. Physiol., 33(3): 281-300. 1949.

Khan, S., Culture of algae in the rice-fields of Kashmir. Biologia, 3(1): 29-43. 1957.

Kniep, H., *Die Sexualität der niederen Pflanzen*. Jena. 1928.

Komarek, J., Utility of synchronized algal cultures in experimental taxonomy. Plant and Cell Physiol., 5: 385-391. 1964.

Krauss, R. W., Nutrient supply for large-scale algal cultures. Sci. Month., 80(1): 21-28. 1955.

Kufferath, H., Note sur la forme des colonies de Diatomées et autres algues cultivées sur milieu nutritif mineral gelose. Ann. Biol. Lac., 9: 12-24. 1919.

————, Recherches physiologiques sur les algues vertes cultivés en culture pure. Bull. Soc. Roy. Bot. Belg., 54: 49-77. 1921.

————, La culture des algues. Rev. Algol., 4: 127-346. 1928.

Lefèvre, M., Recherches sur la biologie et la systématique de quelques algues obtenues en culture. Rev. Algol., 6(34): 313-338. 1932.

————, M. Nesbit, and H. Jakob, Action des substances excretées en culture par certaines algues sur le metabolisme d'autres espèces d'algues. Trav. Assoc. Inter. Limnol. Théor. Appl. Congr. de Suisse, 1948-1949, 10: 259-264. 1949.

Lewin, R. A., The isolation of algae. Rev. Algol., 4(3): 170-180. 1959.

————, (ed.), *Physiology and Biochemistry of Algae*. New York: Academic Press, 1962.

Loeblich, A. R., III, Aspects of the physiology and biochemistry of the Pyrrhophyta. Phykos, 5(1/2): 216-255. 1966 (1967).

McLachlan, J., The growth of unicellular algae in artificial and enriched sea water media. Canad. Jour. Microbiol., 5(9): 9-15. 1959.

————, Some considerations of the growth of marine algae on artificial media. Canad. Jour. Microbiol., 10: 769-782. 1964.

————, and P. R. Gorham, Growth of *Microcystis aeruginosa* Kuetz. in a precipitate-free medium buffered with tris. Canad. Jour. Microbiol., 7: 869-882. 1961.

————, and C. S. Yentsch, Observations on the growth of *Dunaliella euchlora* in culture. Biol. Bull., 116(3): 461-471. 1959.

McLaughlin, J. J. A., Chrysomonads: nutrition and toxigenesis in *Prymnesium parvum*, with notes on *Isochrysis galbana* and *Monochrysis lutheri*. Jour. Protozool., 5(1): 75-81. 1958.

————, and P. A. Zahl, Axenic zooxanthellae from various invertebrate hosts Ann. New York Acad. Sci., 77(2): 55-72. 1959.

————, P. A. Zahl, A. Nowak, J. Marchisotto, and J. Praeger. Mass cultivation of some phytoplanktons. Ann. New York Acad. Sci., 90(3): 856-865. 1960.

Moewus, F., Die Analyse von 42 erblichen Eigenschaften der *Chlamydomonas eugametos* Gruppe I. Ibid. Gruppe II. Zeit. f. Induk. Abst. u. Vereb., 78: 418-462, 463-500. 1940.

Myers, J., The growth of *Chlorella pyrenoidosa* under various culture conditions. Plant Physiol., 19: 579-589. 1944.

Myers, J., and L. B. Clark, Culture conditions and the development of the photosynthetic mechanism. II. An apparatus for the continuous culture of *Chlorella*. Jour. Gen. Physiol., 28: 103-112. 1944.

————, J. N. Phillips, and J. P. Graham, On the mass culture of algae. Plant Physiol., 26: 539-548. 1951.

Newell, J. T., Notes on mass growing of algae in pure culture. Trans. Amer. Microsc. Soc., 78(2): 237-240. 1959.

Nieuwland, J. A., Hints on collecting and growing algae. Midland Nat., 1(4): 85-97. 1909.

Noll, F., Ueber die Kultur von Meeresalgen in Aquarien. Flora, 75: 281-301. 1892.

Petersen, J. B., Studies on the biology and taxonomy of soil algae. Dansk Bot. Arkiv., 8(9): 1-180. 1935.

Prát, Sylvestr., The culture of calcareous Cyanophyceae. Stud. Physiol. Lab. Charles Univ., 3: 86-88. 1925.

Pringsheim, E. G., Die Kultur der Desmidiaceen. Ber. d. Deutsch. Bot. Ges., 26: 482-485. 1918.

————, Die Kultur von *Micrasterias* und *Volvox*. Arch. f. Protistenk., 72: 1-48. 1930.

————, *Pure Cultures of Algae*. Cambridge: Cambridge Univ. Press, 1949.

Provasoli, L., S. H. Hutner, and A. Schatz, Streptomycin-induced chlorophyll-less-races of *Euglena*. Proc. Soc. Exper. Biol. & Med., 69: 279-282. 1948.

————, J. J. A. McLaughlin, and M. R. Droop, The development of artificial media for marine algae. Arch. Mikrobiol., 25: 392-428. 1957.

Reynolds, N., Methods for culturing epiphytic algae. New Phytol., 49(2): 155-162. 1950.

Rich, L. G., and W. M. Ingram, A balanced ecological system for space travel. Journ. Sanit. Eng. Div., SA-6: 87-94. 1959.

Rodhe, W., Environmental requirements of fresh-water algae. Symbol. Bot. Upsal., 10(1): 1-149. 1948.

Sauvageau, C., Sur la culture d'une algue phéosporée épiphyte, *Strepsithalia Liagorae* Sauv. Compt. Rend. Acad. Sci., Paris, 180: 1464-1467. 1925.

Schiller, J., Über Kultur und Methodik beim Studium Meerespflanzen. Abd. Handb. d. Biol. Arbeit, Abt. 9, 5(2): 181-309. 1928.

Schoenborn, H. W., Nutritional requirements and the effect of pH on growth of *Euglena viridis* in pure culture. Trans. Amer. Microsc. Soc., 69(3): 217-221. 1950.

Schomer, H. A., and C. Juday, Photosynthesis of algae at different depths in some lakes of northeastern Wisconsin. Trans. Wis. Acad. Sci., 29: 173-193. 1935.

Schreiber, E., Zur Kenntnis der Physiologie und Sexualität höherer Volvocales. Zeit. f. Bot., 17: 336-376. 1925.

————, Die Reinkultur von marinem Phytoplankton und deren Bedeutung für die Erforschung der Produktionsfähigkeit des Meereswassers. Wiss. Meeres. Abt. Helgoland, 16(10): 1-34. 1927.

Shrift, A., Sulphur-selenium antagonism. I. Antimetabolite action of selenate on the growth of *Chlorella vulgaris*. Amer. Jour. Bot., 41(3): 223-230. 1954.

Skinner, C. E., Isolation in pure culture of green algae from soil by a simple technique. Plant Physiol., 7: 533-537. 1932.

Sorokin, C., and R. W. Krauss, Maximum growth rates of *Chlorella* in steady-state and in synchronized cultures. Proc. Nat. Acad. Sci., 45(12): 1740-1744. 1959.

Sparling, S. R., A report on the culture of some species of *Halosaccion, Rhodymenia* and *Fauchea*. Amer. Jour. Bot., 48(6): 493-499. 1961.

Spencer, C. P., On the use of antibiotics for isolating bacteria-free cultures of marine phytoplankton organisms. Jour. Mar. Biol. Assoc., U. K., 31: 97-106. 1952.

————, Studies on the culture of a marine diatom. Jour. Mar. Biol. Assoc., U. K., 33: 265-290. 1954.

Starr, R. C., A method of effecting zygospore germination in certain Chlorophyceae. Proc. Nat. Acad. Sci., 35: 453-456. 1949.

————, Isolation of sexual strains of placoderm desmids. Bull. Torr. Bot. Club, 82(4): 261-265. 1955.

Thomas, E. A., Über eine blasenbildende Krankeit von kultivierten grünen Fadenalgen (*Cladophora* und *Rhizoclonium*). Viertel. Naturf. Ges. Zurich, 106(2): 277-288. 1961.

Tiffany, L. H., A physiological study of growth and reproduction. Ohio Jour. Sci., 24: 65-98. 1924.

Trainor, F. R., The morphology of a *Scenedesmus* in pure and contaminated culture. Bull. Torr. Bot. Club, 90(2): 137-138. 1963.

Trelease, S. F. and M. E. Selsam, Influence of calcium and magnesium on the growth of *Chlorella*. Amer. Jour. Bot., 26: 339-341. 1939.

Valare, M. de, Note on the difference in growth of *Enteromorpha* species in various culture media. Kgl. Fysiogr. Sallsk Lund Förhandl., 10: 52-58. 1940.

Wann, F. B., The fixation of nitrogen by green plants. Amer. Jour. Bot., 8: 1-29. 1921.

Wetherell, D. F., Culture of fresh water algae in enriched natural sea water. Physiol. Plant, 14(1): 1-6. 1961.

Wiedling, S., Die Kultur der Diatomeen. Mikrokos., 36(6/7): 80-83. 1943.

Williams, A. E. and R. Burris, Nitrogen-fixation by blue-green algae and their nitrogenous composition. Amer. Jour. Bot., 39(5): 340-342. 1943.

Yendo, K., On the cultivation of seaweeds, with special accounts of their ecology. Roy. Dublin Soc. Econ. Proc., 2: 105-122. 1914.

5. SELECTED REFERENCES

Bornet, E. and Ch. Flahault, Revision des Nostocacées hétérocystées contenues dans les principaux herbiers de France. Ann. Sci. Nat. Bot., 3(Sér. 7): 323-381. Ibid., Part II., Ibid., 4(Sér. 7): 343-373; Ibid., Part III, Ibid., 5(Sér. 7): 51-129; Ibid., Part IV., Ibid., 7 (Ser. 7): 177-262. 1886, 1887.

Bourrelly, P., Les Algues d'Eau Douce. Paris: Boubée & Cie., 1966.

Chapman, V. J., The Algae. New York: Macmillan Co., 1962.

Collins, F. S., The green algae of North America. Tufts College Studies, Sci. Ser., 2: 79-480. 1909.

Copeland, J., Yellowstone Thermal Myxophyceae. Ann. New York Acad. Sci., 36: 1-232. 1936.

Dawson, E. Yale, How To Know the Seaweeds. Dubuque, Iowa: Brown Co., 1956.

Desikachary, T. V., Cyanophyta. Bombay, 1959.

Eddy, Samuel, The fresh-water armored or thecate dinoflagellates. Trans. Amer. Microsc. Soc., 49: 277-321. 1930.

Feldmann, J., Les algues marines de cote des Albères. I-III. Cyanophycées, Chlorophycées, Phaeophycées. Rev. Algol., 9: 141-335. 1937.

————, and G. Feldmann, Additions à la flore des algues marines de l'Algérie. IV. Bull. Soc. Hist. Nat. Afr. N., 38: 80-91. 1947.

Frémy, P., Les Myxophycées de l'Afrique équatoriale française. Caen. 1930.

Fritsch, F. E., The Structure and Reproduction of the Algae. Vols. I, II. New York: Macmillan Co., 1935, 1945.

Geitler, L., Cyanophyceae. Rabenhorst's Kryptogamen-Flora. Bd. XIV. Leipzig, 1932.

Gemeinhart, K., Oedogoniales. Rabenhorst's Kryptogamen-Flora. Bd. XII. Leipzig, 1939.

Gojdics, Mary, The Genus Euglena. Madison: Univ. of Wisconsin Press, 1953.

Gomont, M., Monographie des Oscillariées (Nostocacées homocystées). Paris, 1893.

Hansgirg, A., Prodromus der Algenflora von Böhmen. Erster und Zweiter Theils, 1886, 1892 (1893).

Hirn, K. E., Monographie und Iconographie der Oedogoniaceen. Acta Soc. Sci. Fenn., 27: 1-395. 1900.

Hoyt, W. D., Marine algae of Beaufort, North Carolina and adjacent regions. U. S. Bur. Fish. Bull., 36: 367-556. 1917.

Huber-Pestalozzi, G., Die Binnengewässer. Bd. XVI, 2 Teil. Chrysophyceen. Farblose Flagellaten Heterokonten. Bd. XVI, Teil 3. Cryptophyceen. Chlormonadinee, Peridineen; Bd. XVI, Teil 4. Euglenophyceen; Bd. XVI, Teil 5. Chlorophyceae (Grunalgen) Ordnung Volvocales. 1941, 1950, 1955, 1961.

Islam, Nurul, A Revision of the Genus Stigeoclonium. Stuttgart: Cramer, 1963.

Krieger, W., Die Desmidiaceen. Rabenhorst's Kryptogamen-Flora. Bd. XIII. Leipzig, 1937.

Kuetzing, F. T., Species Algarum. Leipzig, 1849.

Kylin, H., Die Gattungen der Rhodophyceen. Sweden: Lund, 1956.

Loeblich, A. R., and A. R. Loeblich, III, Index to the genera, subgenera, and sections of the Pyrrhophyta. Stud. Trop. Oceanogr., Univ. Miami, No. 3. 94 pp. 1966.

Okamura, K., Icones of Japanese algae. Tokyo, 1909.

Pascher, A. (Aut. et Ed.), Die Süsswasserflora Deutschlands, Oesterreichs und der Schweiz. Heft 1-12. Jena: Fischer, 1913-1925.

————, Heterokonten. Rabenhorst's Kryptogamen-Flora. Bd. XI. Leipzig, 1939.

Patrick, Ruth and C. W. Reimer. The Diatoms of the United States. Vol. I. Philadelphia, 1966.

Prescott, G. W., Algae of the Western Great Lakes Area. Dubuque, Iowa: Brown Co., 1962.

————, How To Know the Fresh-Water Algae. Dubuque, Iowa: Brown Co., 1964.

Printz, H., Die Chaetophoralen der Binnengewässer (eine systematische Übersicht). Den Haag: Junk, 1964.

Ramanathan, K. R., Ulotrichales. New Delhi, India: Indian Council Agric. Res., 1964.

Schiller, J., Flagellatae. Dinoflagellatae. Rabenhorst's Kryptogamen-Flora. Bd. X. Teil 1, 2. Leipzig, 1933.

Setchell, W. A., and N. L. Gardner. Algae of Northwestern America. Univ. Calif. Publ. Bot., 1: 165-418. 1903.

Sirodot, S., Les Batrachospermes. Organisation, Fonctions, Développement, Classification. Paris, 1884.

Smith, G. M., ed., Manual of Phycology. Waltham, Mass.: Chronica Botanica, 1951.

————, Phytoplankton of the inland lake of Wisconsin. Part I. Myxophyceae, Phaeophyceae, Heterokontae, and Chlorophyceae exclusive of the Desmidiaceae. Wis. Geol. and Nat. Hist. Surv., 57: 1-243; Ibid. Part II. Desmidiaceae., Ibid., 57-II): 1-227. 1920, 1924.

————, The Fresh-Water Algae of the United States. New York: McGraw-Hill Co., 1950.

————, Marine Algae of the Monterey Peninsula. Stanford, Calif.: Stanford Univ. Press, 1964.

Söderströn, J., Studies in Cladophora. Göteborg, 1963.

Taylor, Wm. R., Marine Algae of the Northeastern Coast of North America. Ann Arbor: Univ. of Michigan Press, 1957.

Tiffany, L. H., Oedogoniales. Oedogoniaceae. North American Flora, 11(1): 1-102. 1937.

————, and M. E. Britton. The Algae of Illinois. Chicago, Ill.: Univ. of Chicago Press, 1952.

Transeau, E. N., The Zygnemataceae. Columbus: Ohio State Univ. Press, 1951.

Van den Hoek, C., A Revision of the European Species of Cladophora. Leiden: Brill, 1963.

Venkataraman, G. S., Vaucheriaceae. New Delhi, India: Indian Council Agri. Res. 1951.

Ward, H. B., and G. C. Whipple. Freshwater Biology, ed. W. T. Edmondson. New York: John Wiley and Sons, 1959.

West, W., G. S. West, and Nellie Carter. Monograph of the British Desmidiaceae. Vols. I-V. London: Ray Society. 1904-1924.

Wood, R. D. and K. Imahori. A Revision of the Characeae. Vols. I, II. Weinheim: J. Cramer. 1965.

Glossary

absciss   to cut off a part of an organ by constriction or by a wall; to cast away.

acronematic   type of flagellum which bears a flimmer or fine fibril at the tip.

adeloparasite   parasitism between two closely related organisms.

akaryotic   without nuclei.

akinete   a thick-walled, reproductive spore formed by the modification of a vegetative cell in which food has been concentrated.

alloparasitism   parasitism between two unrelated organisms.

alveola   a shallow, minute pit or cavity.

amitosis   nuclear division without chromosomes and spindle fibers; equal cleavage of the nucleus (as in Chara).

amoeboid   moving like an amoeba; with pseudopodia.

androspore   a special spore (Oedogoniales) which germinates to form only a dwarf male filament; androspores are produced in specialized cells, androsporangia.

anisogamete   gametes (sex cells) which show scarcely any difference in respect to sex; similar in some respects but different in another so that a slight degree of sexuality is identifiable.

antapical plates   plates in the wall of dinoflagellates which are at or which form the posterior pole of the organism.

antheridium   in the algae, a single, specialized cell in which one or two sperm are produced; a male sex organ (cells sometimes occurring in series).

antherozoid   a motile, male gamete; a spermatozoid or sperm cell.

antibiotic   a chemical agent or substance produced by an organism which inhibits the growth of another (or itself).

apical   at the anterior end (at the apex).

apical plates   plates in the wall of dinoflagellates which occur at or form the apex of the organism.

aplanospore   a non-motile spore formed (many) within a vegetative cell by the cleavage of the protoplast into small fragments, accompanied by nuclear division; the portions become invested by a wall. (Compare with endospore.)

arbuscular   growing in the form of a tree; a bush-like thallus.

areola   a minute cavity or depression; a space between other configurations.

Aufwuchs   a layer of miscellaneous organisms and detritus forming a film on submerged surfaces.

autocolony   a new colony, formed within the cells of a parent colony; replica of the parent colony.

autogamy   union of sex cells which originated in the same gametangium.

autophytic   see autotrophic

autopotamic   organisms which are normally present in streams; completing the life history in streams (sometimes strictly planktonic).

autospores   internal "spores" which are formed by cell division within a mother cell, forming replicas of the parent cell.

autotrophic   self-feeding; producing organic matter through photosynthesis (autophytic).

auxiliary cell in the Rhodophyta, a specialized or selected cell near the female organ to which the zygote nucleus migrates thereafter giving rise to gonimoblasts (which see).

auxospore a spore formed within the frustule of a diatom which has been reduced in size through cell divisions, returning the diatom to a "normal" size when it germinates; also, the spore resulting from gametic union in diatoms (a zygospore).

auxotrophic nutrition in which organic compounds such as vitamins are required.

axial a central, elongated zone, position, filament, or region from which peripheral or lateral parts may be related.

benthic in an aquatic habitat, attached to a substrate (often implying great depth); non-planktonic.

blade a thin expansion, or a less thick, flattened portion of a thallus (as in Laminaria).

blepharoplast a special granule from which a flagellum arises.

bloom a profuse growth of microscopic or semi-microscopic algae which discolors water; may be of short duration; appears and disappears suddenly.

bulbil a small cluster or knot of cells cut off from a thallus, often in the basal portion, functioning as a vegetative reproductive element.

bullate balloon-like or sac-like, a pustule.

calciphilic organisms well-adapted to or seeking calcium-rich waters.

calyptra a thickening of the cell wall at the apex of a filament; forming a membranous cap; applied to a lid-like covering.

canal a narrow connecting tube through mucilage or, as in the diatoms, through the wall, adjoining the fissures of the raphe; in the Euglenophyta, as an exit tube around the basal part of the flagellum; connecting pusules to the exterior of the cell as in the dinoflagellates.

capitate enlarged or swollen at the apex; with a head.

carpogonial branch a special branch of few or several cells in the Rhodophyta, the terminal cell of which serves as the female sex organ, the carpogonium.

carpogonium the female sex organ in the Rhodophyta, usually terminal on a branch, sometimes a metamorphosed cell which develops a protrusion.

carpospore in the Rhodophyta, a haploid or diploid spore produced either directly from the carpogonium after fertilization of the egg, or indirectly at the completion of a filamentous development following fertilization.

carposporophyte the complete development which follows fertilization of the egg in the Rhodophyta, involving the carpogonium, accessory cells, and spore-producing connecting filaments.

carpotetraspores in the Rhodophyta, spores produced in a quartet within a carpogonium.

cellulose I a somewhat modified form of ordinary cellulose, occurring in the walls of several algae, the crystals arranged with axes in two directions.

cellulose II a form taken by cellulose when precipitated; crystals with axes in one plane; rarely if at all occurring in alga walls.

centriole a dense granule, internal or just external to the nucleus; related to the neuromotor apparatus (which see).

centroplasm a central area of the cyanophyte cell (the central body), with less pigment than the peripheral; the region containing the granules (plates) of nuclear material.

centrosome an area or body lying just external to the nuclear membrane, often including a small grain, the centriole; functions in cell division.

chemolithotrophy see chemosynthetic.

chemosynthetic synthesizing by uptake of inorganic substances (especially in artificial culture media).

chemotrophic see auxotrophic.

chitin an insoluble carbohydrate occurring in the walls of some algae (common in the exoskeleton of insects and other Arthropoda).

chondriosome see mitochondria.

chromoplasm the peripheral plasm of a blue-green algal cell, usually more densely pigmented than the central body.

cingulum a band interspersed between the two valves of a diatom frustule, holding the valves in place.

clone a sexually different or a physiological "race" within a single species population; one of possibly many expressions of a single species.

coccoid round or subsphaerical cells, usually lying free from one another within mucilage.

coccolith a calcareous ring or button on the walls of the *Coccolithophoridae*.

coenobium an association of cells forming an organized colony of definite form and configuration (*Coelastrum*, *Crucigenia*).

coenocytic a cell or thallus unit containing many nuclei.

commensal organisms living in close association with mutual benefit.

compensation point the level of respiration which just equals or balances the rate of organic synthesis by photosynthesis.

conceptacle a chamber within the thalli of Phaeophyta (usually opening to the exterior) in which reproductive organs are borne.

corona a crown; in Charales the terminal cells of the spirally wound investing cells of the oogonium; in *Acetabularia*, the whorl of lobes around the axis at the base of the radiating lobes which comprise the fertile disc. When below the disc, the corona is inferior; when above, superior.

cortex, cortical, cortication cells or tissues external to a central axis or inner core.

costa a rib; a narrow wall thickening.

cover cells in the Rhodophyta, sterile cells cut off from one surface of the daughter cell in the divisions which form the tetrasporangium and tetraspores.

cruciate cross-form, one of the arrangements taken by tetraspores when cut out by the spore-mother cell; spores lying in three planes.

cryoconite the organisms and wind-blown detritus inducing surface melt pits in glaciers.

cryoplankton ice- and snow-inhabiting organisms, occupying films of water within snow banks and glacial ice.

cryptostomata   surface pits in such brown algae as *Fucus*, in which there are tufts of outwardly directed hairs.

cyst   a thick-walled, dormant cell or stage, usually a metamorphosed vegetative cell in a resting stage; regenerates by forming one or more new organisms.

cystocarp   the structures that develop after fertilization in the red algae, involving either carpospores or filaments from the carpogonium which bear carpospores; sometimes enclosed by a pericarp (which see).

cytokinesis   activities within the cytoplasm or division of the protoplast with or without division of the nucleus.

dendroid   branching irregularly, similar to that of a root system.

diastolic   expanding phase of a contractile vacuole as opposed to the systolic phase.

dichotomous, dichotomy   branching in a forking fashion to form two branches (usually equal).

dimorphous   a life history in which there are two phases, one bearing sex organs, and one bearing sporangia or asexual reproductive elements.

dioecious   a situation in which male and female sex organs are borne on separate plants; in reference to sporophytes, with mega- and microspores produced on separate plants.

diplohaplont   a life cycle involving an alternation of haploid and diploid generations, morphologically similar or dissimilar.

diploid   a plant or cell having the double or unreduced number of chromosomes; usually a sporophyte generation.

diplont   a plant which is a diploid gametophyte, producing haploid gametes, there being no 2n sporophyte other than the zygote.

DNA   deoxyribonucleic acid, a component of chromatin material.

dorsiventral   showing two surfaces, morphologically different; upper and lower surfaces identifiable.

dystrophic   not "feeding," referring to a lake which in aging has passed into a marsh and is no longer productive of water biota.

edaphophyte   plants (especially algae) forming an association on or immediately beneath soil.

endemic   referring to organisms which appear, at least, to be confined to a particular area or geographical position.

endochite   the inner one of three wall layers of the oögonium in the Fucales.

endophytic   organisms existing within cells or among tissues of a plant.

endospore   a spore formed by multiple division of a protoplast to form reproductive elements, not enclosed by a thick wall but only a membrane; usually formed many within a cell (see Chamaesiphonales, p. 142).

endotoxins   poisonous substances produced and retained within a cell, and released only after death of the cell.

endozoic   organisms living in the cells or among the tissues of an animal.

epicone   the upper or anterior portion of a cell which is divided by a median girdle or sulcus into an anterior and posterior section.

epilimnion   the upper zone of a lake (or the sea) characterized by having more or less equal distribution of oxygen and in which the temperature is uniform throughout.

epiphytic organisms growing on a plant (sometimes specifically associated).

epiterranean subaerial or terrestrial algae, forming an association only at the surface of the soil.

epizoic organisms living on animals (sometimes specifically associated).

eupotamic inhabiting a stream incidentally; not necessarily confined to a stream type of habitat; but able to complete a life history within a stream.

euplankton true plankton, the drifting organisms of open water or main body of a lake or sea.

euryhaline organisms truly salt-water-inhabiting; poorly or not at all adjusted to brackish waters.

eutrophic a lake type which because of its chemical and hydrographic features is relatively highly productive; a true "feeder."

exochite the outermost of three wall layers of the oögonium in the Fucales.

false branching a type of lateral proliferation of a filament which is not formed by vertical division of a cell in the main axis, but by the turning to one side of a broken section of the filament.

fertile disc a whorl of closely arranged rays at the summit of the axis in Acetabularia in which reproductive cysts are produced.

filament a type of thallus consisting of one or more rows of closely adjoined cells, with or without a gelatinous or mucilaginous sheath.

fissure a definite crack or linear-shaped cleavage (usually in reference to a character of the cell wall).

flimmer lateral fibrils on some flagella (pleuronematic flagella).

floridean starch a starch-like carbohydrate peculiar to the Florideae of the Rhodophyta; a glucose residue.

foliaceous, foliose like a leaf in form.

frustule the shell (cell wall), the capsule of diatoms.

gametangium a cell, specialized or not, which produces a sex cell (gamete).

gamete a sex cell; general term for reproductive elements which fuse.

gametophyte a plant which produces gametes (usually haploid).

girdle structurally, a transverse band; a band within the valve portions of the diatom cell which aids in keeping the two valves in position; ecologically, a horizontal extension of a habitat type, or a horizontal association of organisms which are representative of a type of habitat.

girdle band cingulum (which see).

Golgi apparatus vesicles in the cytoplasm, associated with various organelles of the cell, often showing layers of flat vesicles.

gonimoblast an elongation or filament developing from the carpogonium in the red algae, formed after fertilization and producing at the tip a carpospore.

grana areas between the discs which compose the chloroplast (mostly in chloroplasts of higher plants, Angiosperms).

gynandrosporous species of Oedogoniales in which androspores are produced in androsporangia occurring in the same filament that bears the oögonia.

haplobiont   a species which has but a single phase in the life history wherein a diploid phase produces diploid tetraspores.

haploid   a plant or cell which has one-half or the reduced number of chromosomes.

haplont   a species which has a life cycle involving a gametophyte stage, alternating with a diploid zygote.

hapteron   a root-like, branched basal portion of an alga thallus which forms a hold-fast.

haptonema   a special flagellum, long or short, often coiled; sometimes used as an attaching organ, sometimes partly buried in the cell.

heleoplankton   plankton of small ponds

heterococcoliths   the larger of two types of coccoliths, composed of rib-like or plate-like calcareous structures on the wall of Coccolithophoridae.

heterocyst   an enlarged, thick-walled, and mucilage-filled cell differentiated in the cyanophyte trichome, occurring either basally or intercalary.

heterodynamic   a flagellum which has more than one type of movement or function.

heterogamete, heterogamous   gametes which are clearly differentiated as to maleness and femaleness; reproduction by egg and sperm.

Heterogeneratae   plants which have an alternation of generation in which the sporophyte and gametophyte are different morphologically; a group of orders in the Phaeophyta (as opposed to the Isogeneratae).

heteromorphic, heteromorphous   different in form; plants which assume two different expressions in completing the life history.

heterospore   spores different from one another in shape, size, or sometimes function.

heterothallic   a situation in which two kinds of gametes are produced on separate plants; gametes which unite must come from different plants or be of different "strains."

heterotrichous   a thallus which is partly prostrate and partly erect.

heterotrophic   obtaining food from organic substances in the medium.

holococcoliths   minute and ultramicroscopic plates of crystals on the wall of the Coccolithophoridae.

holophyte   entirely plant-like in nutrition; producing food by photosynthesis.

homothallic   plants in which two kinds of gametes are borne on the same plant; gametes capable of uniting with one another, coming from the same plant.

hormogonium   a short section of a cyanophyte filament.

hormomorphous   plants which have two generations in the life cycle that are morphologically similar.

hormospore   a "spore"-like body formed by a short section of a filament becoming invested by a thick membrane and acting as a dormant reproductive element.

hypha, hyphal   colorless, thread-like growths within or extending from a parenchymatous (usually) thallus, especially in Laminariales.

hypnospore   a thick-walled spore formed indefinitely in the basal portion of coenocytic plants.

hypocone   the lower or posterior portion of a dinoflagellate cell in which there is a median sulcus separating an upper and lower portion.

hypolimnion   a zone or stratification of water below the thermocline (which see) where the temperature is uniformly low to the bottom, the epilimnion being of a higher and more or less uniform temperature because of mixing.

idioandrosporous   species of the Oedogoniales in which the androspores are formed in androsporangia that are borne in filaments separate from those in which the oögonia occur.

infralittoral   see sublittoral.

intercalary   occurring interspersed among other cells of a filament or plant, rather than being localized at the base or apex.

intercalary plates   plates in the wall of dinoflagellates which lie between the cingular plates (near the transverse furrow) and the apical or antapical plates.

internode   a section of a filament or a thallus lying between two nodes or nodal regions.

intertidal   the coastal zone which lies within the upper level of high tide and the lowest level of low tide; roughly the zone which is alternately covered and uncovered by tidal action.

isodiametric   a figure with the diameter more or less equal in all planes (theoretically a sphere or a circle).

isodynamic   a flagellum which shows only one type of movement, or performs but one function.

isogametes   sex cells which are equal to each other in size, shape, and behavior; undifferentiated in respect to sexuality.

Isogeneratae   a group of orders in the Phaeophyta in which the sporophyte and gametophyte generations are morphologically similar.

isokont   flagellation in which the flagella are apical and equal in length and form, usually two (but sometimes four or eight).

isomorphic   plants in which the two generations, sporophyte and gametophyte, are similar morphologically.

isthmus   a neck or narrowed portion of a cell or thallus between two larger portions.

keel   a ridge or a flange arising from a plane surface, as the longitudinal flange on a diatom valve.

lamella, lamellate   a layer; with successive parallel plates.

lamina, laminate   layered; with one or more parallel plates.

laminarin   a carbohydrate (polysaccharide) formed in most Phaeophyta.

lateral conjugation   joining of two cells in the same filament by a tube formed laterally around the cross wall permitting the passage of a gamete from one cell to the other.

leucosin   a chrysophycean food reserve (chrysolaminarin or chrysose; a $B_{-1,3}$-linked glucan).

lignophilic   living on or boring in wood.

lithophilic   living on or forming a film over rock; boring in calcareous formations.

littoral   referring to the ocean shore (usually the intertidal zone).

longitudinal furrow   a sulcus (groove) extending parallel with the long axis, often at right angles to a transverse furrow.

lorica   a shell or capsule formed externally to the cell, usually found in flagellated species.

lumen   the cavity or volume of the cell within the cell wall.

mannan   a carbohydrate known to occur in several *Rhodophyta*, composed of D-mannopyranose residues.

manubrium   a handle-like extension; in Charales the radiating cells from the center of the spherule which bear at their outer ends the broadened shield cells that form the shell of the organ.

mastigonemes   the flimmers or fibrils lateral on the flagellum of the pleuronematic type.

medulla   the inner or central region of a thallus, variously formed, of isodiametric cells or of elongate, filamentous cells.

meiosis   nuclear division wherein the chromosome number is reduced by one-half; passing from a diploid to a haploid state.

meiospore   a spore produced as a result of meiotic or reductive division.

meristoderm   the outer layers (dermis) of cells in an algal thallus constructed by the continued division of the cells that extend outwardly from the units that are cut off from the apical cell or meristem.

mesochite   the middle of three layers in the oögonium of the Fucales.

mesotrophic   a moderate "feeder"; a lake which has aged and which is passing out of its original capacity to produce aquatic biota; a lake passing into a marsh-like area and thence to dystrophy.

metabolites   products of metabolism (usually not reserve food substances) which are cast off or which escape to the surrounding medium as extrametabolites.

metachromatic granules   polyphosphate bodies within the cytoplasm, involved some way in metabolism; thought to be identical with volutin grains.

metamorphosis   undergoing change directly as when a cell becomes a thick-walled spore, or when it modifies itself to become a zoospore.

micromeres   bodies along the inner wall of some cells which give rise to inward-projecting tongues of material (trabeculae, which see).

mitochondria (*chondriosomes*)   minute rod-like or spherical granules in the cytoplasm; of uncertain function, possibly related to enzyme action.

mitosis   nuclear division involving the duplication of chromosomes to form two daughter nuclei.

mixotrophic   nutrition both by photosynthesis and by heterotrophy (using organic compounds).

monoecious   a condition in which both male and female sex organs or sex cells are produced on the same plant; in reference to sporophytes, with mega- and microspores produced on the same plant.

monomorphous a life cycle which involves but a single type of plant, as opposed to dimorphous.

monospores spores borne singly within a vegetative or an unmodified cell (sometimes slightly enlarged), as in some Rhodophyta.

multiaxial with more than one axis; growth at several points in an apical region.

multiseriate thallus composed of several series of cells; of more than one filament.

nannandrous species of the Oedogoniales which use dwarf male plants that are epiphytic on the female.

necridium a dead cell; a cell in the trichome of the Oscillatoriales which dries, becomes filled with mucilage, and so forms a weak link, providing for fragmentation.

nemathecium a cavity on the thallus (Rhodophyta) in which one or more sori of reproductive organs are borne.

neuromotor apparatus the granules and interconnecting fibrils in motile cells which together form a sensitization system that regulates motility.

neuston organisms which are suspended or are carried along beneath the surface film of water.

neutral spores spores formed by internal division of the protoplast to form several elements which escape without having special walls; capable of regenerating a new plant.

nodal, node a joint or area in a filament or thallus from which lateral organs or branches develop; a multicellular area which bears sex organs, alternating with an internodal, branchless area.

nodule (central or polar) an internal thickening of the wall of a diatom cell, the central nodule median, and a nodule at either pole.

nucule the branch consisting of a short stalk and an enlarged oögonium; the female sex organ of the Charales.

nurse cell(s) a special cell or a short filament of cells differentiated within the thallus of some Rhodophyta, acting as nutritive elements in the development of gonimoblasts and the carposporophyte.

ocellus an eye-spot with an associated lens-like organelle.

oligotrophic a poor "feeder"; a type of lake with few electrolytes and with other hydrographic features which render it low in productivity of biota.

ooblast a filament in the development of the carposporophyte in the red algae which connects the carpogonium with an auxiliary cell, through which the diploid nucleus (zygote) migrates.

oogamous sexual reproduction involving an enlarged, non-motile gamete, or egg.

oogonium a cell, usually somewhat specialized, producing the egg: a female sex organ.

operculate, operculum with a lid; opening by a slit which forms a cap that lifts away.

ostiole a mouth; a small opening leading to a cavity (as in the conceptacles of the Fucales).

palmelloid a thallus involving an indefinite arrangement of many (usually spherical) cells embedded in mucilage that is sometimes lamellate.

pantocronematic a flagellum which has both lateral flimmers and a terminal one (see mastigonemes).

pantonematic lateral flimmers on two sides of the flagellum

papilla a slight, nipple-like elevation.

paradesmose a fibril which interconnects the granules at the base of flagella; part of the neuromotor apparatus.

paramylum a solid carbohydrate which is starch-like, found in the Euglenophyta.

paraphysis a hair, often club-shaped, borne near or in association with reproductive organs.

parasite an organism which attaches on or in another, causing a pathological condition.

parenchymatous a thallus composed of a cushion-like mass of cells all about the same size and shape.

parietal peripheral; lying along the inner wall of a cell (as opposed to axial).

parthenospore a spore similar in size and shape to a zygospore, but formed without gametic union.

pedicel a stalk, usually short.

pellicle a skin; outer membrane continuous with the cytoplasm of a cell (see periplast).

penicillate brush-like.

pericarp a basket-like envelope of sterile cells developed around the carposporophyte (Rhodophyta).

pericentral cells segmented or cut off around a central axis; sometimes forming a cortex around a central filament.

periphyton association of organisms attached to and/or growing over submersed plants, often at the water level of an emergent aquatic plant.

periplast a firm, outer skin or membrane continuous with the cytoplasm (see pellicle).

perithecium a cavity or pit in the thallus of an alga, lined with an epidermal-like layer; an enclosure, opening externally.

phagotrophic feeding like or taking particulate food, as do animals.

phosphorylation the formation of phosphorus compounds in or after the photosynthetic process, involving a chemical energy exchange.

photo-receptor a granule which receives light stimulus from an eye-spot.

phototactic response to or moving in reaction to light of various intensities.

phototropic reacting positively to light; moving in the direction of light source.

pinnate with branching like a feather; an elongate main axis with lateral branches or lobes.

pit, pit connection a pore-like opening in the wall of the Florideae (Rhodophyta) coordinated with a similar opening in an adjoining cell wall through which cytoplasmic strands (plasmodesmata) pass.

placenta a composite, multinucleate cell produced when the carpogonium (Rhodophyta) fuses with the auxiliary and other sterile cells in the vicinity; a cell from which gonimoblasts develop.

plakea a plate (often somewhat rectangular) composed of spermatozoids arranged with their long axes parallel (see *Pleodorina* and *Volvox*).

plankton drifting or floating organisms, not capable of swimming against currents (see tychoplankton; euplankton).

pleuronematic flagellum with numerous lateral flimmers or fibrils (see mastigonemes).

plurilocular gametangium an aggregation of regularly arranged cells formed on a short branch or in a special intercalary series in each one of which a gamete is produced (sometimes acting as zoospores).

pneumatocyst a swollen, blister-like or bladder-like pocket filled with gas and aiding in flotation of the thallus (especially in some Phaeophyta).

polyhedron a thick-walled, angular resting cell produced from a zoospore that has come from a germinating zygospore of the Hydrodictyaceae.

polysiphonous a thallus which is multiseriate, with several siphons; filaments of the thallus with intercellular connections and not completely segregated.

polyspores spores formed by a few successive divisions following meiotic division so that more than four tetraspores (meiospores) result.

postcingular plates plates in the wall of dinoflagellates which lie in the hypocone (which see) adjoining the transverse furrow.

potamoplankton potamic stream or river plankton.

precingular plates plates in the wall of dinoflagellates in the epicone (which see) adjoining the transverse furow.

procarp the carpogonial branch (Rhodophyta) and its associated auxiliary cell; the essential structure for the development of a carposporophyte (which see).

propagulum a special, tri-part, hooked branch (*Sphacelaria*) which, abscissed, is able to reproduce the thallus; a fragmentation method of vegetative reproduction.

psammon the biota existing immediately below the upper layer of sand on beaches, existing in films of water in the interstices.

pseudocilia false flagella; fine, gelatinous hairs arising from cells in some members of the Tetrasporales.

pseudofilamentous incidental linear arrangement of cells to form a somewhat filamentous type of thallus.

pseudoparenchymatous a false cushion, i.e., an essentially filamentous plant growing in a prostrate fashion, the cells so arranged as to appear as a cushion or mound.

pseudoraphe a clear, smooth, axial zone in the wall of a diatom valve resulting from the incomplete or interrupted striations extending laterally from the margins.

pseudovacuole a false vacuole; a gas-filled pocket in cells of many cyanophyte species; usually light refractive.

pulsule a sac-like vacuole at the base of flagella in the dinoflagellates, connected to the exterior by canals.

punctum   a minute depression or pit in the cell wall; scattered or arranged in linear series; pits may or may not extend through the wall.

pyramidate   a geometric, three-dimensional or plane figure somewhat like a pyramid in shape or outline.

raphe   a longitudinal fissure extending through the wall of the diatom valve; V-shaped (but lying horizontally) in cross section and so presenting an inner and an outer groove.

receptacle   the swollen apices of branches in the Fucales, or swollen lateral members in which are located the conceptacles containing reproductive structures.

reniform   bean- or kidney-shaped.

reservoir   a sac-like chamber in the anterior end of some euglenoids into which the flagellar canal opens from the exterior.

reticulate   in the form of a net; mesh-like markings.

rheophilic   living in or selective of water currents.

rhizoplast   a fibril connecting the basal granule (of a flagellum) to the centriole that lies within or near the nucleus, involved in the neuromotor apparatus.

rhizopodial   amoeboid type of cell; with pseudopodia.

RNA   ribonucleic acid, a component of nuclear material.

saccate   balloon- or sac-like.

saprophyte   a plant obtaining nutrition by using dead organisms or dead organic matter.

scalariform conjugation   reproduction by formation of tubes between cells of two adjoined filaments to provide movement of gametes; forming a ladder-like association.

scrobiculate   wall or shell with deep pits or depressions (sparse or dense) often pattern-like in arrangement.

sedentary   attached, stationary; sessile or stalked.

semicells   half-cells; the portions of a desmid cell resulting from a deep or shallow median invagination (sinus), the two halves being mirror images of one another.

septa   cross partitions or walls, usually complete, sometimes interrupted.

sessile   attached without a stalk.

setae   hairs, either outgrowths from a wall, or hair-like extensions of a cell or filament of cells.

sheath cells   cells forming an external covering or involucre.

shield cell   a cell terminating the manubrium in the Charales, forming with other shield cells the external shell of the male reproductive branch or spherule.

silicalemma   a thin layer of material immediately within the siliceous shell of diatoms which functions in maintaining or adding to the diatom frustule.

simple flagellum   a smooth whip, without lateral flimmers.

sinus   a narrow (or wide) incision or invagination, forming the semicells of desmids, or the lobings of semicells.

siphonaceous a thallus which is tubular or saccate, without cross walls; multi-nucleate.

spermatozoid a motile sperm; male gamete which swims.

spermocarp an investment of the oögonium by proliferations of sterile cells in the vicinity of the oögonium, thus forming a protective covering (*Coleo-chaete*).

spherule a highly modified branch forming a spherical body that serves as a complex antheridium (Charophyta).

spore a one-celled (usually), non-sexual reproductive element; motile or non-motile asexual reproductive cell.

sporophyte a plant which produces spores, usually by meiosis; a diploid phase of the life history.

stalk cell a sterile cell at the base of a tetrasporangium (Rhodophyta); a cell at the base of the oögonium (Charophyta).

statospore a spore formed when a cell or a portion of a protoplast becomes invested by a siliceous wall (diatoms and other Chrysophyta).

stauros a laterally extended and enlarged central nodule of some diatom cell walls.

stellate star-shaped; usually axial and radiate, as applied to chloroplasts.

stephanokont flagellation in which there is a crown-like circle of flagella arising from a series of blepharoplasts.

stichonematic a flagellum of the pleuronematic type in which flimmers arise from one side only.

stipe a stalk or stem.

stria a linear etching or fine rib; a line-like marking.

subaerial growing on exposed surfaces, using only a film of moisture; algae of rocks, trees, and soil.

sublittoral the coastal zone lying just below lowest low water of tidal action; the zone never uncovered by tide movements (infralittoral).

suffultory cell the cell of oedogoniaceous filaments which lies immediately below the oögonium, the cell usually distinctly inflated and showing the influence of hormones.

supporting cell the cell (Rhodophyta) which gives rise to the carpogonial branch.

supralittoral the coastal zone just above the littoral, or above the intertidal zone; sometimes includes the "splash zone."

symbiotic, symbiotism two or more organisms living together or in close association, with various degrees of interdependence or parasitism.

syngamy union of sex cells; uniting of nuclei to form a diploid cell.

syntagmatic germination formation of a single thallus by the germination of several tetraspores within a tetrasporangium.

systolic the contracting phase of a pulsating vacuole.

taxon a recognized, systematic entity at whatever rank.

tenaculae interconnecting pads and branches between principal axes of a branched thallus.

tetrasporangium, tetraspore spores formed in groups of four by meiosis within a special cell (sporangium), the spores linear, pyramidately or cruciately arranged.

tetrasporophyte a diploid plant which produces tetraspores, usually by meiosis.

thallus a plant body not differentiated into true roots, stems, and leaves.

theca the investment or thickened wall of a cell; in dinoflagellates the wall composed of regularly arranged plates; epitheca and hypotheca, the two parts of the wall separated by a transverse furrow.

thermocline a stratum of a lake or sea immediately below the epilimnion in which temperature decreases with depth to the hypolimnion which is a zone of more or less uniform temperature.

tonoplast membrane of a vacuole.

trabeculae tongues or plates of material extending from a cell wall into the lumen of the cell.

transverse furrow a sulcus or groove extending transversely around a cell, as in the dinoflagellates.

trichoblast a branch of a thallus (Rhodophyta) which in rebranching forms hair-like cells; branches bearing hairs and sex organs, or sterile.

trichocyst an organelle within the periplast of a cell which throws off fibrils (thought to be poisonous or stinging).

trichogyne the extended, neck-like portion of a carpogonium, the female organ of the Rhodophyta.

trichome a hair or gelatinous bristle, or an extension of the cell wall; name applied to the thread of cells in filamentous cyanophytes, minus the sheath.

trichothallic growth of the thallus occurring by meristematic cells lying at the base of apical hairs.

trichotomous dividing or forking in three more or less equal parts or branches.

true branching branching produced by the vertical division of cells in a main axis, as in *Hapalosiphon*.

trumpet hyphae elongated, filamentous cells in the medulla of some brown algae which are distinctly enlarged at the cross walls in which there are sieve plates.

tufa a form of limestone, often formed by blue-green algae.

tychoplankton free-floating organisms living near shore and intermingled with other growths, but not attached.

umbrophilic shade loving; referring to subdued light.

uniaxial a thallus or filament in which there is a single row of cells; or a single apical growing cell which produces one series of cells.

unilocular sporangium a sporangium which is one-celled, sometimes stalked, producing spores usually by meiosis (Phaeophyta).

uniseriate a filament in which there is a single series of cells, as opposed to a filament (*Stigonema*) with more than one series.

utricles swollen, sac-like branches or portions of a thallus.

vacuole a region of the cell enclosed by a membrane, containing cell sap or crystals of waste material.

valve, valve view the flat portions of a diatom cell wall, the two forming the top and bottom of the "box"; when seen from top or bottom, the valve view as opposed to a view from the side, a girdle view; the upper valve (larger) known as the epivalve, the lower (smaller) the hypovalve.

vesicle, vesicular sac-like; a utricle or bladder-like swollen portion of a thallus.

volutin metachromatic granules of a polyphosphate compound; possibly a food reserve; found more commonly in bacteria.

zoospore an animal-like spore with organs of locomotion and usually with an eye-spot; a spore capable of producing a new plant independently.

zygospore a thick-walled resting stage (diploid; formed from a zygote).

zygote a diploid cell resulting from a union of sex cells; a fertilized egg.

Index

Page numbers in italics refer to illustrations; those in bold-face to pages where plants are discussed or especially noted; those in light-face refer to pages where organisms are considered, or terms defined.

Acanthoica Schilleri *161*
Acetabularia 31, 35, 42, **106,** 301, 306; *mediterranea, 107*
Acontochrysophysidae 180
Acrochaete 79, **80;** *repens, 82*
Acrochaetiaceae 249
Acrochaetium **250,** *251,* 256
Acronematic flagella *24*
Acrosiphonia 102
Adeloparasites 323
Adenosine diphosphate 343
Adenosine triphosphate 343
Aegagropila 97
Aerial, Subaerial 17
Aeronautics 352
Africa 305
Agar-agar 235, 262, 267, 333, 354, 359
Agarum 227, 303
Aglaozonia 216
Ahnfeltia 235, 354
Akaryotic 6
Akinete 15, 16, 32, 135, 148, sq.
Alaria 227, 301, 303, 307, 350
Albrightia 151
Alcohol 30, 207, 333, 350
Algae: Classification 4, 6; Cytology, 18; Definition of, 3; Duration, 35; General characteristics, 3; Growth, 30; Importances, 5; Life histories, 33; Occurrence (Habitats), 16; Phyla and orders, 7; Pigments, 24; Reproduction, 31
Algicides 361
Algin, Alginic Acid 222, 333, 350, 355
Alginates 355
Algonkian 372
Alkaline phosphatase 338
Allergies 360
Alloparasites 323
Alpine 50, 69, 285, 326
Alsidium 359

Alternation of generations 33, 42, 209, 241, 371
Alysiella 325
Amanita phalloides 363
Amanori 351
Ambrosia 58, 324
Amino Acids 350, 352
Amitosis 20, 103, 106
Ammonium sulphate 351
Amoeboid, Amoeboid gametes 10, 157, 170, 183; *Chromulina,* 156, 168; Conjugatae, 118; *Draparnaldia,* 77; Eyespot, 21
Amphidinium 197; *amphidinioides, 199*
Amyloids 18
Amylopectin 30, 332
Amyloproteins 42
Amylose 332
Anabaena 17, 139, *146,* **149,** 289, 292, 320, 334, 336, 362; *Azollae,* 325; *Cycadearum, 325; flos-aquae,* 284
Anabaenin 243
Anabaeniolum 325
Ancylonema **120,** 327; *nordenskioldii, 116, 326*
Anadyomenaceae **104**
Anadyomene **105;** *stellata, 107*
Androsporangium 32, 95
Androspore 32, 95
Androtermones 50
Anemia 359
Animal deaths: See Deaths
Anisogametes, Anisogamy 7, 8, 11, 12, 33, 42
Anisomonas 23, 41
Ankistrodesmus **69;** *falcatus, 59; spiralis, 59*
Annual Plants 34, 306
Antarctic 29, 60, 103, 284, 303, 305, 312, 319, 344; Plankton, 319

Antheridium 33, 95, 132
Anthoceros 139, 325
Anthocyans 25, 38
Antibiotics 345, 346, 347, 352, 359
Antifouling fungicides 355
Antipernicious anemia 347
Antithamnion 233
Aonori 351
Aphanizomenon **149,** 289, 292, 296, 298, 359, 361, 362; flos-aquae, 146, 284, 290, 314
Aphanocapsa **141,** 325; Grevilliei, 130
Aphanochaetaceae **79**
Aphanochaete 79, **80;** repens, 81
Aphanothece **141,** 289, 370; stagnina, 131, 292
Apical cell 132
Apiocystis **54;** Brauniana, 49
Aplanospores 34, 45, 138
Apodinium 326
Arabinose 332, 346
Araceae 114, 324
Archaeozoic 135, 371
Arctic 29, 63, 171, 281, 284-286, 303, 310, 312, 319, 344; Plankton, 319
Areolae 182
Arisaema 115
Arthrospira 139, 148
Ascomycetes 324
Ascophyllum 209, 215, **230,** 301, 346; nodosum, 224, 355
Asexual reproduction 8, 9
Ash 352, 356
Asparagopsis 242, **258,** 259
Asperococcus 35, 306
Associations of species 290
Astasia 190
Astasiaceae 193
Asterionella 187, 289, 337; formosa, 290, 314
Asterocystis 233, 236, **246;** Smaragdina, 225
Astrephoneme 29
Atlantic 304, 319
Attheya 318
Audouinella **249;** violacea, 239
Aufwuchs 17
Aurosphaera **179**
Australia 305
Autocolonies 9
Autopotamic 297
Autospores 11, 32

Autotrophic 30, 332, 339
Auxiliary cell 14, 15, 240, 242, 243
Auxin 31
Auxospore 183, 185
Auxotrophic 332, 339
Azolla 76, 77, 139, 325
Azoosporic 56

B$_{12}$ 309, 339
Bacillaria paradoxa 184
Bacillariophyceae 4, 7, 10, 28, 155, **179** (see Diatoms); Cell wall, 180
Bacteria 18, 40, 135, 307, 310
Ballia callitriche 303
Bangia **247,** 302, 310; astropurpurea, 247; ciliaris, 323; fuscopurpurea, 225, 247
Bangiaceae 246
Bangiales 14
Bangioideae 14, 233, 235, **243**
Bar Kanten 354
Barnacles 302
Basal Granules 22
Basicladia 17, **98,** 325; chelonum, 100
Basidiomycetes 324
Batophora **110,** 303; Oerstedi, 109
Batrachosphermaceae **250**
Batrachospermum 241, **250,** 251, 295; sinense, 251
B-D-glucopyranose 30, 350
B-D-mannopyruronic Acid 350
Belts (Horizontal) 304
Benthic 17
Benzedine 347
Bible of Poems 63
Bicarbonates 289, 290
Bicarinella 373
Biddulphia 185, **186;** granulatum, 175
Biercherella 373
Bifurcaria 228
Bilichromoproteins 203
B-Indol-acetic acid 347
Binuclearia **72;** tatrana, 67
Biological assay 192, 359
Biotin 339
Bipedinomonas 23, 41
Blade 208
Blasia 139, 325
Blepharoplast 21, 22, 24
Bloom 53, 56, 61, 138, 144, 150, 153, 170, 194, 205, 292, 315, 317, 342, 347

Blue flagellates 16
Blue-Green algae 15
Bodanella 207; *Lauterbornii, 283*
Boghead coal 372
Bolbocoleon 76, 79, **84**
Boldia 295
Bonnemaisonia 252, **258**
Bonnemaisoniaceae **257**
Boodlea **105,** 301; *siamensis, 107*
Boodleaceae 105
Bostrychia 233, 289, 301, 351
Bosworthia 371
Botrydiaceae 165
Botrydiopsis 157
Botrydium 157, **165;** 321; *granulatum,*
62, 160
Botryococcus **61,** 372; *Braunii, 59,* 292,
314
Botulina 365
Braarudosphaera 170
Brachiomonas 45, 46
Brackish water 17, 45, 132, 288, 289
Bracteococcus 332
Bradypus 79
Branchipus 325
Bromine 356
Brown algae 12
Bryopsidaceae 112
Bryopsis 31, 39, 41, **112,** 301, 333;
plumosa, 108, 112
Bryozoa 250
Bulbils 128
Bulbochaete 91, 93, **95,** 289, 294

C^{14} 282, 313
Caespitella 74
Calcareous, Calcification: *See* Calcium
Calciphilic 18
Calcisphaerella 373
Calcium (lime) 18, 39, 40, 290, 291, 293,
334; Encrusted algae, 37, 40, 104, 106,
110, 118, 132, 139, 216, 233, 263, 328,
342, 370
Calcium salts 334
Calleocolax 234
Callithamnion 301
Callophylis 234
Callose 18, 39, 42, 333
Caloglossa 301
Calothrix 137, **152,** 159, 327, 336; *Con-*
torenii, 302; *parietana,* 152; *scopu-*
lorum, 302

Calyptra 144
Cambium 209
Cambrian 370
Campylodiscus 175, **187**
Canal (Diatoms) 182
Capitate 144
Carbohydrates 30, 352
Carbon 353
Carbonates 296, 309, 341
Carbon dioxide 40, 310
Carex Meadow 292
Carotenes 11, 19, 25, 38, 350, 351
Carotenoid hydrocarbons 25
Carpogonial branch 14, 15, 240, (initial)
255; *See* Red Alga genera
Carpogonium 14, 32, 236
Carpomitra **218**
Carposporangium 240
Carpospore 32, 236, 240
Carposporophyte 240, 243
Carpotetraspores 240
Carrageen, Carrageenin 268, 333, 351,
354
Carteria 44, 47, **51,** 326; *ovata,* 51
Cassiopeia 196, 325
Casuals 320
Catenella opuntia 301
Caulerpa 42, 109, **111,** 112, 301, 304,
333
Caulerpaceae **111**
Cave algae 138
Cellulose 18, 39, 333, 350
Cellulose-I 18, 19, 39
Cellulose-II 18, 39, 63
Cell Wall 6, 18, 39; Bacillariophyceae,
180; Chlorophyta, 39; Chrysophyta,
155; Coccolithophoridaceae, 170; Cy-
anophyta, 137; Fibrils, 19, 39, 235;
Phaeophyta, 208; Rhodophyta, 235;
Silicoflagellatae, 179; Xanthophyceae,
157
Cenozoic 371
Central Body: *See* Centroplasm
Centrales (Centricae) 11, 181, **185**
Centriole 21, 24
Centritractaceae **163**
Centritractus **163;** *belanophorus, 160*
Centrobacillariophyceae **185**
Centroplasm 137
Centrosome 22
Cephaleuros 17, 85, **86,** 324; *virescens,*
89, 324

Ceramiaceae   272, **273**
Ceramiales   15, 243, **272**
Ceramium   273, **274**, 301; *diaphanum,*
   270; fastigiatum, 270
Ceratiaceae   198
Ceratium   11, 194, 195, 196, **198**, 293;
   hirundinella, 194, 198, 200, 290; *tripos,*
   319
Ceratocolax   233, 323
Ceratophyllum   324
Cercaria   153
Chaetangiaceae   **257**
Chaetoceros   175, **186**
Chaetomnion   74
Chaetomorpha   **98,** 102, 103, 323; *area,*
   100; linum, 98; media, 102
Chaetonema   79, **80;** *irregulare, 82*
Chaetophora   43, 74, **77;** *pisciformis, 75*
Chaetophoraceae   70, **74**
Chaetophorales   8, 10, 11, 70, **73**
Chaetosphaeridium   **85;** *globosum, 83*
Chaetotheke   74
Chamaeophyceae   35, 306
Chamaesiphon   **143;** *incrustans,* **145**
Chamaesiphonaceae   143
Chamaesiphonales   15, 32, 138, **142**
Champia   303
Champiaceae   272
Chantransiaceae   **249**
Chara   7, 35, 37, 42, *129, 132,* **133**, 337,
   372
Characeae   133
Characiaceae   62
Characiopsidaceae   **162**
Characiopsis   62, **162,** 325; *pyriformis,*
   160
Characium   17, *59,* **62,** 162, 325
Charales   9, 20, 37, 39, 41
Chareae   133
Charophyceae   7, 9, **128**
Charophyta   128
Chemical factors   288; Fresh-water, 287;
   Marine, 307; Toxic, 290
Chemolithotrophy   30, 332
Chemosynthesis   30
Chemotrophic   332
Chilodon   318, 353
Chilomonas   23, 203
Chionaster nivalis   326
Chitin   18, 39, 40
Chlamydobotrys   30
Chlamydomonadaceae   46

Chlamydomonas   17, *23,* 24, 25, 42-45,
   46, *47,* 50, 51, 283, 296, 346; *halophila,*
   50; *nivalis,* 326; *Reinhardii,* 346; *vari-*
   abilis, 51
Chlorallanthus   **162;** *oblongus, 159*
Chlorangiaceae   55
Chlorangium   **55,** 325; *stentorinum, 57*
Chlorella   6, 17, 38, 56, **64,** 69, 320, 325,
   336, 340, 343, 344, 345, 351, 352, 359;
   conductrix, 325; Cultured for food, 352;
   parasitica, 325; *stigmatophora,* 346; *vul-*
   garis, 65
Chlorellin   345, 352, 359
Chlorobotrys   **162;** *regularis, 160*
Chlorobrachis gracillima   45, 46
Chlorochytrium   43, **60;** *Lemnae, 58,* 324
Chlorococcaceae   **60**
Chlorococcales   9, 10, 11, **56**
Chlorococcum   57, **60,** 320
Chlorogonium   46
Chloromonadales   16
Chloromonadophyceae   7
Chloromonadophyta   16, **204**
Chlorophyceae   4, 7, 42
Chlorophyll   25, 28, 38
Chlorophyta   4, 7, 20, 22, 25, 29, 30, **37;**
   Cell wall, 39; Cytology, 38; Life his-
   tories, 43; Pigments, 38; Representative
   orders, 42; Reproduction, 42; Reserve
   food, 42
Chloroplast   29, 38, 234
Chlorosaccaceae   158
Chlorotheciaceae   **163**
Chlorothecium   164
Chlorotylium   78
Cholesterol   30, 333
Chondria   208
Chondrillosterol   333
Chondriosomes   20, 41
Chondrus   **267,** 301, 303, 306; *crispus,*
   29, 234, 268, 269, 351, 354, 359
Chorda   221
Chordaria   **218;** *flagelliformis, 215*
Chordariaceae   **217**
Chordariales   13, 209, 217
Choreocolax   233
Choreonema   234, 323
Chromatin   20, 137
Chromatophore   29
Chromolipoid   25
Chromonemata   137
Chromoplasm   29, 136, 137

Chromosomes 20, 45, 97, 102; Sex, 20
Chromulina 23, 156, *161,* **168**
Chromulinaceae **168**
Chromulinales **168,** 180
Chromulineae 180
Chroococcaceae **140**
Chroococcales 15, **140**
Chroococcus 135, **140,** 328, 334; *limne-ticus,* 140; *turgidus,* 130, 140, 293
Chroodactylon 246
Chroothece 140
Chrysapioninae 180
Chrysocapsa **176;** *planctonica,* 173
Chrysocapsaceae **176**
Chrysocapsales 10, 176
Chrysochromulina 23, 24, 30, **172;** *parva,* 173
Chrysolaminarin 155, 167, 183, 371
Chrysolykos 156, 327
Chrysomonadales 10, **168**
Chrysophyceae 4, 7, 10, 155, **167;** Classification, 180
Chrysophycophyta 7
Chrysophyta 10, 20, 28, 30, **155,** 286, 339; Cytology, 155; Distribution, 156; Flagella, 156; Pigments, 155; Repro-duction, 156; Reserve food, 155
Chrysosphaeraceae **178**
Chrysosphaerales 10, **178**
Chrysosphaerella **169**
Chrysosphaerella longispina 161
Chrysosphaerineae 180
Chrysostomataceae 178
Chrysostrella **178;** *furcata, 174*
Chrysotrichales 10, **177**
Cingulum 181
Citron 350
Citrus 86, 324
Cladophora 17, 18, 20, 22, 35, 39, 42, 43, 76, **96,** 98, 102, 295, 297, 306; balls, 97; *clavuligera, 97; glomerata,* 96, 99, 295; *pellucida,* 41; *profunda,* 283
Cladophoraceae 96
Cladophorales 8, 9, 39, 73, **96,** 103
Cladophoropsis **105,** *107*
Cladostephus 35, 306
Claudia 273
Clavator 372
Clearing Agent 351
Cloniophora 74
Closteriaceae 119, 121
Closterieae 127

Closterium 116, 121, 126
Clostridium 346
Clumping of gametes 110
Coccogoneae 15, 140
Coccolithineae 170
Coccolithophoridaceae, Coccolithopho-ridae 156, **170**
Coccoliths 170
Coccomyza 324, 340
Coccomyxaceae **55**
Coccophora 281
Codiaceae 112
Codiolum 39, 103; *petrocelidis,* 102
Codium 19, 20, 35, 43, *108,* **112,** *303,* 306, 351, 359, 372; *fragile,* 113; *mag-num,* 112; *mamillosum,* 305
Coelastraceae 64
Coelastrum **64,** 334; *microporum,* 65, 292
Coelosphaerium 57; *Kuetzingianum,* 290, 314
Coenobium 56
Coenocytes, Coenocytic 8, 9, 20, 56
Coenogonium 38, 86
Co-enzyme 28
Colaciaceae 193
Colaciales 10, 189, 193
Calocium 55, 189, **193,** 325; *calvum,* *199*
Colacopsis 234, 323
Coleochaetaceae **84,** 103
Coleochaetales 8, **79**
Coleochaete **84;** *orbicularis, 82; nitel-larum,* 84, 324; *scutata,* 84
Collenia 370
Collinsiella 88
Colorless 25, 325, 347
Colteronema 328
Commensal 18
Commercial products 353
Compensation point 344
Composition 333
Compsopogon 234, 235, **248;** *coeruleus,* *238*
Compsopogonaceae 248
Compsopogonales 14, 248
Conceptable 13, 228, 230, 263
Conchocelis 247, 248
Condyleatis 196
Conferva 7
Conjugales 9, 37, 43, **118**

Conjugatae 9, **118;** Classification, 122, 123

Conjugation 9, 10, 11, 119, 127; Geniculation, 127; Lateral, 127; Scalariform, 127

Connecting filaments 240

Contractile vacuoles 24

Convoluta 326

Copepoda 315

Corallina 233, *260*, **264,** 301, 304, 359, 371

Corallinaceae 103, **263**

Corallinoideae 263

Coral Reefs 17, 309

Corals 17

Corona: *Acetabularia,* inferior, superior, 106; Characeae, 133

Cortex, Cortical Cells 13, 133, 253, 275

Coscinodiscus **185;** *perforatus, 174*

Cosmariaceae 119, 121

Cosmarieae 127

Cosmarium **121,** 346, 347; *quadri-farium, 116*

Costa 182

Costaria 208, 307

Cover Cells 277

Cretaceous 110, 171, 179, 356, 371-373

Crocetin 50

Crucigenia 55, **70;** *crucifera, 66; tetra-pedia, 66*

Crustacea 325

Cryoconite 327

Cryoplankton, Cryovegetation 17, 50, 69, 326, 327

Cryptococcaceae 204

Cryptococcales 16, 204

Cryptomonadaceae 203

Cryptomonadales 16, 203

Cryptomonas 23, **203,** 286; *pusilla, 286; splendida, 201*

Cryptonemiales 14, 242, **262**

Cryptophyceae 7, 203

Cryptophyta 16, 189, **203;** Cytology, 203; Pigments, 203; Reserve food, 203

Cryptophytes 320

Cryptostomata 228

Cryptozoon 370

Ctenocladus 85

Culturing 375; Agar, 380; Axenic, 377; Bacteria free, 377; Chlorophyta, 379; Continuous flow, 376, 377; Cyanophyta, 379; Desmids, 380; Flagellata, 379; Food for Man, 352, 375; Formulae, 378, sq.; Gross, 377; Growth, 376, sq.; Marine, 380, sq.; Media, 378, sq.; Objectives, 375; Soil-water, 377; Synchronous, 377; Techniques, 376, sq.; Temperature, 376; Unialgal, 377; Volvocales, 380

Currents: Convection 294; Fresh-water, 294; Marine, 319

Cutleria **212,** 372; *multifida, 214*

Cutleriaceae **212**

Cutleriales 13, 209, 212

Cyanella 325

Cyanoderma bradypodis 326

Cyanophyceae 4, 7

Cyanophycin 137

Cyanophyta 15, 18, 19, 28, 29, 33, **135,** 189, 292, 324, 372; Cell wall, 137; Cytology, 136; Cytoplasm, 137; Fossil records, 135; Habitats, 138; Movement, 139; Nitrogen-fixation, 139; Pigments, 136; Representative orders, 140; Reserve food, 137

Cycads, *Cycas* 17, 325

Cyclops 347

Cyclosporales **227**

Cyclosporeae 13, **227**

Cyclotella 184

Cylindrocapsa **72,** 73; *geminella, 68*

Cylindrocapsaceae 72

Cylindrocapsales 8, 72

Cylindrocapsella 72

Cylindrocystis *116,* **120,** 322, 327

Cylindrospermum 139, 336

Cymbella 187, 292, 295

Cysta 167

Cystocarp 240, 264, 266

Cysts 11, 33, 195

Cystodinium. **202;** *iners, 200*

Csytophyllum, fusiforme 335

Cystoseira 301, 306, 324

Cytochrome-f 343

Cytokinesis 56

Cytology: Cell wall, 18, 39, 137; Centrosomes, 22; Chloromonadophyta, 204; Chlorophyta, 38; Chloroplasts 29,; Chrysophyceae, 167; Chrysophyta, 155; Cryptophyta, 156, 203; Cyanophyta, 136; Cytoplasm, See: Desmids, 118; Diatoms, 180; Euglenophyta, 189; Eye-spot, 21; Flagella, 22; Mitochondria, 19, 20; Nucleus, 30; Phaeophyta, 207; Pig-

ments, 25-28; Rhodophyta, 235; Silicoflagellata, 179
Cytoplasm   19, 40, 41, 137, 182, 190

Dalyia   371
Daphnia   347
Dasycladaceae   106, 372
Dasycladales   37, 42, 103, **106,** 110, 373
Dasycladus   110
Daughter Cell *(Polysiphonia)*   277
Death: Animals   6, 362; Fish, 6, 141,
    288, 361, 362; Fowl, 362; Man, 6, 361,
    364
Debarya   127
Delesseria   303, 312
Derbesia   22, 41, 110, **114,** *115, 118*
Derbesiaceae   **114**
Derbesiales   114
Dermatodea   303
Dermatophyton   **78**
Dermocarpa   **143;** *pacifica, 145*
Dermocarpaceae   **143**
Desert   322
Desiccation   321, 322
Desmarestia   219, 303; *viridis,* 303
Desmarestiaceae   **219**
Desmarestiales   13, 219
Desmidiaceae   121, 127
Desmidiales   118, sq.
Desmidium   121; *Swartzii, 129*
Desmids   19, 20, 37, 39, 43, **118,** 285,
    289, 290; Cell division, 126; Classifi-
    cation, 122; Phylogeny, 124; Zygote-
    formation, 125
Desmococcus   78
Desmokontae   12, 196, 197
Desmomonadales   197
Desmophyceae   12
Diabetis   350
Diaminopimelic Acid   18
Diastolic   41
Diatomin   25
Diatomite, Diatomaceous Earth   356, 357
Diatoms,   4, 10, 17, 19, 20, 155, 174,
    175, 292, 303, 319, 326, 327, 338, 352,
    356-359
Dichotomosiphon   9, 110, **113,**   295;
    tuberosus, 113, 115, 283
Dichotomosiphonaceae   113
Dictyochaceae   179
Dictyosiphon   **220;** *Eckmanii, 323*
Dictyosiphonales   13. **220**

Dictyosphaeria   104
Dictyosphaeriaceae   61
Dictyosphaerium   61; *pulchellum, 58*
Dictyota   208, **216,** 301, 372; *dichotoma,*
    214
Dictyotaceae   179, **216**
Dictyotales   13, 208, 209, 216
Digenea   359
Dillick   351
Dilsea   308; *corallina,* 235
Dimorphococcus   **61;** *lunatus, 59*
Dimorphosiphon   372
Dimorphous   242
Dinamoebidium   194
Dinobryon   19, 171, **172,** 292, 314, 332,
    359; *cylindricum, 173*
Dinocapsales   12
Dinoclonium   **194,** 373; *Conradi, 201*
Dinococcales   12, **202**
Dinoflagellata: See Pyrrhophyta
Dinokontae   12, 196, 197
Dinophyceae   7, 12, 20, 195, 197
Dinothrix   4, 194, **202,** 373; *paradoxa,*
    201
Dinotrichales   12, **202**
Dioecious   95, 242
Diplochaete   79
Diplohaplont   241
Diploid   20, 32, 34, 45, 51, 60
Diplont   241
Dispora   **55;** *crucigenioides, 57*
Distephanum   179
Distribution: Disjunct, 305; Freshwater,
    280; Geographical 305; Horizontal, 28,
    210, 280, 284, 304, 319; Marine, 304,
    305; Vertical, 28, 233, 282, 284, 285,
    312, 316; Zonation, 299, 300
Diurnal variation   294, 298
DNA   137, 195, 334, 347
Draparnaldia   23, 74, **77,** 295; *glomerata,*
    76
Draparnaldiopsis   74, 77, 281; *indica, 77*
Dudresnya   260, **263**
Dulcitol   351
Dulse   351
Dumontia   263, 303
Dumontiaceae   **263**
Dunaliella   42, 45, **46,** 289, 302, 346;
    paupera, 47; teritolaeta, 46
Duration   35, 306
Durvillea   227, 281, 359
Dystrophic   292

Ecklonia bicyclis 335
Eclipsiophyceae 35, 306
Ecology **279;** Biological factors, 280; Brackish water, 17, 45, 288, 289; Chemical factors, 279, 287, 307; Currents, 279, 294, 299, 309; Desiccation, 321, 322; Duration, 306; Factors, 279; Freshwater, 281; Gases, 279; Habitats, 16; Ice, 285; Light, 279, 281, 284, 311; Marine, 298, sq.; Physiographic Factors, 280; Soil, 320; Substrate, 280, 295; Temperature, 279, 284, 285, 309, 310, 319, 322; Tidal Marsh, 138, 300, 301; Tides, 299; Winds, 310; Zones, 300
Economics 349; Commercial Products, 353; Diatoms, 356; Food for Man, 349; Food for Fish; Food Chain, 5, 6, 56, 64, 102, 208; Medicine, 359; Phaeophyta, 355; Rhodophyta, 354; Toxins, 360, sq.; Water Supplies, 359
Ectocarpaceae 210
Ectocarpales 12, 209, 210
Ectocarpus **211,** *213,* 242, 372
Ectochaete 80, 84
Edaphophytes 320
Egg 33
Egregia *224,* **227,** 301
Ehriaceae 179
Eisenia 355
Eklonia 355
Elakatothrix **55;** *viridis,* 49
Electrolytes 290
Elittoral 303
Embryo, Embryonic Development 229; *Fucus,* 229
Emulsifiers 350
Endemic 281, 305
Endochite 229
Endocladia 324
Endoderma 76, **78**
Endophytes, Endophytic 17, 56, 60, 114, 139, 142, 143, 192; Chlorophyta, 60, 61, 80; Cyanophyta, 142; Rhodophyta, 323
Endophyton ramosum 78, *81,* 323
Endosphaeraceae **60**
Endospores 15, 32, 136, 138, 142, 143
Endozoic 17, 56, 325
Enteromorpha 17, 18, 31, 35, **88, 89,** 289, 295, 301, 303
Entocladia 78
Entophysalidaceae **142**
Entophysalis *131,* **142**

Enzymes 19, 333, 372
Eocene 233, 371, 373
Eodina 373
Ephemerophyceae 35, 306
Epibolium 78
Epichrysis *173,* **178**
Epicone 195
Epilimnion 284, 318
Epilithic 294
Epipelic 294
Epiphloeophytes 324
Epiphyllous 324
Epiphytes, Epiphytic 17, 110, 143, 158, 176, 233, 234, 250, 294, 324
Epiterranean 320
Epitheca 181, 195
Epithemia 292
Epivalve 181
Epizoic 17, 193, 250
Eremosphaera **69,** 292; *viridis,* 66, **69**
Erythrotrichaceae **246**
Erythrotrichia *237,* **246**
Escherichia coli 359
Euastrum *117,* 121
Eudorina 44, **52;** *elegans,* 48
Euglena 4, 19, 23, 190, **191,** 283, 296, 320, 347, 359; *acus,* *175;* *deses,* 191; *gracilis,* 191; *sanguinea,* 192; *viridis,* 296
Euglenaceae, Euglenoids 20, 21, **191;** 292, 322
Euglenales 10, 191
Euglenarhodone 25
Euglenomorpha 191
Euglenophyceae 7
Euglenophyta 10, 24, 28, 30, 38, **189,** 372; Cytology, 190; Pigments, 190; Phylogeny, 372, 373; Reserve food, 190
Euglenophytina 38
Eukaryotic 6
Eupotamic 297
Euplankton, Euplanktonic 17
Euryhaline 17
Eutrophic 290, 314
Evolution 37, 367, sq.
Exochite 229
Extrametabolites 279, 280, 289, 290, 319, 345–347
Exuviella 197
Eye-spot 21, 24

Falkenbergia rufanilosa 258
False branching 16, 135, 150, 151

Fat choy 351
Fats, fat-producers 352
Fatty acids 340, 345
Fertile disc 106
Fertile Trichoblast; See Trichoblast
Fertilizers 288, 315, 337, 355
Fibrils 19, (flagella) 22, 235
Fish deaths: See Death
Fish, parasites on 17, 325, 326
Fish Production 313
Fission 138; Fission plants, 135
Fissure (Diatom wall) 181
Flagella, Flagellation 6, 22; Acronematic, 24; Ancestry of Algae, 367; Chloromonadophyta, 204; Chlorophyta, 41; Chrysophyta, 156; Coccolithophoridaceae, 170; Euglenophyta, 189; Fibrils, 22; Flimmers, 24; Pantocronematic, 24; Pantonematic, 24; Pleuronematic, 24; Pyrrhophyta, 194; Simple, 24, 40; Stichonematic, 24; Xanthophyceae, 157
Flagellated phyla 189
Florideae 14, 233, 235, 243, **248**
Floridean starch 14, 30, 234, 332
Floridoside 234
Flour 352
Fodder 350
Food chain 5, 6, 56, 64, 102, 298, 316, 351
Food for man 6, 111, 149, 248, 316, 351
Food reserve, Nutrition 6; Arctic Species, 344; Bacillariophyceae, 183; Chloromonadophyta, 205; Chlorophyta, 42; Chrysophyta, 155; Cryptophyta, 203; Cyanophyta, 137; Phaeophyta, 207; Pyrrhophyta, 195; Rhodophyta, 234; Xanthophyceae, 157
Fossil Algae 63, 367, 370; Characeae, 128, 372; Chlorophyta, 63, 372; Chrysophyta, 356, 373; Coccolithophoridaceae, 171; Cyanophyta, 370; Diatoms, 356; Phaeophyta, 371; Phylogeny, 367; Pyrrhophyta, 196, 373; Records, 37; Rhodophyta, 370; Silicoflagellata, 179
Fragilaria 175, 187
Fridaea 74
Fritschiella 74, 320
Fructose 42
Frustule 180
Fucaceae **227,** 299
Fucales 210, **227**
Fucoidin 333

Fucosan 207
Fucosterol 208, 333
Fucoxanthin 12, 28
Fucus 4, 7, 18, 31, 35, 209, 227, **229,** 230, 237, 301, 306, 312, 336, 355, 372
Fuller's Earth 356
Fungi 18, 56, 307, 327
Funori 354
Furcellaria **268,** 269
Furcellariaceae **268**
Furcellarin 333
Fuxochlorin 137
Fuxorhodin 137

Gaidukov Phenomenon 136
Galactose 333, 346
Galactose sulphuric acid 351
Galaxaura 249; Diesingiana, 239
Gambusia 361
Gametangia 33, 42
Gamete 33
Gametophyte 33, 34, 371
Gamone 50
Gastroclonium 303
Gelidiales 14, 242, **258**
Gelidium 241, **258,** 259, 301, 333, 354; cartilagineum, 335
Gels 267, 351, 354
Genera, morphological comparison 368, 369
Geological history: See Fossil
Gibberillic Acid 347
Gigartina 241, 261, **267,** 303; mamillosa, 354; stellata, 351
Gigartinaceae **266**
Gigartinales 14, 242, **265**
Girdle, Girdle Band, Girdle View 180, 181; Cell Division, 31; Desmids, 125, 126; Diatoms, 180; Ecological, 304
Gizzard shad 315, 352
Glaciation 372
Glaucocystis 56, **142,** 325; Nostochinearum, 131
Globule 132
Globulin-protein 25
Gloeobotrydiaceae **162**
Gloeocapsa 18, 130, 138, **140,** 326, 370; rupestris, 283
Gloeochaete **142,** 325; Wittrockiana, 131
Gloeochloris **158;** Smithiana, 159
Gloeocystis 283

Gloeotaenium **69;** *Loitelsbergerianum,* 65

Gloeotrichia **153,** 347, 362; *echinulata,* 153, *159,* 284, 314; *natans,* 153

Gloiopeltis furcata 354

Glucose 42, 332

Glycerol 351

Glycogen 30, 137, 332

Glycolic Acid 346

Glycoside 333

Golden-yellow algae 167

Golenkinia **61,** 292; *radiata, 58*

Golgi apparatus 20, 41

Gomontia 18, 85

Gomphonema 292, 295

Gonatoblaste 79

Gonatozygaceae 119, **121**

Gonatozygon **121;** *pilosum, 116*

Gongrosira 85, 294, 325

Gonimoblast Filament 240

Goniotrichaceae **246**

Goniotrichales 14

Goniotrichum 224, **246,** 309

Gonium **52;** *pectorale,* 45 *48,* **52**

Gonyaulax 196, 364, 365; *catenella,* 196, 361; *moniliata,* 196; *polyedra,* 196; *Tamarensis,* 196, 361

Gonyostomum 204, **205;** *semen, 201*

Gracilaria 261, **266,** 303, 333, 349, 354

Gracilariaceae **265**

Grana 39

Grateloupia 303

Great Lakes 97

Griffithsia 273, 306; *globulifera,* 270; *pacifica, 270*

Grinnellia 273 ·

Growth 30

"Growth Rings," 222

Gulf of California 148, 361

Gulf of Maine 282, 317

Gulf of Mexico 306, 361

Gulf Weed 231

Gums 354

Gunnera 139, 325

Gymnodiniaceae 197

Gymnodiniales 12, 197

Gymnodinium 19, 196, **197,** 199, 347, 361; *adriaticum,* 325; *brevis,* 361; *splendens,* 196, 197; *veneficum,* 361, 362

Gymnogongrus 35, 306

Gynotermones 50

Gypsum granules 41, 120, 125

Gyrodinium 23

Gyrogonites 372

Gyttja 291

Habitats: Cryovegetation 17; Cyanophyta, 135; Definitions, 16, 17; Occurrence, 16; Plankton, 313; Psammon, 16, 321; Soil, 16; Symbiosis, 18 (See Epiphytic, Epizoic); Thermal, 17

Haematochrome 17, 21

Haematococcaceae **51**

Haematococcus 23, 25, 38, 41, 283; *lacustris, 48,* **51;** *pluviale, 346*

Halicystidaceae 114

Halicystis 39, 114

Halimeda 109, 110, 304, 372

Halophytic 289

Hantzschia amphioxys 320

Hapalosiphon **151,** 289; *pumilus, 147*

Haplobiont 241

Haplodiplont 242

Haploid generation 32, 34

Haplont 241, 242

Haptera 105, 208, 299

Hapterophycus 209

Haptonema 24, 156, 171, 172, 176

Haptophyceae 170, 172

Hardwater: See Lakes

Heleoplankton 17

Helminthocladiaceae **255**

Hemicellulose 39

Hemicryptophyceae 35

Hemiphanerophyceae 35

Heribaudiella 207

Heterocapsales 11, **158**

Heterococcales 11, **158**

Heterochrysophycidae 180

Heterococcoliths 170

Heterococcus 165; *caespitosus, 160*

Heterocysts 15, 135, 136, 336

Heterodynamic 22

Heterogametes, Heterogamy 7, 12, 14, 33, 42

Heterogeneratae 13, 34, 210, **217**

Heterohormogonium 328

Heterokont, Heterokontae 11, 155, 157, 171

Heteromorphic 13, 33, 242

Heterosiphonales 157, **165**

Heterospores 228

Heterothallic 33, 45

Heterotrichales   11, **164**
Heterotrichy, Heterotrichous   208, 248, 371
Heterotrophic   30, 317, 332
Hildenbrandtia   35, *261,* **265,** 283, 295, 303, 306
Hildenbrandtiaceae   265
Hold-fast   208
Holococcoliths   170
Holophytic   30, 195, 332
Holozoic   167, 195, 332
Homomorphous   242
Homothallic   33, 45
Homotrichous   371
Hormidium   67, **71,** 320
Horizontal distribution: *See* Distribution
Hormogonales, Hormogoneae   15, 140, **143**
Hormones   30, 50
Hormosira   227, 301
Hormospore   33, 138
Hormothamnion **149;** *entero-morphoides, 146*
Hornellia   204, **205;** *marina, 201*
Hot springs (*See* Thermal)   370; Chemistry, 328; pH, 328; Temperature, 328
Hyalophacus   190
Hyalotheca   121; *dissiliens, 117*
Hyalothecaceae   121
Hyalotheceae   119
Hydra   17, 56, 325
Hydrodictyaceae   **62**
Hydrodictyon   39, 56, **63,** 64; *patenae-forme, 63; reticulatum, 63, 65*
Hydrogenase   344
Hydrogen Sulfide   332
Hydruraceae   **177**
Hydrurus, 177; *foetidus,* 173, 177, 296
Hyella   18
Hymenoclonium   258
Hymenomonas   171
Hyphal Filaments   254
Hypnea   301
Hypnodinium **202;** *sphaericum, 200*
Hypnophyceae   35
Hypnospores   32, 165
Hypnum   354
Hypocone   195
Hypolimnion   284, 318
Hypotheca   181, 195
Hypovalve   181

Ice (*See* Cryoplankton)   285, 289, 302
Ichthyosarcotoxin   365
Idioandrosporous   95
Inclusions   333
Index organisms: Pollution   296; Productivity, 290; Quantitative, 292, sq.
Indolyl acetic acid   31
Infralittoral   302
Inhibitors   126, 345
Insecticides   356
Insolation   309, 317
Internode   9, 128; Characeae, **128**
Intertidal   300 sq.
Inulin   42
Iodine   222, 356, 358, 359
Iodoamino acid   208
Ireksokonia   74
Iridaea   303, 308; *cordata, 281*
Iridiophycin   333
Irish moss   267, 351
Iron   18, 19, 40, 121, 290, 315, 334
Isochrysidales   180
Isochrysophycidae   180
Isodynamic   22
Isogametes   7–12, 33, 42
Isogeneratae   12, 34, 210
Isokont   41, 167
Isomorphic   13, 33
Isotherms   310
Isthmia   183
Iwanoffia   74

Janczewskia   234
Jania   234
Jurassic   171, 356, 372, 373

Katharobic zone   152
Katodinium   346
Keel (Diatoms)   181, 186
Kelp   207, 220, 355; harvesting, 355
Kelp ore   359
Kentrosphaera   58, **60**
Kephyrion   156
Ketonic carotinoids   25
Kieselguhr   356
Kinetin   347
Kombu   350
Kylinia   323

Lagynion **176;** *ampullaceum,* 173; *Scherfellii, 173*

Lakes: Baltic, 288; Brine, 289; Calcium rich, 289; Caledonian, 288; Classification, 290, 291; Dystrophic, 292; Eutrophic, 290, 291, 292, 314; Hardwater, 132, 288, 289; Mesotrophic, 292; Oligotrophic, 290, 291, 292, 315; Panoligotrophic, 291; Productive, 314; Siderotrophic, 291; Softwater, 289; Trophic nature, 313

Lamellae 39, 40, 136, 234; Chloroplasts (*See also* under descriptions of algal groups), 29, 39; Wall, 208

Laminaria 35, 208, **221,** 301, 303, 306, 307, 323, 333, 336, 346, 347, 349, 355; *Agardhii,* 223; *Farlowii,* 221; *japonica,* 335; *saccharina, 303*

Laminariaceae 221

Laminariales 13, 210, **220**

Laminarin 30, 333, 350, 371

Laminariose 333

Lamprothamnus 133

Lateral sterile filaments: *See Polysiphonia*

Laurencia 208, 234, 301

Laurentian 371

Laver 351

Leathesia **217**; *diffoemis, 215*

Lemanea 251, **254,** 295, 306; *fluviatile, 251*

Lemaneaceae **254**

Lemna 58, 60; *trisulca, 324*

Lessonia 227, 303

Lessoniaceae **227**

Lessoniopsis 308

Leucosin 10, 20, 30, 155, 333

Liagora 252, **256;** *erecta, 252; farinosa, 256*

Lichens 18, 56, 60, 139, (marine) 302, 324

Life histories 6, 33, 371; Algae, 3; Alternation of generations, 33, 42; Chlorophyta, 209; Rhodophyta, 241, sq.; Volvocales, 45

Light Absorption, 28, 282, 311, 312; Adaptation, 29; Distribution of algae, 282; Latitudes, 282; Marine, 311; Penetration, 282, 283, 311; Periodicity of species, 284; Photosynthesis, 342; Pigments, 282; Rays, 28; Reflection, 282, 311; Suspended matter, 283; Temperature, 282

Lignophilic 18

Lime: *See* Calcium

Limnology 5, 279 sq.

Limu 350

Lipids 137, 333, 340, 352

Lipoproteins 29

Lithodinia 373

Lithophilic 17, 18

Lithophyllum 35, 304, 306

Lithothamnion 233, 304, 309, 371

Littoral 301, 308, 310, 312

Liverworts 139

Lobomonas 46

Lomentaria 241, **272,** 301; *Baileyanum, 270; rosea, 241*

Lomentariaceae **272**

Longitudinal furrow 11, 12, 194

Lorica 19, 193

Lubricants 354

Luminescence 196

Lychnothamnus 133

Lyngbya 144 *145,* **148,** 301, 346; *aestuarii, 290; Birgei, 290; major, 290; majuscula, 302*

Macrandrous 95

Macrocystis 209, **226,** 303, 311, 355; *pyrifera, 4, 224*

Magnolia 86, 89, 324

Mallomonadaceae **168**

Mallomonas 23, 155, 156, **169,** 170, 292; *pseudocoronata, 161*

Mammals 17

Manganese 315

Mangrove swamp 301

Mannitol 30, 333, 350

Mannoglycerate 234

Mannose 18, 39, 40, 333

Manubrium 132

Marl 328, 372

Martensia 273

Mass Culture: *See* Culture

Mastigoclodus 139, 151, 336

Mastigonemes 24

Medicine 5, 358

Mediterranean 304, 305, 311

Medulla 13, 209

Megaplankton 316

Megasporangium 228, 229

Megaspore 228

Meiosis 14, 20, 33, 34

Meiospore 20, 33, 34

Melobesoideae 263

Melosira 174, 183, **185,** 314; *italica, 283*

Meridion 187, 292
Merismopedia **141;** *tenuissima, 131,* 142
Meristerm, Meristematic 221
Meristoderm 209
Mermaid's Wineglass 106
Merotrichia 205
Mesochite 229
Mesoplankton 316
Mesosaprobic 152
Mesotaeniaceae 119, 127
Mesotaenium Bergrenii var. *alaskanum,* 326
Mesotrophic 292
Mesozoic 371
Metabolic *(Euglena)* 190
Metachromatic granules 20, 41
Metamorphosis 9
Methionine 352
Micractiniaceae **61;** *Micractinium,* **61;** *pusillum, 58*
Micrasterias 39; *depauperata, 117*
Microcoleus 143, *145,* **148,** *289; 320; paludosus,* 292
Microcystis **141,** 289, 292, 296, 328, 336, 337, 346, 347, 359, 361, 362, 364, 370; *aeruginosa, 130, 284, 290, 314; toxica,* 362; toxins, 362, 363
Microdictyon **105;** *mutabile, 101*
Microfibrils 18, 39, 40
Micromeres 111
Micromonas 23
Microplankton 316
Microscope lens testing 358
Microspora **72;** *pachyderma, 68*
Microsporaceae 72
Microsporales 8, 70, 72
Microsporangium 228
Microspores 185, 228
Microthamnion 74
Miocene 167, 371, 373
Mitochondria 19, 20, 41, 235
Mitosis 20
Mixotrophic 30, 332
Mollusca 80
Molybdenum 336
Monaxial 248
Monocilia **165;** *viridis, 160*
Monociliaceae 165
Monoecious 95, 242
Monomorphous 242
Monosporangium 32
Monospores 32, 236, 246

Monostroma 35, 43, **87,** 88, *89,* 103, 295, 301, 303, 306, 351
Monostromaceae 87
Monothallic 242
Mosquito larvae 17
Mougeotia 38, *120; capucina,* 38
Mougeotiaceae 119
Mougeotiopsis 127
Movement: Cyanophyta 139, 144, 282; Desmids, 124; Diatoms, 184; Light, and, 282; *Oscillatoria,* 144
Mucilage 18, 335
Mugil: poecilus 326; *troscheli,* 326
Multiaxial 135, 233, 248
Mussels 361, 362
Mycacanthococcus **69;** *antarcticus, 66*
Myriophyllum 153
Myxophyceae 7, 137
Myxophycophyta 7

Nannandrous 95
Nannochloris 327
Nannoplankton 316
Nautococcus 17; *pyriformis, 47*
Navicula *175,* 182, 187, 320, 353
Necridia 144
Nemalion 14, 249, 252, **255;** *multifidum, 252; vermiculare,* 256
Nemalionales 14, 242, **249**
Nemathecia 240, 267
Nematochrysis **178;** *sessilis, 173*
Neomeris annulata 305
Nereia 306
Nereocystis 209, **222,** 333; *Luetkeana,* 223
Neretic 318
Netrium *115,* **120**
Neuromotor apparatus 21, 22, *24*
Neuston 17
Neutral Spores 218, 246
Niche associations 320
Nitella 84, 128, *130,* 132, **133,** 283, 289, 290, 324
Nitelleae 132, 133
Nitellopsis 133
Nitrates 287, 288, 296, 308, 317
Nitrogen 5, 45, 138, 289, 334, 336
Nitrogen-fixation 139, 322, 336
Nitzschia 183, 320, 346, 359; *linearis, 183, 297; palea, 296; paradoxa,* 184
Noctiluca 192, 196, *199*
Node 9, 128

Nodularia   **150,** 322, 362; *spumigena, 147*
Nodules   182
Nori   351
Nostoc   138, 139, *146,* **148,** 322, 324, 336, 346, 351; *commune,* 149; lichens, 324; *muscorum,* 322; *parmeloides,* 18, 149, 295; *pruniforme,* 292, 325
Nostocaceae   **148**
Notheia   227
Notheiaceae   228
Nucleolus   20
Nucleus   20
Nucule   132
Nullipores   371
Nurse cells   240
Nutrients, Elements   287, 315, 317, 334
Nutrition   5, 331; Autotrophic, 30; Auxotrophic, 339; Heterotrophic, 30, 339; Mixtrophic, 30; Parasitic, 323; Phagotrophic, 30, 339; Required elements, 287; Stream, 295; Symbiosis, 323

Objectionable algae, 359; Fish deaths, 361; Human deaths, 361, 364; Water supplies, 359
Occurrence   *See* Ecology
Oceanography   5
Ocellus   21
Ochromonadaceae   **171**
Ochromonadales   180
Ochromonadineae   180
Ochromonas   *23, 332, 339, 345*
Odonthalia   307
Oedocladium   93, **95;** *Hazenii, 91*
Oedogoniaceae   **93**
Oedogoniales   9, 22, 39, **93**
Oedogonium   31, 43, 73, *90,* **93,** 94, 95, 294, 306
Oil   11, 16, 30, 42, 61, 137, 155, 332, 333, (Geological) 358
Oleander   86, 324
Oligochaetophora   79
Oligosaprobic   152
Oligotropic: *See* Lakes
Onychonema   121; *laeve, 129*
Ooblastic filaments   240, 264
Oocardium   118
Oocystaceae   **64**
Oocystis   32, 56, **69,** 142, 292, 325; *parva, 65*
Oodinium limneticum   326
Oogamy, Oogamous   7-11, 13, 236

Oogonium   33, 132
Oolith   139, 370
Operculum, Operculate   94
Ophiocytium   157, **163;** *arbuscula,* 163; *capitulum, 160*
Ophrydium   56, 325
Ordovician   37, 106, 110, 371, 372
Organic acids   333
Oscillatoria   139, **144,** 148, 283, 296, 301, 320, 328, 347; *limosa,* 296; movement, 139; *nigra, 145; rubescens,* 144, 284; *tenuis, 296*
Oscillatoriaceae   144
Oscillatoriales   15, **143**
Oscillospira   325
Osmotic pressure   307, 308
Ostioles   228, 230
Ostreobium   **114,** *115*
Over-turn   284
Oxidation   19, 344
Oxycarotenes   25
Oxygen   309, 310; depletion, 338; tension, 344
Oxyrrhis   332
Oxytrichia   353

Pachymeniopsis   241
Pacific   305, 306
Padina   208, 216, 372
Paints   354, 355
Palaeodasycladus   372
Palcoto   359
Paleozoic   171, 233, 371, 372
Palmella   **54;** *mucosa, 49*
Palmellaceae   **54**
Palmella Stage, Palmelloid   10, 60, 72, 79, 142, 151, 171, 172, 177, 178, 189, 191, 194
Palmodictyon   54; *viride, 48*
Pandorina   *44,* **51;** *morum, 48*
Panoligotrophic   291
Pantocronematic   24
Pantonematic   24, 41
Paradesmose   22, *24*
Paramecium   325
Paramylum   10, 190, 191, 332
Paraphyses   228
Parasites, Parasitic   17, 61, 114, 323, 332; Chlorophyta, 114, 323; Cryptophyta, 204; Dinoflagellata, 196; Phaeophyta, 227, 323; Rhodophyta, 233, 323; Sporophyte, 3

Parthenospores 9
Pascherina 44
Pasturage of the sea 298
Pectin 18, 39
Pectodictyon **70;** *cubicum, 66*
Pediastrum 56, **62**, 292, 314, 346; *Boryanum, 59, 290*
Pedicel: *See* Stalk cell
Pedinomonas 20, 23, 41, **46;** *minor, 47*
Pelagophycus 226, 303
Peliaina 325
Pellicle: *See* Periplast
Pelvetia 350; *caniculata, 301*
Penicillin 346
Penicillus 301
Penieae 127
Pennales, Pennatae 11, 180, 181, **186**
Pennatobacillariophyceae **186**
Pentalith 170
Peranema 190
Peranemaceae 193
Perennial 35, 306
Pericarp 240, 257, 258, 266, 277
Pericentral 15, 243, 248, 254, 273
Peridiniaceae 197, 293
Peridiniales 12, 197
Peridinium 11, **197;** *anglicum, 200; limbatum, 200; wisconsinense, 200*
Periodicity 284, 303, 319; Plankton, 284
Periphyton 17
Periplast 19, 190
Perithecium 264
Permian 37, 372
Perone 164
Petalonia 219
pH 288, 293; Fresh-water, 288, 290; Hot springs, 328; Marine, 288, 308; Respiration, 345
Phacus 190, **192, 199**
Phaeophila 79, **80**, *82*
Phaeophyceae 4, 7
Phaeophyta 12, 22, 28, 30, **207;** Alternation of generations, 12; Architecture, 208; Cell wall, 208; Composition, 350; Cytology, 207; Flagella, 208; Growth, 208; Habitats, 207, 301; Phylogeny, 231; Pigments, 207; Reproduction, 209
Phaeoplacales 180
Phaeosporeae 12
Phaeostrophion 220
Phaeothamniales 177
Phaeothamniaceae 177

Phaeothamnion 4, **177;** *confervicola, 173*
Phaeothamnionineae 180
Phagotrophic 30, 156, 327, 332, 339
Phanerophyceae 35
Pharmaceutical products 359
Pharyngeal rods 190
Phialopore 52, 53
Phloeospora brachiata 323
Phormidium 18, 295, 301, 320, 326, 328, 346, 347; *corium, 302; persicinum, 136*
Phosphates, Phosphorus 287, 288, 289, 296, 308, 317, 336–338
Photo-organotrophic 30
Photophosphorylation 343
Photoreceptor 21
Photosynthesis 5, 19, 28, 29, 30, 340; Carbon, 341; Enzymes, 340; Formula, 340, 343; Light, 340, 342, 344; Pigments, 28, 340, 342
Photosynthetic zone 283, 311
Phototactic 21
Phototrophic 282, 331
Phycobilins 25, 29
Phycochromoproteids 25
Phycocyanin 28
Phycoerythrin 14, 28
Phycopeltis 85, 324
Phykos 4
Phyla 7
Phyllaria 303
Phyllobium **60;** *sphagnicola, 58*
Phyllophora 303, 306; *Brodiaei, 245; membranifolia, 245*
Phyllosiphon **114;** *Arisari, 115*, 324
Phyllosiphonaceae **114**, 324
Phylogeny 44, 367; Bacillariophyceae, 373; Characeae, 372; Chlorophyta, 44, 372; Chrysophyceae, Chrysophyta, 371, 373; Cryptophyta, 371, 373, 374; Cyanophyta, 18, 370; Desmidiales, 124; Euglenophyta, 373; Fossil records, 367, sq.; Phaeophyta, 371; Pyrrhophyta, 373; Rhodophyta, 370
Physiology 3, 5, 331
Physolinum 85
Phytoflagellata 4
Phytophysa 324
Pia 372
Pickles 350
Pigments 3, 6, 10, 11, 24–27; Adaptation, 29; Bacillariophyceae, 26; Check list, 26; Chloromonadophyta, 27; Chry-

sophyceae, 26; Chrysophyta, 26, 155; Cryptophyta, 27; Cyanophyta, 27, 136; Euglenophyta, 26; Light absorption, 28, 282, 311, 312; Photosynthesis, 340, 342; Phaeophyta, 207; Pyrrhophyta, 194; Rhodophyta, 27, 234; Xanthophyceae, 26
Pigment-spot 21, 24
Pilea 324
Pilinia 74
Pinnularia 358; *lata, 175*
Pithophora **98;** *varia, 99*
Pits 151, 182, 235, 324
Placenta 240
Placoderm desmids 119, **121**
Placosphaera perforata 176
Plakea 52
Plankton 17; Blooms, 53, 56, 61, 138, 144, 150, 194, 205, 292, 315, 317, 342, 346; Classification, 316; Composition, 316, 318; Fresh-water. *See* Blooms, Ecology; Marine, 298, 307, 308, 315, 316, 319, 353; Periodicity, 319; Productivity, 293, 314; Pulses, 284, 315; Vertical Distribution, 318
Plasma membrane 19
Plasmodesmata 19, 235
Plates (Pyrrhophyta cell wall) 195
Platymonas 23, **51,** 288, 289, 326; *elliptica, 48*
Plectonema 327, 328, 346
Pleodorina **52**
Pleodorina californica 48
Pleurocapsa fuliginosa 302
Pleurocapsaceae **143**
Pleurocapsales 15
Pleurochloridaceae **158**
Pleurocladia 207
Pleurococcus 78
Pleuronematic 24, 41
Pleurotaenium 121; *Ehrenbergii, 116*
Pleurothamnion 78
Plurilocular gametangium 211
Pneumatocysts 209, 226, 227, 231
Polar: *See* Arctic, Antarctic
Polarity 31, 229
Pollution 296, 297; Indicators, 296
Polyblepharidaceae **45**
Polyblepharides 45
Polychaetophora 79
Polyhedra 63
Polyides 235

Polykrikos 194
Polypeptids 333
Polyploidy 20
Polysaccharides 333
Polysiphonia 35, 82, 236, 241, 242, 245, 273, **275,** 276, 301, 306, 308, 346, 356; *denudata, 276; Harveyi, 276*
Polyspores 236
Polytoma 22, 25, 41, 42, 46; *uvella, 347*
Pontosphaera 171
Pores, Pit connections 19, 151, 208
Porphyra 35, 60, 235, 236, *238,* 241, 242, **247,** 306, 308, 323, 351; *tenera, 335*
Porphyridaceae 243
Porphyridales 14, **243**
Porphyridium 234, 236, **243;** *cruentum, 225*
Porphyrin 333
Porphyrosiphon 144, 320
Postelsia 18, **222,** 303, 307; *palmaeformis, 223, 299*
Potamoplankton 17, 296, 297
Potash 222, 356
Potassium 334, (nitrate) 351
Prasinocladus **55;** *lubricus, 57*
Prasinophyceae 45
Prasiola 17, *90,* 92, 324; *crispa, 302; stipitata,* **92**
Prasiolales 8
Primary feeders 352
Primicorallina 372
Pringsheimiella 79
Procarp 240
Productivity 313, 352; Fresh-water, 288, 290, 293, 313; Index of, 290; Marine, 319
Propagula 209, 212
Prorocentraceae 194, 197
Prorocentrum **197,** *199*
Proteins 18, 350, 352; Cell wall, 18
Proterozoic 370, 372
Protista 4
Protococcaceae 79
Protococcus **78,** *81*
Protoderma **78;** *viride, 81,* 320
Protodermataceae **78**
Protoeuglena **192;** *noctilucae, 199*
Protoflorideae **243**
Protonema (Characeae) 133
Protosiphon 25, **62,** 165; *botryoides, 59,* **62**
Protosiphonaceae 62

Protozoa, Algae and 4
Prymnesiaceae **172**
Prymnesiales 180
Prymnesium 172
Psammon 16, 321
Pseudendoclonium **78,** *81*
Pseudochaete 74
Pseudocilia 54
Pseudopodium 176
Pseudoraphe 11, 181
Pseudoulvella 79
Pseudovacuoles 138, 149, 284, 333
Pteromonas 19
Pterospermaceae 178
Pterygophora 209, 303
Pulses (Plankton) 284, 315
Pulsule 194
Puncta 182
Punctaria **219;** *latifolia, 223*
Punctariaceae 219
Punctariales **219**
Pyramimonas 19, **46;** *tetrahynchus, 47*
Pyrenoid 29, 39
Pyrobotrys gracilis 45
Pyrodinium phoneus 361
Pyrrhophycophyta 7
Pyrrhophyta 4, 11, 20, 21, 25, 30, 189;
194, 302, 308, 319, 339, 361, 373, 374;
Classification 196; Cytology, 194; Flag-
ellata, 194; Fossil, 196, 373; Parasitic,
194, 196; Phylogeny, 373; Pigments,
194; Toxic, 364; Wall, 195
Pyxidicula 373

Raciborskia 194, 202; *bicornis, 201*
Ragweed 61
Ralfsia 210, **211,** *213*
Ralfsiaceae **211**
Raphe 11, 181
Raphidonema 17, 326
Ratio (K–Na/Ca–Mg) 293
Ray cells 254
Receptacle 228, 230
Red algae 3
Red Sea 144, 305
Red tide 6, 194, 196, 197, 317, 361, 362
Regulators 30
Reproduction 6, 31; Asexual, 31; Ba-
cillariophyceae, 183, 186; Chlamy-
domonadaceae, 50; Chlorophyta, 42;
Chrysophyta, 156; Cryptophyta, 203;
Cyanophyta, 138; Euglenophyta, 191;

Phaeophyta 209; Pyrrhophyta, 195;
Rhodophyta, 236; Sexual, 33; Vegeta-
tive, 31; Zoospores, 32
Reserve Food: See Carbohydrates, Pro-
tein, Oil, Paramylum, Floridean Starch
Reservoir 21
Respiration 312, 344; Anaerobic, 345;
pH, 345
Rheophilic 18
Rhizochloridales 11, **157**
Rhizochrysidales 10, **176, 180**
Rhizoclonium 76, **97,** 295, 324; *hiero-
glyphicum, 97; Hookeri, 99; lubricum,
98*
Rhizolekane 324
Rhizoplast 21, 22, 24
Rhizosolenia 139, *174,* 180
Rhodochorton 233, **250,** *251*
Rhodochytrium 61, 324; *spilanthidis, 58*
Rhodomela 356
Rhodomelaceae **274**
Rhodophyceae 4, 7
Rhodophyta 14, 19, 22, 28, 29, 30, 189;
Cell wall, 235; Cytology, 235; Distribu-
tion: See Ecology, 305; Food reserve,
234; Life histories, 241, 244; Light ab-
sorption, 311, sq.; Phylogeny, 277; Pig-
ments, 234; Representative orders, 243;
Reproduction, 236; Symbiotism, 323;
See Parasitic
Rhodospora 246
Rhodymenia **271,** 323, 350; *palmata,
269, 351; pseudospinnata, 269*
Rhodymeniaceae **271**
Rhodymeniales 15, 242, **268**
Richelia 139
Rickertia 204
Rimu 350
Rivularia 138, **152,** 159, 301, 370; *atra,*
302
Rivulariaceae **152**
Rivulariales 16, 152
RNA 137
Rubber 355

Saccate thallus 13, 295
Saccoderm desmids 119
Salinity 288, 289, 307, 308
Salmo fario 315
Salt Water: See Brackish, Salinity
Saphophytes 320

Saprophytes, Saprophytic 56, 195, 321, 325, 332
Sargasso Sea 148, 282, 317
Sargassum 35, 227, **231,** 237, 301, 302, 304, 306; *filipendula,* 237
Sarumen 350
Scalariform Conjugation: See Conjugation
Scenedesmaceae **70**
Scenedesmus 56, 66, **70,** 292, 296, 333, 345, 347, 352; *quadricauda,* 290
Schizochlamys **54;** *gelatinosa,* 57
Schizogonales 8, **92**
Schizogonium 92
Schizomeridaceae **88**
Schizomeris **88;** *Leibleinii,* 90
Schizophyta 18, 135
Schizothrix 139
Scinaia 241, 252, **257;** *furcellata,* **257**
Scotiella 17, 66, **69,** 326
Scytonema 137, 138, 139, *147*, **150,** 283, 328
Scytonemataceae **150**
Scytonematales 16, 150
Scytonemin 137
Scytosiphon 303, 323
Scytothamnus australis 281
Sea anemone 325
Sea holly 237
Sea of Japan 281
Sea Palm 222
Sea water: Chemistry 307; Composition, 307; pH, 308; Salinity, 307
Sea weeds 3
Secondary feeders 352
Segregative cell division 104, 111
Semicells 118, 121
Septa 182
Sex organs 3: See Group Names of Algae; Characeae, 132
Sheath, Sheath cells 132, 133, 135 (pigmented sheaths), 283
Shield cell 132
Siderotrophic 291
Sieve plates, Tubes 221, 228
Silicalemma 182
Silicoflagellatae 155, **179,** 338
Silicon 18, 289, 318, 334, 338
Silurian 37, 372
Simonsiella 325
Simple flagella 24
Sinus 121
Siphonales 9, 11, 20, 41, 104, **110**

Siphonocladaceae 105
Siphonocladales 9, 39, 96, **103**
Siphonous, Siphonaceous 11, 37, 103, 156, 165
Sirodotia **253**
Sitosterol 333
Skeletonema 338
Skujapelta 142
Sloke 351
Sloth 326
Snapping turtle: See Turtle
Snow 326; Cryoplankton, 326; Green, 327; pH, 326; Red, 326; Yellow, 196
Sodium 334
Sodium Alginate: See Alginates
Soft-Water Lakes: See Lakes
Soil 16, 320, 332; Acid, 320; Alkaline, 320; Desert, 322; Flora, 321; Pioneers, 322; Psammon, 321; Temperature, 322; ˙Tropical, 321
Solenoporaceae 371
Sorbitol 351
Sori 240
Sperm 33
Spermatangial branch 255
Spermatangium 236
Spermatium 240
Spermocarp 84, 85
Sphacelaria 209, **212,** *213*
Sphacelariaceae 212
Sphacelariales 12, 209, 212
Sphaerellaceae **51**
Sphaerocystis Schroeteri 314
Sphaeroplea **73,** *75;* *annulina,* **73**
Sphaeropleaceae 73
Sphaeropleales 8, **73**
Sphagnum 58, 126, 202, 253, 324
Spherule 132
Spindle fibers 20, 22
Spirogyra 35, 40, *120,***128,** *129*
Spirulina 139, **148;** *princeps,* **145**
Splash zone 152, 302
Sponge 17, 96, 325
Spongiochloris 332
Spongocladia 105
Spongomorpha coalita *100,* **102**
Sporochnaceae **218**
Sporochnales 13, 218
Sporochnus 35, *215,* **218,** 306
Sporophyte 3, 33, 45, 371
Squamariaceae 265
Stabilizers 351, 354

Stalk, Stalk Cell 132, 273, 277; Characeae, 132; *Polysiphonia*, 277
Staphylococcus aureus 346
Starch, Starch producers 11, 16, 30, 37, 41, 332
Statospores 10, 33, 156, 168, 169
Staurastrum 117, 121; *paradoxum*, 293; *polonicum*, 280
Stauroneis 182
Stentor 325
Stephanodiscus 174, **185;** *Niagarae*, 290
Stephanokont 41
Stephanoptera **46;** *gracilis*, 47
Stephanosphaera 289
Sterile filament, Filament initial 275, (lateral) 275, (basal) 275
Sterile hairs 106
Sterols 333
Stichococcus **71,** 320; *bacillaris*, 67; *cylindricus*, 72
Stichogloeales 180
Stichonematic 24
Stigeoclonium 18, **74,** 75, 152, 294, 296, 325; *subspinosum*, 77; *tenue*, 296
Stigonema 18, 138, **151,** 283, 289; *ocellatum*, 147, 293
Stigonemataceae **151**
Stigonematales 16, 151
Stimulators 340, 345, 346
Stipe 208
Stipitococcaceae 157
Stipitococcus **157;** *urceolatus*, 159
Stomatochroon 85, 324
Stoneworts 9, **128**
Stratification 284
Stream 18, 294; Flora, 294, 297, 298; Plankton, 294, 297; Soft-water, 296; Types, 298
Streptomycin 347
Striae 182
Strombomonas 189, 193
Strychnine 365
Stylosphaeridium **55;** *stipitatum*, 57
Subantarctic 29
Sublittoral 301, 308, 310, 312
Subterranean 16, 320
Sucrose 42, 234, 350
Suffultory cell 95
Sulphates, Sulphur 290, 296, 334
Supporting cell 15, 240, 275
Supralittoral 302, 310
Surirella 187

Swimmer's itch 153
Symbiosis 323; Chlorophyta, 324; *Cladophora*, 96; Cyanophyta, 139, 324; Fresh-water, 324; Marine, 96, 323
Synechococcus 135
Syngamy 33, 34
Syntagamatic germination 241
Synthesis 19, 30
Synura 23, **170,** 359; *uvella*, 161, 292, 314
Synuraceae **169**
Synzoospore 166
Systolic 41

Tabellaria 175, **186**
Tea *(Thea)* 17
Tellamia 74
Temperature 285; Arctic and Antarctic, 285; Distribution, 284; Hot springs, 17, 138, 285; Optimum, 285; Productivity, 286; Range, 285; Soil, 322
Tenaculae 105
Terramycin 347
Tertiary 196, 356, 373
Tetradinium 194; *javanicum*, 200
Tetraedron 32, 64; *limneticum*, 65; *muticum*, 65; *regulare*, 65
Tetragonidium **204;** *verrucatum*, 201
Tetrallantos 292
Tetraodontoxin 365
Tetrapyrrolic compounds 25
Tetraselmis 46, 51
Tetraspora **54,** 295; *cylindrica*, 49; *gelatinosa*, 53, 54
Tetrasporaceae **54**
Tetrasporales 7, 10, 11, 45, **53,** 69, 70
Tetrasporangium 32, 240
Tetraspores 20, 32, 34, 236, 240, 242
Tetrasporophyte 14, 15, 32, 240, 242, 243
Thalassiosira 184
Thalassomonas 23
Thallochrysineae 180
Thallus 3
Thalophila 151
Thamniochaete 79
Theca 195
Thermal 17, 135, 138, 327, 328, (pH) 328, 370
Thermocline 284, 309, 317, 318
Thiamine 339
Thylakoids 194

Tidal flats   *See* Ecology
Tide pools   301, 302, 303, 308
Tides, Tide levels   18, 299, 304; Designa-
tions, 304; Neap, 299; Spring, 299
Tilopteridales   13
Tolypella   128, *130,* 132, 133
Tolypothrix   139, *147,* **151,** 336; *tenuis,*
139
Tonoplast   19
Toxic Toxins   6, 149, 150, 172, 196, 345,
361, 362, 364; Composition, 363, 364
Trabeculae   111
Trachelomonas   19, 21, 189, **193,** *199*
Trachychloron   164
Trailiella   258
Transverse furrow   11, 12, 194
Travertine   370
Trebouxia   18, 56, **60,** 324; *Cladoniae, 57*
Trehalose   137, 234, 332
Trentepohlia   18, 25, 31, 38, **85,** 86, 283,
302, 324; *aurea, 83*
Trentepohliaceae   **85,** 103, 324
Trentepohliales   8, 85
Treubaria   292
Triassic   371
Tribonema   19, 157, *160* **164;** *utriculo-
sum,* 160
Tribonemataceae   **164**
Tricarboxylic acid   19, (cycle) 344
Trichoblast   274, 275, (fertile) 274
Trichocyst   16, 203–205
Trichodesmium   **144,** 336; *erythraeum,*
144; *lacustre, 145*
Trichodiscus   74, **77;** *elegans, 76*
Trichogyne   84, 240
Trichome   135
Trichophilus   **79;** *Welcheri, 81,* 326
Trichosarcina   88, 92; *polymorpha, 90,*
92
Trichothallic growth   13, 209
Trifolium   139
Trigonidium   56
Triphosphopyridine Nucleotide   343
Tripoli earth   356
Trochiscia   326, 327
Tropical   304; Plankton, 319; Soils, 321
Trout   315
True branching   135, 151
Trumpet hyphae   221, 222, 226
Tsao   350
Tsats' ai   351
Tsunami   302

Tube cells   132
Tufa   328
Turbidity   318
Turbinaria   355
Turtles   17, 325
Tychoplankton   17, 297

Udotea   304
Ulothrix   18, 31, 35, 43, **71,** 88, 301, 306;
australis, 302; *flaccida,* 326; *zonata, 67,*
71
Ulotrichaceae   71, 92
Ulotrichales   7, **70,** 73, 87, 103
Ultranannoplankton   316
Ultraviolet   29
Ulva   7, 18, 21, 22, 31, 88, 301, 347; *latis-
sima, 89*
Ulvaceae   87, 299
Ulvales   8, 70, **87,** 92, 303, 351
Undaria pinnatifida   335
Uniaxial   135, 233
Unilocular sporangium   211
Urococcus   194, 324
Uroglenopsis   **171;** *americana, 161,* 171
Uronema   70
Urospora   39, *101,* 102, **103,** 310
Utricles   112

Vacuoles   19, 41
Valonia   19, **104;** *utricularia,* 101; *ven-
tricosa, 101*
Valoniaceae   **104**
Valve   181; Jacket, 181; View, 11, 180
Vaucheria   19, *23,* 35, 156, **166,** 295,
302, 306, 321, 327; *geminata, 161;
Jonesii, 327; sessilis,* 292
Vaucheriaceae   166
Vaucheriopsis   166
Vermilion Sea   148
Verrucaria   302
Vertical distribution   29, 282
Vidalia   234
Virus   346
Vitamins   5, 30, 288, 289, 296, 309, 316,
318, 339, 340, 343, 347, 350, 357
Volutin   20, 183
Volvocaceae   **51**
Volvocales   4, 7, 21, 39, 41, **42,** 54, 70,
372
Volvophyceae   42
Volvox   42, 45, **53;** *aureus, 49*

Wahpia 371
Wall: *See* Cytology
Water blooms: *See* Blooms
Water supplies 359
Wittrockiella **102;** *paradoxa, 101*

Xanthophyceae 4, 7, 11, 155, 156, **157;**
  Cytology, 157; Pigments, 157
Xanthophylls 11, 19, 25
Xenococcus *131,* **143**
Xylose 39, 40

Yellow-Green algae, 10, 155; *See* Xanthophyceae
Yuycho 351

Zanardinia 212
Zonation, Zones 299, 300; Black, 302;
  Fucoid, 301; Horizontal, 304; Infralit-
  toral, 302; Littoral, 301; Midlittoral, 301,
  303; Splash, 302; Supralittoral, 301, 302
Zoochlorella 17, 325
Zooplankton 315
Zoospores 8, 10, 16, 45
Zoosporic 56
Zooxanthellae 17, 204, 304, 325
Zygnemataceae 118, **127**
Zygnematales 9, 118, 119
Zygogonium 127, 320
Zygospore 33, 34
Zygote 33, 34

P. H. WELSHIMER MEMORIAL LIBRARY
MILLIGAN COLLEGE. TENN. 37682